SEPUP   SCIENCE & GLOBAL ISSUES

BIOLOGY

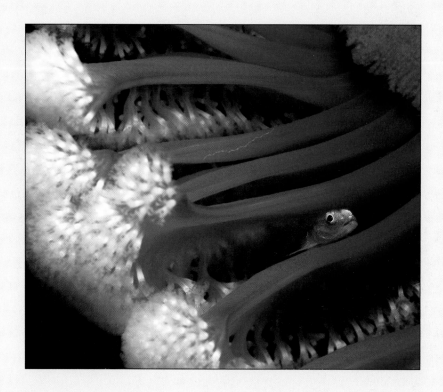

SCIENCE EDUCATION
FOR PUBLIC UNDERSTANDING
SEPUP   PROGRAM

UNIVERSITY OF CALIFORNIA, BERKELEY
LAWRENCE HALL OF SCIENCE LHS

LAB-AIDS
INCORPORATED

This material is based upon work supported by the National Science Foundation under Grant No. ESI-0352453. Any opinions, findings, and conclusions or recommendations expressed in this material are those of the authors and do not necessarily reflect the views of the National Science Foundation.

For photo and illustration credits, see pages 609–612, which constitute an extension of this copyright page.

The preferred citation format for this book is:
SEPUP. (2011). Science and Global Issues: Biology. Lawrence Hall of Science,
University of California at Berkeley. Published by Lab-Aids ®, Inc., Ronkonkoma NY

3 4 5 6 7 8 9   14 13 12 11

©2011 The Regents of the University of California

ISBN:
1-60301-328-8
978-1-60301-328-4

SEPUP
Lawrence Hall of Science
University of California at Berkeley
Berkeley CA 94720-5200
e-mail: sepup@berkeley.edu
Website: www.sepuplhs.org

Published by:

LaB-aiDS
INCORPORATED
17 Colt Court
Ronkonkoma NY 11779
Website: www.lab-aids.com

Acknowledgments

SCIENCE AND GLOBAL ISSUES PROJECT

Barbara Nagle, Ph.D., *Project Director*

Sara Dombkowski Wilmes, *Project Coordinator*

Maia Willcox, *Field Test and Publications Coordinator*

SEPUP SCIENCE AND GLOBAL ISSUES DEVELOPMENT TEAM

Janet Bellantoni

Laura Lenz

Sara Dombkowski Wilmes

Barbara Nagle

John Howarth

Maia Willcox

Christopher Keller

UNIT AUTHORS

Sustainability

Janet Bellantoni, Maia Willcox, and Sara Dombkowski Wilmes

Ecology: Living on Earth

Maia Willcox, John Howarth, and Sara Dombkowski Wilmes

Cell Biology: World Health

Laura Lenz, Barbara Nagle, and John Howarth

Genetics: Feeding the World

Sara Dombkowski Wilmes, Maia Willcox, and Barbara Nagle

Evolution: Maintaining Biodiversity

Laura Lenz, Barbara Nagle, and John Howarth

OTHER CONTRIBUTORS

Kristin Nagy Catz

Patty Kreikemeier

Raquel Gomes

Donna Parker

Christopher Keller

CONTENT AND SCIENTIFIC REVIEW

Evolution: Maintaining Biodiversity

Kefyn Catley, Ph.D., *Department of Biology, Western Carolina University, Cullowhee, North Carolina*

Nicholas J. Matzke, *Department of Integrative Biology, University of California, Berkeley, California*

PRODUCTION

Copyediting: Trish Beall

Index: Dick Evans

Design, illustration, photo research and composition: Seventeenth Street Studios

Administrative assistance: Roberta Smith and Anna Vorster

FIELD TEST CENTERS

The following centers participated in field testing *Science and Global Issues: Biology*. We are extremely grateful to the center directors, teachers, and their students for their significant contributions to the development of this course.

REGIONAL CENTER, IOWA

Phyllis Anderson and Christopher Soldat, *Center Directors*

Anthony Brack, Jason Cochrane, Dawn Posekany

REGIONAL CENTER, WESTERN NEW YORK

Kathaleen Burke and Tammy Martin, *Center Directors*

Elizabeth Brunn, Nathan Kahler, Christen LaBruna, Heather Maciewjeski, Julie Sek, Susan Wade

BALTIMORE, MARYLAND

Keely Brelsford, *Center Director*

Dana Johnson, Aubrey Melton

BOULDER VALLEY, COLORADO

Kristin Donley, *Center Director*

Eliza Bicknell, Martina Kastengren, Kelly Ksiazek, Alberto Real

DUBLIN, OHIO

Donna Parker, *Center Director*

Chuck Crawford, Henry Lee, Heather Moore, Becky Saylor

GRAND RAPIDS, MICHIGAN

William Smith, *Center Director*

Jackie Billingsley, Abby Velie

LOS ANGELES, CALIFORNIA

Tammy Bird, *Center Director*

Brandie Borges, Elisa de la Pena-Nagle

NEW YORK, NEW YORK

Marc Siciliano, *Center Director*

Jared Fox, Leah McConaughey, Patrick Whelton

TUCKER, GEORGIA

Lisa Martin-Hansen, *Center Director*

Jeb Fox, Kelly Voss

WAKE COUNTY, NORTH CAROLINA

Michael Tally, *Center Director*

Jennifer Morrison, Tracey Myer, Tina Robinette, Rebecca Townsend, Susanne Turley

WHITTIER, CALIFORNIA

Tara Barnhart, *Center Director*

Jeff Varney

INDEPENDENT

Alameda, California: Patricia Williamson

Floyd, Kentucky: Angela King

Hartford, Connecticut: Angela Kumm

Hickory, North Carolina: Linda Culpepper

Oakland, California: Sam Tsitrin

Parkersburg, West Virginia: Nathan Alfred

Contents

A Letter from SEPUP *xxi*

About SEPUP and *Science and Global Issues* *xxiii*

How to Use *Science and Global Issues* *xviii*

Sustainability 1

1 *Our Global Community* 3
▶ What do indicators tell us about regions of the world?

2 *Life in Other Countries* 8
▶ What can indicators reveal about the sustainability challenges facing different countries?

3 *Sustainability Case Studies* 14
▶ What steps have communities taken to live in ways that are more sustainable?

4 *Ecological Footprint* 22
▶ Can the earth's ecosystems sustain our current use of resources?

5 *Jaffrey City's Problem* 26
▶ How can phosphate and nitrate indicators help identify the contamination problem in Jaffrey Lake?

6 *Jaffrey City's Master Plan* 31
▶ How can a sustainability plan be developed for Jaffrey Lake that will balance the interests of all of the stakeholders?

Unit Review: Sustainability 41

Ecology: Living on Earth   43

1   *Ecosystems and Change*   45
▶ How does change affect ecosystems?
- CASE STUDY 1: THE CRAB JUBILEE   **48**
- CASE STUDY 2: THE MARCH OF THE TOADS   **50**
- CASE STUDY 3: THE BLEACHING OF THE REEFS   **52**
- CASE STUDY 4: THE YELLOWSTONE FIRES OF 1988   **54**

2   *A Population of Duckweed*   57
▶ How quickly can a population grow? How does the size of a population change through time?

3   *Biomes*   62
▶ How do the characteristics of a biome determine the types of organisms found there?

4   *Invasive Species*   70
▶ How do certain characteristics increase the likelihood that a nonnative species becomes an invasive species?
- CASE STUDY 1: THE ROUND GOBY   **72**
- CASE STUDY 2: THE INDIAN MONGOOSE   73
- CASE STUDY 3: ZEBRA MUSSEL   **74**
- CASE STUDY 4: GIANT SALVINIA   **75**
- REPORT SUMMARY: CHESAPEAKE BAY OYSTERS   **78**

5   *The Tragedy of the Commons*   80
▶ How can the overuse of an ecosystem service be prevented?

6   *Producers and Consumers*   85
▶ How do plankton populations affect the sustainability of a fishery?

7   *Energy Flow through an Ecosystem*   90
▶ How can we use food webs to predict the short- and long-term effects of particular events on an ecosystem?

8   *Carbon Cycle*   96
▶ How does human activity affect the movement of carbon through the carbon cycle?

9   *The Photosynthesis and Cellular Respiration Shuffle*   100
▶ How do carbon and oxygen cycle through the environment?

10   *Respiring Beans*   103
▶ How do various factors affect the rate of cellular respiration?

11 *Respiration and Photosynthesis in Plants* 107
   ▶ How does changing one variable affect photosynthesis
     and cellular respiration in plants?

12 *Too Much Life* 111
   ▶ How does the rate of cellular respiration affect the oxygen levels
     available in an aquatic ecosystem?
     • BACKGROUND INFORMATION: CHESAPEAKE BAY   93

13 *Symbiotic Relationships* 116
   ▶ How do organisms gain or lose from their interactions with each other?

14 *Investigating Population Growth Rates* 119
   ▶ How do changing variables alter population growth rates and ecosystem
     carrying capacities?

15 *Changes Due to Population Growth* 123
   ▶ How can the environmental harm from salmon farming be minimized?

16 *Ecosystems Out of Balance* 129
   ▶ How does information about relationships among organisms help to
     determine the sustainability of a species and an ecosystem?

17 *Ecosystem Change and Resiliency* 134
   ▶ What determines if an ecosystem can recover from a major event?

18 *Fishery Case Studies* 139
   ▶ How can case studies guide what should be done with the Avril Gulf
     tuna fishery?
     • CASE STUDY 1: CREATION OF THE GOAT ISLAND MARINE RESERVE   141
     • CASE STUDY 2: OPEN-OCEAN AQUACULTURE IN HAWAII   143

19 *Making Sustainable Fishery Decisions* 145
   ▶ Which fishery management strategy is the best choice for the
     sustainability of the Avril Gulf tuna fishery?

    Unit Review: Ecology 148

Cell Biology: World Health 155

1 World Health and Sustainability 157
▶ What do health indicators show about world health and sustainability?

2 Cells and Disease 161
▶ How do observations of cells help doctors and scientists diagnose and study diseases?
  ◦ CASE STUDY: MALARIA 167

3 What Is a Cell? 171
▶ What are the similarities and differences in cells from various living organisms?
  ◦ CASE STUDY: TUBERCULOSIS 177

4 What Do Cells Do? 180
▶ What are the functions of the structures in cells?

5 What Do Specialized Cells Do? 184
▶ What are the specialized structures and functions of cells?

6 Cell Structure and Function 186
▶ What are the fundamental structures and functions of cells?

7 A Model Membrane 191
▶ What structures and characteristics help the cell membrane perform its functions?
  ◦ CASE STUDY: DIABETES 196

8 The Cell Membrane and Diffusion 198
▶ What factors determine whether a substance moves across a model of the cell membrane?
  ◦ CASE STUDY: HIV/AIDS 203

9 Cell Membrane Structure and Function 206
▶ How do the structures of the cell membrane help it function?

10 Functions of Proteins in Cells 213
▶ What are the functions of proteins in cells and viruses?

11 Investigating Enzyme Function 216
▶ How do pH and temperature affect the function of the enzyme lactase?

12 *Photosynthesis and Cellular Respiration* 219
   ▶ How do photosynthesis and cellular respiration meet the energy needs of all organisms?

13 *The Cell Cycle* 229
   ▶ What happens during each phase of the cell cycle, and how are the phases regulated?
   • CASE STUDY: CANCER 233

14 *Stem Cell Differentiation* 236
   ▶ How do stem cells produce specialized cells?

15 *Stem Cell Research* 240
   ▶ What are the current scientific understandings and social debates about stem cell research?

16 *HIV/AIDS Infection and Cell Organelles* 244
   ▶ How does HIV take over a cell's structures and organelles during infection and use them to reproduce?
   • CASE STUDY: ROTAVIRUS 247

17 *Disease Interventions* 250
   ▶ What are the benefits, drawbacks, and trade-offs of some disease interventions?

18 *World Health Proposal* 252
   ▶ How should funding be allocated to address sustainability problems related to world health?

Unit Review: Cell Biology 254

Genetics: Feeding the World 259

1   *A Genetically Modified Solution?*   261
  - ▶ Should your country allow farmers to grow genetically modified corn?

2   *Creating Genetically Modified Bacteria*   269
  - ▶ How do scientists genetically modify an organism?
    - • CASE STUDY: MODIFYING BACTERIA TO PRODUCE BIOFUELS   274

3   *Mitosis and Asexual Reproduction*   278
  - ▶ If a genetically modified cell undergoes mitosis, how likely is it that the daughter cells will contain the inserted gene?

4   *Breeding Corn*   282
  - ▶ How can information about the genetic makeup of plants help farmers breed plants for desirable traits?

5   *Genes and Traits*   290
  - ▶ What can we infer about genes and traits based on heredity patterns?

6   *Breeding Corn for Two Traits*   300
  - ▶ How do scientists predict the results of crossing corn for two kernel characteristics: color and texture?
    - • CASE STUDY: GOLDEN RICE   304

7   *Breeding Better Rice*   307
  - ▶ What trade-offs are involved in selectively breeding a desirable strain of rice?
    - • CASE STUDY: HISTORY OF SELECTIVE CORN BREEDING   311

8   *Interpreting Pedigrees*   316
  - ▶ What information can geneticists obtain by analyzing a pedigree?

9   *DNA Isolation*   324
  - ▶ How is DNA isolated from an organism?

10   *Modeling DNA Structure*   328
  - ▶ What is the molecular structure of DNA?

11   *Genomics*   334
  - ▶ How has genomics contributed to our understanding of heredity?

12   *DNA Replication*   343
- ▶ How does DNA replicate?

13   *Meiosis and Sexual Reproduction*   346
- ▶ How do chromosomes divide during the formation of egg and sperm cells?
  - ◦ CASE STUDY: FAST-GROWING SALMON   **350**

14   *Genes and Chromosomes*   353
- ▶ How do genes and chromosomes behave during meiosis and sexual reproduction?

15   *Evaluating Genetically Modified Organisms*   361
- ▶ What are the benefits and trade-offs of using genetically modified organisms?

16   *Protein Synthesis: Transcription and Translation*   366
- ▶ How does a cell make proteins with the information from DNA?
  - ◦ CASE STUDY: SEEING THE RESULTS OF GENE THERAPY   **372**

17   *Cell Differentiation and Gene Expression*   376
- ▶ How does the same set of genes direct the activities of 220 human cell types?
  - ◦ CASE STUDY: TERMINATOR TECHNOLOGY   **382**

18   *Which Corn is Genetically Modified?*   385
- ▶ Which samples contain genetically modified corn?
  - ◦ CASE STUDY: VIRUS-RESISTANT PAPAYA   **389**

19   *Biopharming Edible Vaccines*   393
- ▶ What are the benefits and trade-offs of genetically modifying crops to contain edible vaccines?

20   *Are GMOs the Solution?*   400
- ▶ Should the government Panel on Genetic Modification approve the planting of genetically modified soybeans?

  Unit Review: Genetics   408

Evolution: Maintaining Diversity 413

1 Biodiversity and Sustainability 415

▶ How are the biodiversity of an ecosystem and the sustainability of human communities related?

2 Human Activities and Biodiversity 422

▶ How do humans alter the biodiversity of groups of taxa?

3 Geologic Time 432

▶ What are the key events of geologic time?

4 Darwin and the Development of a Theory 436

▶ How did Darwin build on his and others' work to develop his ideas about natural selection and evolution?

5 Using Fossil Evidence to Investigate Whale Evolution 443

▶ How does fossil evidence determine the relationships of whale ancestors and their descendants?

6 Evidence from the Fossil Record 446

▶ How do scientists interpret evidence in the fossil record?

7 The Phylogeny of Vertebrates 454

▶ How do you test a tree hypothesis for a group of tax a?

8 Studying Hominids 459

▶ How do biologists study the evolutionary relationships of hominids?

9 Studying Lineages for Conservation 465

▶ How does evidence about phylogenetic relationships assist evolutionary biologists and conservationists in making sustainable conservation decisions?

　• CASE STUDY: MADAGASCAR **469**

10 What Is a Species? 472

▶ How do new species separate from existing species?

11 Natural Selection 482

▶ How does natural selection lead to speciation?

12 *The Genetic Basis of Adaptation* 484
   ▶ How did a change in the environment lead to genetic changes in populations of the rock pocket mouse?

13 *The Processes and Outcomes of Evolution* 489
   ▶ How do evolutionary processes lead to changes in biodiversity?

14 *Ideas about Evolution* 498
   ▶ What scientific evidence and reasoning supports ideas about evolution?

15 *Conservation of an Island Biodiversity Hotspot* 500
   ▶ Which of four areas should receive priority for conservation?

Unit Review: Evolution 507

Appendices

A Literacy Strategies 513

B Science Tools and Skills 523

C Assessment in *Science and Global Issues* 533

D Science Classroom Safety 541

E The International System of Units 543

F Elements and Organisms 545

G Classifying Living Organisms 547

H The Geologic Time Scale 565

I Media Literacy 567

J What is Science? 571

Glossary 573

Index 585

Credits 609

A Letter from SEPUP

SEPUP'S *SCIENCE AND GLOBAL ISSUES: BIOLOGY* is a different kind of science course in three important ways. First, it is student-centered, with the goal of helping all students to understand and enjoy science. Second, it is authentic to the way scientists work, and it asks you to begin to think and investigate as a scientist does. Finally, it is organized around important global issues related to sustainability.

Students and their teachers around the United States tested this course and gave feedback, which we used to revise and improve the program. From this testing we learned what high school students find interesting, what is easier or more difficult for you to learn, and how to provide learning experiences to help you progress in your understanding of science. During this course you will participate in a wide range of activities, including hands-on labs, hands-on models, interactive computer simulations of scientific concepts, readings describing how scientific theories are developed and are applied today, and discussions and debates. You will also connect what you learn to your own life, your community, and the world.

In this course, you will engage in a process of inquiry similar to that which scientists use. Scientific inquiry involves asking questions about the natural world, gathering evidence, and constructing logical explanations to answer those questions. The activities in this course will help you become more confident, competent, and independent in designing, analyzing, and communicating scientific investigations. They will also show you how scientists develop new hypotheses and theories, and help you develop your own explanations of important findings in science.

Like all SEPUP courses, this one teaches science in the context of important issues of our times. In this course all issues relate to the theme of sustainability. Sustainability refers to the ability of a community to meet its present needs without compromising the ability of future generations to meet their own needs.

Each of the scientific topics in this course relates to sustainable development— that is, humans' use of environmental resources in a responsible way to ensure that they will continue to be available for future generations. Issues of science and sustainability directly affect your personal life, your community, and the world as a whole. By considering some of these important issues in this course, you will gain the skills necessary for making decisions critical to your future and the future of other living things on earth.

This course will prepare you with the scientific background and problem-solving skills to help you shape evidence-based opinions and make personal decisions about such global concerns as the sustainability of fisheries, health disparities between developing and developed countries, the development of genetically modified crops as a possible food source, and conservation of diverse ecosystems. You will evaluate scientific evidence to determine which proposed solutions are most likely to be effective. In some cases you will develop your own solutions.

We hope that this course will show you that learning more about science is valuable, enjoyable, and relevant to your life and the future of the world.

The SEPUP *Science and Global Issues* Staff

About SEPUP and *Science and Global Issues*

SEPUP DEVELOPS BOTH comprehensive and supplemental science programs for middle school and high school learners. All SEPUP programs are issue-oriented, and provide learning resources that promote scientific literacy and the importance of evidence in decision making.

Science and Global Issues includes the following features common to SEPUP materials.

Science and Global Issues is research-based.

Units and activities are based on research on how students learn science, including the specific concepts in this course. The course is designed and tested through several rounds of classroom field testing, and revised based on the evidence we gather from students and their teachers. At each phase, several scientists working in fields related to each unit provide insight on current work by scientists and review the written materials.

Science and Global Issues is student-centered.

Because the ideas and knowledge you already have are important starting points for your learning, activities in *SGI* begin with what you know and think about science concepts and sustainability issues. As you conduct the activities, you will expand your understanding, and sometimes you may find that your ideas are changing. You will have many chances to connect what you are doing in science class to your own life and to the world around you.

Science and Global Issues emphasizes inquiry.

In many *SGI* activities you will follow an inquiry approach to learning. Inquiry is a process of asking and answering questions. In this approach, you will analyze data collected by you and by others, investigate the evidence that supports scientific ideas, develop and evaluate explanations, and communicate explanations verbally and in writing. This process of asking questions and searching for logical, evidence-based answers is similar to the processes of inquiry that scientists employ.

Science and Global Issues is an issue-oriented approach to science.

Each *SGI* unit focuses on a major issue related to sustainability. You will build knowledge and understanding of the science concepts most important for understanding the issue. Throughout each unit you will also learn more about the issue and about the perspectives of various people affected by it. In the final activity of each unit, you will apply what you learned to make personal or group decisions about the most sustainable course of action.

Science and Global Issues includes an embedded research-based assessment system.

Research has shown that SEPUP's assessment system helps students learn science, conduct scientific investigations, and apply scientific knowledge to recommend evidence-based choices about issues. The assessments in *SGI* assess your work in the following five key areas:

- Understanding of science concepts
- Ability to design and analyze investigations
- Ability to use evidence and the concept of trade-offs to recommend decisions related to sustainability issues
- Ability to communicate ideas clearly
- Contributions to group activities

Science and Global Issues provides embedded literacy support.

These tested strategies help you to learn how to better read science texts, write clear descriptions of your laboratory results and conclusions, and explain scientific ideas. The strategies also help you to express and discuss your ideas verbally, and engage in scientific argument—a process by which scientists evaluate scientific claims and hypotheses.

How *Science and Global Issues* is organized:

SGI UNIT	SCIENCE CONTENT	ISSUE FOCUS
Sustainability	Sustainability Indicators Life cycle of products Correlation and causality	Aspects of sustainability from a personal, community, and global perspective
Ecology: **Living on Earth**	Biomes Stability and change in ecosystems Invasive species Population dynamics Energy flow through ecosystems Carbon and nitrogen cycles Photosynthesis and cellular respiration Symbiotic relationships Predator–prey relationships	Sustainability from an ecosystems perspective, with a focus on humans' impacts on ecosystems Making decisions regarding fisheries management
Cell Biology: **World Health**	Cellular nature of life Cell structure and function Cell specialization and differentiation Cell division and the cell cycle Microbes and infectious diseases Breakdown of cellular function in diseases, such as diabetes and cancer Respiration, photosynthesis, and cellular macromolecules	Disparities between developing and developed countries in terms of diseases' impacts on life Making decisions about priorities for disease interventions to prevent or treat diseases that limit social, economic, and environmental progress
Genetics: **Feeding the World**	Sexual and asexual reproduction Mitosis and meiosis Genotype and phenotype Mendel's research Genetic crosses, Punnett squares, and pedigrees Patterns of inheritance Genes, alleles, chromosomes, and DNA Flow of genetic information Selective breeding Genetically modified organisms	Comparison of selective breeding and genetic modification Use of genetically modified organisms, particularly in the production of agricultural crops
Evolution: **Maintaining Diversity**	Biodiversity Ecosystem services and humans' impact on species Natural selection and adaptation Darwin's research Geologic time Interpreting the fossil record Phylogeny Microevolution and macroevolution Biological species concept and speciation The genetic basis of evolution	Conserving genetic, species, and ecosystem diversity Ecosystems services and intrinsic value models for conservation

How to Use *Science and Global Issues*

THIS IS AN innovative science program. During this biology course you complete a series of activities, many of them with a partner or in a group of four students. To learn the material in this course, read and conduct each activity carefully. It takes more than simply reading the book to understand the ideas being presented. Participate fully in the laboratory, investigation, simulation, and discussion activities to get the whole picture!

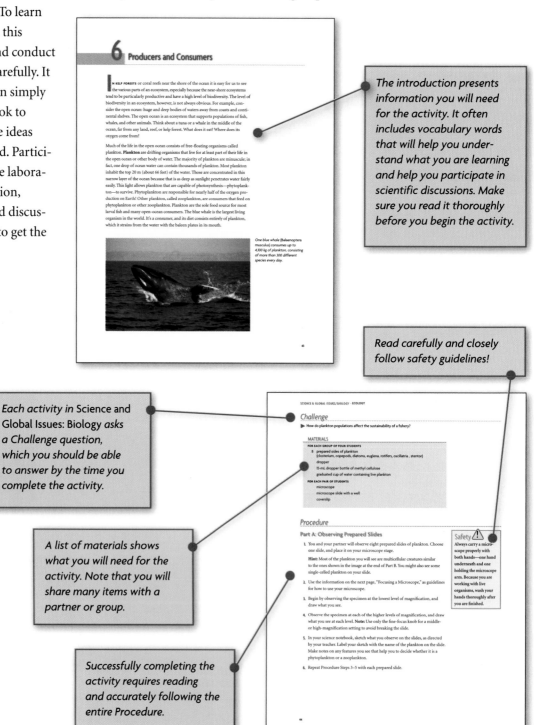

The introduction presents information you will need for the activity. It often includes vocabulary words that will help you understand what you are learning and help you participate in scientific discussions. Make sure you read it thoroughly before you begin the activity.

Read carefully and closely follow safety guidelines!

Each activity in Science and Global Issues: Biology asks a Challenge question, which you should be able to answer by the time you complete the activity.

A list of materials shows what you will need for the activity. Note that you will share many items with a partner or group.

Successfully completing the activity requires reading and accurately following the entire Procedure.

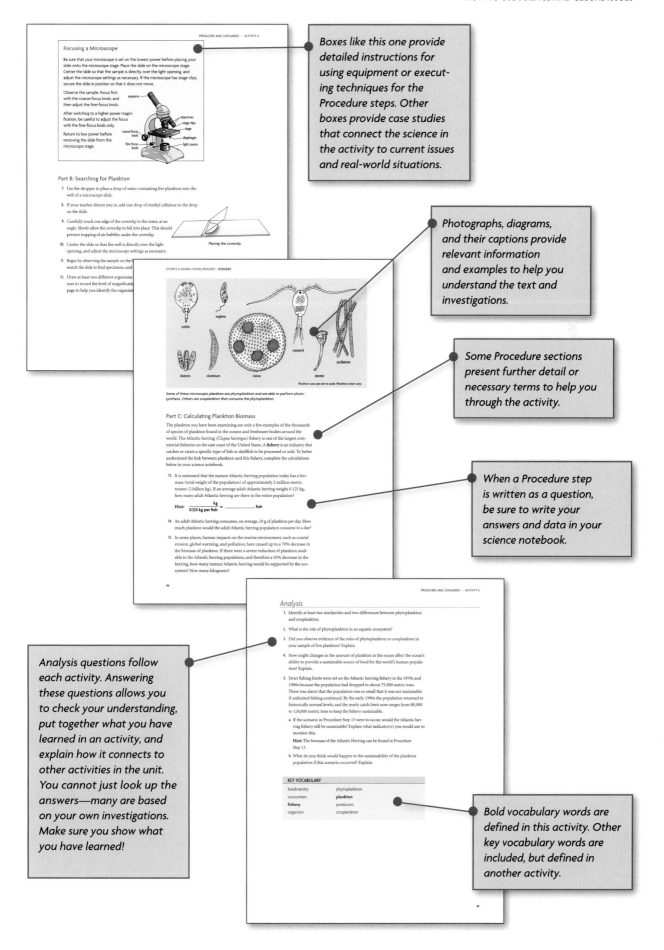

Boxes like this one provide detailed instructions for using equipment or executing techniques for the Procedure steps. Other boxes provide case studies that connect the science in the activity to current issues and real-world situations.

Photographs, diagrams, and their captions provide relevant information and examples to help you understand the text and investigations.

Some Procedure sections present further detail or necessary terms to help you through the activity.

When a Procedure step is written as a question, be sure to write your answers and data in your science notebook.

Analysis questions follow each activity. Answering these questions allows you to check your understanding, put together what you have learned in an activity, and explain how it connects to other activities in the unit. You cannot just look up the answers—many are based on your own investigations. Make sure you show what you have learned!

Bold vocabulary words are defined in this activity. Other key vocabulary words are included, but defined in another activity.

Sustainability

ONE OF THE MOST critical global issues of our time is how to live in ways that will sustain our planet's systems and resources. In this introductory unit to *Science and Global Issues*, you will investigate what it means to live in a sustainable world. You may be familiar with the term sustainability and perhaps have heard it used in different contexts. As you will discover in this unit, however, investigating sustainability often raises more questions than it can answer.

Most sustainability problems are a result of people's overuse and misuse of the earth's resources. The environmental, economic, and social consequences of unsustainable practice affect us on all levels—individually, locally and globally. In this unit, you will identify sustainability challenges in towns, countries, and larger regions around the world. You will learn about communities that have applied scientific knowledge and technology to address their local resource challenges. You will estimate the impact of your own lifestyle on the ecological sustainability of the planet. Finally, you will apply the fundamentals of scientific inquiry to investigate a city facing a sustainability dilemma. The evidence gathered will then be used to suggest a course of action for the community.

1 Our Global Community

PEOPLE ACROSS the world share the same basic needs, despite many differences. Food, water, energy, and shelter sustain our human communities. Any group of people with a common interest living in a particular area—from the smallest village to the largest country—is a community. All the people of the world form a global community, with diverse governments, environments, and cultures. A community is **sustainable** if it meets its present needs without compromising the ability of future generations to meet their own needs. Sustainable activities do not press nature beyond its capacity to regenerate. A sustainable solution to a difficult situation must consider the environmental, economic, and social impacts on the community.

In this course, *Science and Global Issues*, you will explore ways science helps people to understand and develop solutions to sustainability challenges. You will begin this activity by analyzing some statistical indicators from around the globe. An **indicator** is an observation or calculation that shows the presence or state of a condition or trend. By looking at a set of indicators, you will explore the sustainability of human activities in populated regions of the world.

Challenge

▶ What do indicators tell us about regions of the world?

Researchers tag a lemon shark in the Bahamas (left). Students study marine life on the coast of Vancouver Island (above).

MATERIALS

FOR THE CLASS
  set of large Indicator Pie Graphs
  set of region signs
  small magnets

FOR EACH STUDENT
  calculator

Procedure

Part A: World Data

1. On the world map below, identify the eight geographical regions of the world this activity focuses on:

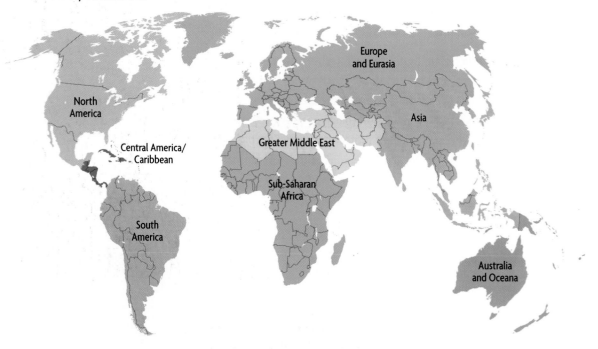

2. Your teacher will designate eight locations in the classroom—one for each region of the world. A sign at each location labels the region.

3. As a class, look at the large Indicator Pie Graph for world population. In this procedure your class represents the entire population of the world. Use the percentages for each region to calculate how many people in your class represent each region.

4. Assign everyone in the class to a region based on the results of the calculation in the previous step. Have each person move to his or her "region" in the classroom.

5. Send one representative from your region to get and bring back the appropriate pie piece from the world population graph.

Indicator Key

INDICATOR	ICON	EXPLANATION
CO_2 emissions		An estimate of the amount of carbon dioxide released into the atmosphere based on United Nations (UN) data.
Energy consumption		The amount of primary energy consumed, on average, by each person living in a particular country or region in a year. All primary sources of energy, such as coal and coal products, oil and petroleum products, natural gas, nuclear power, and hydroelectric power, are included. Energy losses from transportation, friction, heat, and other inefficiencies are included in these totals.
GDP	$ $ $ $ $ $ $ $	The gross domestic product (GDP) is the value of all final goods and services produced within a nation in a given year. It is provided here at purchasing-power-parity (PPP) exchange rates valued at prices prevailing in the United States. This is the measure most economists cite when looking at per-capita wealth and when comparing living conditions or resource consumption across countries.
HIV deaths	HIVHIVHIVHIVHIVHIV	An estimate of the number of adults and children who died of AIDS during a given calendar year.
Internet users		The number of users within an area who access the Internet. Statistics vary from country to country and range from those who access the Internet at least several times a week to those who access it only once in a period of several months.
Malnutrition		The total undernourished population is calculated as the number of people who consume less than a minimum food-energy requirement, which is estimated by sex and age group by a reference body weight. This minimum energy requirement varies by country, but typically averages 1,750–2,030 calories per person daily.
Population		US Census Bureau's International Programs estimates based on population censuses, sample surveys of vital-statistics-registration systems pertaining to the recent past, and assumptions about future trends.
Protected area		The total protected area is the area of land especially dedicated to the protection and maintenance of biological diversity and natural resources. Protected areas include nature reserves, wilderness areas, national parks, natural monuments, habitat-and-species-management areas, protected landscapes and seascapes, and managed-resource areas. The data in this activity excludes marine and intertidal areas.
Threatened species		Critically endangered, endangered, and vulnerable species, including mammals, birds, reptiles, amphibians, fishes, mollusks, insects, and plants.

6. As a class, choose the next indicator to examine. Read aloud the definition of the indicator from the graph. Each piece of the pie represents the region's portion of the world's total for that indicator (not a portion of the regional total).

7. Again, send a representative to get and bring back the appropriate pie piece from the Indicator Pie Graph.

8. Repeat Steps 6–7 until your region has collected all the Indicator Pie Graph pieces.

9. As a class, walk around the room and review the data for each region. Compare

   • the amounts of the indicators relative to other regions

   • how the indicators relate to the population of each region

10. With those in your region, categorize the nine indicators into three groups: economic, environmental, and social. Record the groups, and explain your choices in your science notebook.

11. Using the data on the pie graphs and in the table below, calculate both the gross domestic product (GDP) in U.S. dollars, and the carbon dioxide (CO_2) emissions *per capita* for your region. A sample calculation is shown below the table.

World Data	
INDICATOR	WORLD TOTAL
Population (people)	6,705,900,000
Gross domestic product (US dollars)	69,490,000,000,000
CO_2 emissions (metric tons, per year)	27,246,000,000

SAMPLE CALCULATION: NORTH AMERICA

$$\text{GDP per capita} = \frac{\text{(world total GDP) (North America \% of world total GDP)}}{\text{(world total population) (North America \% of world population)}}$$

$$= \frac{(\$69,490,000,000,000)\,(.25)}{(6,705,900,000 \text{ people})\,(.065)}$$

$$= \$39,856/\text{person}$$

12. Share the per-capita data for all the regions with the class. When the data have been reviewed, discuss
    • how perceptions can change when the data are presented differently
    • what other ways the data could be presented
    • what the indicators in the activity show
    • what the indicators don't show
    • how indicators could be used to evaluate sustainability

Part B: Planet 100

13. Watch the slide presentation "Planet 100." During the presentation, record any
    • information that is surprising.
    • questions the presentation raises for you.

14. When the presentation is over, share your notes according to your teacher's instructions. Discuss what the presentation shows about the sustainability of the global community if the world continues on its current path.

Analysis

1. Did calculating indicators per capita significantly change your perception of the sustainability of a region? Explain why or why not.

2. Indicator levels can vary from country to country within a region. For example, Botswana (population two million) and Ethiopia (population 85 million) are both in Sub-Saharan Africa. However, 95% of the people in Botswana have improved drinking water, compared to 22% of Ethiopians. The average of people with improved drinking water for all countries in Sub-Saharan Africa is 66%.

   a. Use this example to explain how data can be misleading.

   b. Do you think it is better to rely on regional data or data from individual countries when looking at global trends? Support your answer using the example above, and identify the trade-offs of the choice you made.

3. According to the United Nations, South America consumes 4% of the energy generated in the world every year and generates 0.02% of the waste. However, only one country in South America (Brazil) reported its figures to the United Nations.

   a. Make a list of possible reasons why some world data collected by the United Nations is not reported or is underreported.

   b. Describe some consequences of unreported or underreported data.

4. Give an example of at least one potentially useful indicator that was NOT presented in this activity and what it could show about sustainability.

5. Who is responsible for protecting the following resources?

   a. air

   b. water

   c. soil

   d. fossil fuels

KEY VOCABULARY

indicator   **sustainable**

2 Life in Other Countries

IN THE LAST activity you compared indicator data across regions of the world. Within each region, every country and community is unique. Each country has a distinct economy, environment, and society. In this activity you will examine the profiles of four countries. Based on the indicator data provided, you will identify each country's greatest sustainability challenges. You will also explore life in one of the countries by conducting further research.

Challenge

▶ What can indicators reveal about the sustainability challenges facing different countries?

Procedure

1. Assign each of the four countries shown on the following pages to a member of your group. Carefully examine the indicators for your assigned country. Indicators for the United States are also provided for comparison.

2. Think about what the indicator data say about life in your assigned country as compared to life in the United States. Make at least one statement regarding how you think people in your assigned country live. Record your statement in your science notebook. Then, share your ideas with your group.

3. After learning the name of the country you selected, investigate aspects of the country's environment, economics, culture, and history. Record your findings in your science notebook. Make sure to compare life in your assigned country to life in the United States using the following kinds of indicators:

   • economic

   • environmental

   • social

4. Evaluate the statement or statements you made in Step 2 and determine what evidence from your investigation supports it.

An Inuit hunter catches dinner with a fish spear (left). A European woman shops for a meal in a super-market (above).

5. Compare the indicator data provided with the information you collected. Describe how the indicators do or do not adequately show the sustainability issues in that country.

6. Present a summary of life in the country you researched to the others in your group. Be sure to include economic, environmental, and social challenges facing that country.

7. As a group, make a table that shows the most urgent economic, environmental, and social challenges for each country, including the United States. You will need this information to answer the Analysis Questions.

Analysis

1. Which indicator data that were provided were surprising? Describe the data, and explain what they tell you.

2. What other indicator data did you find useful in understanding daily life in other countries? Explain.

3. Look at the economic, environmental, and social challenges in your table from Procedure Step 7. What are the most urgent challenges for each country?

4. Of the countries in the activity, which one(s) have a lifestyle you think is the

   a. most sustainable in the future?

   b. least sustainable in the future?

   Explain the evidence or indicators that support your choices.

5. Suppose representatives from the five countries in this activity came together to discuss improving the sustainability of the planet. Think of the sustainability issues that the countries would want to address by first answering these questions:

   a. Which sustainability challenges might they have in common?

   b. Which sustainability challenges might they NOT have in common?

   c. What challenges does the group face while working together to improve the sustainability of the planet?

6. You find the following posting about the future of the planet on a message board:

   Global Sustainability:
   One challenge
   One solution

   Do you think this should be the slogan for a meeting of world leaders who are trying to improve the environment? Include information from this activity to support your response.

7. How can science contribute to improving the sustainability of the world?

KEY VOCABULARY

indicator   sustainability

Country A

ECONOMIC INDICATORS	
Imported commodities	$121 billion (US) per year
Exported commodities	$161 billion (US) per year
Oil imports	649,000 barrels per day
Oil exports	481,000 barrels per day
ENVIRONMENTAL INDICATORS	
Water shortage	0.3% of area
Basic sanitation	50% population
Fertilizer use	7.7 million metric tons per year
Air quality	28 microgram/m^3 (particulate matter)
SOCIAL INDICATORS	
Population	199 million people
Fertility rate	average 2.3 children per woman
Life expectancy	72 years
Infant mortality	19 per 1,000 live births
Physicians	12 doctors per 10,000 people

Country B

ECONOMIC INDICATORS	
Imported commodities	$219 billion (US) per year
Exported commodities	$146 billion (US) per year
Oil imports	2,159,000 barrels per day
Oil exports	451,000 barrels per day
ENVIRONMENTAL INDICATORS	
Water shortage	80.2% of area
Basic sanitation	72% population
Fertilizer use	16 million metric tons per year
Air quality	72 microgram/m^3 (particulate matter)
SOCIAL INDICATORS	
Population	1,166 million people
Fertility rate	average 3.1 children per woman
Life expectancy	69 years
Infant mortality	57 per 1,000 live births
Physicians	6 doctors per 10,000 people

Country C

ECONOMIC INDICATORS

Imported commodities	$622 billion (US) per year
Exported commodities	$714 billion (US) per year
Oil imports	5,470,000 barrels per day
Oil exports	240,000 barrels per day

ENVIRONMENTAL INDICATORS

Water shortage	9.5% of area
Basic sanitation	100% population
Fertilizer use	1.3 million metric tons per year
Air quality	31 microgram/m^3 (particulate matter)

SOCIAL INDICATORS

Population	127 million people
Fertility rate	average 1.3 children per woman
Life expectancy	82 years
Infant mortality	3 per 1,000 live births
Physicians	21 doctors per 10,000 people

Country D

ECONOMIC INDICATORS

Imported commodities	$23 billion (US) per year
Exported commodities	$59 billion (US) per year
Oil imports	154,000 barrels per day
Oil exports	2,473,000 barrels per day

ENVIRONMENTAL INDICATORS

Water shortage	17.8% of area
Basic sanitation	33% population
Fertilizer use	0.2 million metric tons per year
Air quality	67 microgram/m^3 (particulate matter)

SOCIAL INDICATORS

Population	149 million people
Fertility rate	average 5.8 children per woman
Life expectancy	47 years
Infant mortality	99 per 1,000 live births
Physicians	3 doctors per 10,000 people

United States

ECONOMIC INDICATORS	
Imported commodities	$2,000 billion (US) per year
Exported commodities	$1,163 billion (US) per year
Oil imports	13,710,000 barrels per day
Oil exports	1,165,000 barrels per day
ENVIRONMENTAL INDICATORS	
Water stress	31% of area
Basic sanitation	100% population
Fertilizer use	19.3 million metric tons per year
Air quality	23 microgram/m^3 (particulate matter)
SOCIAL INDICATORS	
Population	307 million people
Fertility rate	average 2.0 children per woman
Life expectancy	78 years
Infant mortality	7 per 1,000 live births
Physicians	26 doctors per 10,000 people

3 Sustainability Case Studies

COMMUNITIES AROUND THE world face a variety of sustainability challenges. Even though the challenges differ from one community to the next, there is often one similarity: many sustainability issues are a result of overuse of the earth's resources. In this activity, you will read about two communities that have taken steps toward more sustainable use of resources.

Challenge

▶ What steps have communities taken to live in ways that are more sustainable?

MATERIALS

FOR EACH STUDENT

Student Sheet 3.1, "Summary Sheet: Sustainability Case Studies"

Student Sheet 3.2, "Three-Level Reading Guide: Sustainability Case Studies"

Procedure

1. As you complete the reading, fill out Student Sheet 3.1, "Summary Sheet: Sustainability Case Studies."

2. When you have finished the reading, complete Student Sheet 3.2, "Three-Level Reading Guide: Sustainability Case Studies."

Reading

EVERYDAY DECISIONS

Every day people make personal decisions about transportation, food, and use of water and other resources. On an individual level, these decisions seem to have little impact on the world. However, when the effects are multiplied by large numbers of people, the results are significant. The sum of many individuals' actions can increase or decrease the sustainability of the community. Here are the true stories of two places where the actions of individuals made a difference in the sustainability issues facing their communities.

BEDDINGTON ZERO FOSSIL ENERGY DEVELOPMENT, ENGLAND

Beddington Zero Fossil Energy Development (BedZED) is one of a handful of developments, or "ecovillages," in the world that were designed and built to encourage people to live using fewer resources. Completed in 2002 near London,

BedZED has 100 living and work spaces. A team of scientists, engineers, and architects designed the community, with help from the local government.

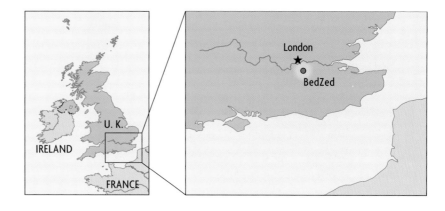

One of the primary goals of BedZED was to reduce the amount of fossil fuels burned for energy. Our continued reliance on fossil fuels is releasing more and more carbon dioxide into earth's atmosphere. A growing body of evidence shows that, as a result, climates around the world are changing—often in harmful ways. Developed countries, in particular, such as England and the United States, give off relatively high amounts of carbon dioxide emissions.

To build BedZED the designers chose cost-effective materials that had a life cycle with a smaller ecological impact than standard products. The **product life cycle** describes the amounts of resources and energy it takes to make a product, the length of the product's usefulness to the consumer, and how the product is disposed of, recycled, or reclaimed when it is no longer needed. In general, a more sustainable product is made from relatively more reclaimed material and less raw material, and requires less energy to produce and transport it.

BedZED is one of the world's best-known eco-villages.

The life cycle of this wood waste could be extended if it were recycled or repurposed instead of being placed in a landfill.

For example, the life cycle of a wooden board includes the energy and resources used in cutting the tree, transporting it to the mill, cutting the board, shipping it to a distributor, and transporting it to the construction site. The "life" of the wooden board continues for however long it is part of the constructed house. The useful life of the board is likely to end when the house is torn down or remodeled. Since construction debris usually ends up in a landfill or is incinerated, more energy is consumed to transport the board to a landfill or incinerator, its final destination. The "life" of the board, however, goes on because there are both economic and environmental costs to maintain it in the landfill or burn it in an incinerator.

Sometimes a board does not go to the landfill or incinerator but is, instead, reused or recycled. Then the materials would be put back into the "cycle," whether to become part of another house or go into another product. In either event more energy and resources go into this next "life." In this way, a product's life cycle is never really a closed loop. The term "cycle" can be misleading because the life cycle of a product does not necessarily mean the resources in the products are reclaimed and continually cycled through different states.

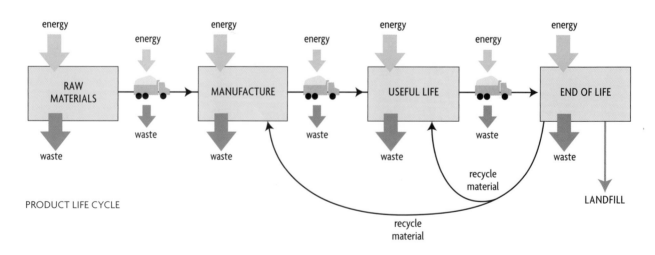

PRODUCT LIFE CYCLE

As well as selecting materials that have a lighter ecological impact, BedZED's builders designed the complex so that residents would rely less on energy and water in their daily routines. For example, the apartments have energy-efficient refrigerators, washers, dryers, and other appliances. Rooms and windows are placed to maximize the amount of sun to heat the house during the day. Water meters are installed at eye level in the kitchens, rather than being put outside of or under the homes, so that residents can monitor the amount of water they use. A community composting and

One of BedZED's goals is to provide alternatives to private car travel.

recycling system begins with a built-in waste collection center in each kitchen. Recycling goes even further with a special office-paper recycling plan in which all used paper is recycled and returned to BedZED for reuse.

BedZED's electrical power was originally generated by solar panels and a biofuel power system. The biofuel power system generated energy by burning recycled garden waste instead of fossil fuels. The biofuel power system supplied electricity and heat to the community. Unfortunately, there were problems with the system. Residents had to use gas-powered water heaters, and a majority of their electricity came from the regional power plant.

Since transportation contributes to carbon dixoide emissions, BedZED was designed to help its residents reduce trips outside the community. For example, there are on-site workspaces, exercise facilities, a community center, and a bicycle repair shop. When residents travel, they do so by taking advantage of BedZED's car-sharing program, electric cars, nearby bus and subway lines, and bicycles. Although BedZED residents travel less frequently by car, they tend to fly more often. As a result, they have a slightly higher than average overall transportation impact.

Having so many resources within BedZED also has the effect of maintaining a strong social community. About 84% of the residents feel that the community is an improvement on their previous neighborhood. On average, they know more than twice as many neighbors as those in the surrounding area. Since the apartments are desirable places to live in, the sale price of a BedZED apartment is higher than similar nearby apartments.

After the project was completed, data from water and energy indicators were collected. In comparison to the average Londoner, BedZED residents use less energy in the home, consume less water, and drive fewer miles.

Some of the indicators, measured five years after project ompletion, are shown in the table below.

BedZED Data

INDICATOR	AVERAGE IN ENGLAND	BEDZED GOAL	2007 BEDZED AVERAGE
Energy consumption			
Electricity consumption at home (kWh/person/day)	4.5	3.0 (33% reduction)	3.4
Heat consumption, space and water heating (kWh/person/day)	21.2	2.1 (90% reduction)	5.2
Total energy consumption (kWh/person/day)	25.7	5.1 (80% reduction)	8.6
Water consumption (liters/person/day)	150	100.0 (33% reduction)	72 + 15 recycled or rain water
Carbon emissions (kg CO_2/person/day)	25	0 (100% reduction)	1.4
Personal fossil fuel car mileage (km/person/year)	6,344	3,172.0 (50% reduction)	2,318

SOURCE: BioRegional, 2009

While BedZED has met its goal of reducing residential energy consumption, it has experienced its share of challenges. Energy consumption has not been reduced as much as planned. The cost to build BedZED ran higher than expected. Critics claim BedZED is a failure because it relies on some fossil fuel for energy. Supporters say BedZED is still successful because it took fewer resources to build than other living complexes, and residents use less water and energy than they would in traditional homes.

The photovoltaic solar panels at BedZED provide electricity and help shade the house in warm weather.

DAREWADI WATERSHED RESTORATION PROJECT, INDIA

Darewadi is a rural village of about 2,500 people located in India, east of the city of Mumbai. The residents of Darewadi are primarily farmers and herders, who make their living raising crops and animals to sell in nearby communities.

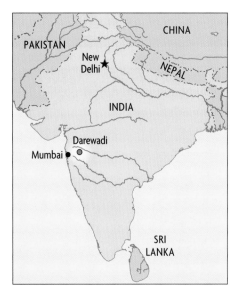

Although the region receives little rainfall each year, the local resources had supported the village population for many years. However, by the early 1980s, overfarming, overgrazing, and population growth caused changes to the local ecosystem. As a result, less arable land was available because farming had exhausted the soil. To create more farmland the residents began clear-cutting the natural landscape, removing trees and shrubs that held water in the ground. This dried out the soil even further. The villagers faced a crisis in the mid-1990s when there was no longer enough water and arable land to support the residents of the village. Not wanting to abandon their homes, the residents of Darewadi had to find ways to support themselves. Many traveled for months on end to neighboring villages and cities to find work. For those who stayed, water was brought in by truck during the extremely dry summer months.

The Darewadi villagers' everyday activities, over the years, had caused their land to degrade. **Land degradation** is the decline in the overall quality of soil, water, or vegetation caused by human activities or natural events. Land degradation caused by human activities is not unique to Darewadi—it occurs all over the world.

In 1996, a nonprofit group together with the Indian and German governments started the Indo-German Watershed Development Project. The project depended on the knowledge of scientists that specialized in agriculture, forestry, and the movement of water. The goal of the project was to restore the Darewadi watershed and land to a condition that could once again support the population.

First, the project convinced Darewadi residents to change their approach to the land and trained them in skills that would restore the ecosystem. Working with the leadership in the village, specialists taught sustainable farming practices, and residents learned how to build trenches and dams to harvest rainwater and underground water. The villagers made a difficult choice when they agreed to stop raising and herding grazing animals. This ban protected the land from further harm and gave it time to recover. To encourage regrowth, the villagers planted native trees and grasses, and prohibited the cutting of all trees and shrubs for five years. In addition, a community board made up of members from every social group was set up to oversee the project. Some indicator data for the project is shown on the next page.

The Darewadi Watershed Restoration Project Data

INDICATOR	BEFORE PROJECT, 1996	AFTER PROJECT, 2001	JANUARY 2005
Months requiring delivery of drinking water by truck	February to June	none	none
Active wells (number)	23	63	67
Livestock	1,507	780	1,007
Agricultural employment (months per year)	3–4	9–10	9–10
Agricultural wage rate (rupees per day)	20–30	40–50	40–50
Kitchen gardens	0	30	30
Televisions	3	76	76
Bicycles	2	122	122
Waste land area (hectares)	167	17	15
Cropped area (hectares)	800	107	1,085

SOURCE: Watershed Organization Trust, 2005

Within five years positive effects were seen in the Darewadi community. The volume of water in the watershed increased, and it was no longer necessary to truck in water. Grasses and trees grew back. Rather than relying on a single grain crop, millet, farmers grew a variety of new crops, including vegetables. More residents were able to stay and farm year-round in Darewadi. Villagers learned to maintain the local resources by using different methods of tending to the soil.

SOLVING SUSTAINABILITY CHALLENGES

These two case studies show the changes communities can make by applying science and technology to improve their lives and maintain natural resources for future generations. In both BedZED and Darewadi, scientific knowledge contributed to improving the economic, environmental, and social lives of the communities. These examples show how science and technology can play an important part in solving sustainability issues.

Analysis

1. For each of the two case studies explain:

   a. What kind of indicators were monitored—economic, environmental, and/or social?

   b. What do the indicators show about the effects of the changes that were made?

2. What specific science- and technology-related changes did the communities make that lowered their

   a. energy use?

   b. water use?

3. Give an example of a potentially unsustainable practice involving natural resources in your community.

   a. Use indicator data to show how it is not sustainable.

   b. Propose alternatives to this activity that might be more sustainable. Explain why your choice(s) are more sustainable.

   c. What are the trade-offs you would have to consider when deciding whether or not to adopt the alternatives?

   d. What indicators would you use to determine if the alternative was sustainable?

KEY VOCABULARY

indicator	**product life cycle**
land degradation	sustainability

4 Ecological Footprint

EVERY HUMAN ACTIVITY involves resources from the earth. An "ecological footprint" is the term often used to describe the impact of an activity on the environment. An **ecological footprint** is a quantitative measurement that estimates the amount of resources consumed and waste produced by an individual, a community, a population, or even a manufactured product. This complicated calculation combines the effects of various environment-related activities, which are measured in different units, into a single indicator of environmental sustainability. It shows the impact in terms of the land area of the earth that is required to sustain the activity.

For an example consider a typical bowl of breakfast cereal. Here is a list of some of the resources involved in getting that bowl of cereal to your table:

- The ingredients in the cereal came from plants, and to get these plants to grow a farmer needed a tract of land, water, soil, and usually, fertilizer.

- Processing and transporting the ingredients required energy (likely fossil fuels) and materials, such as trucks, each of which has its own footprint.

- Your bowl and spoon were made from raw materials that were mined somewhere on earth, and manufactured somewhere.

- The milk in the bowl of cereal came from a cow, which needed space to live, grass or feed to eat, and likely, electrical energy to run the machines that milked the cow. Transporting, pasteurizing, and packing the milk involved

To calculate the ecological footprint of your breakfast cereal, include the cultivation, transportation, and processing of the wheat and other ingredients.

more land for roads, factories, and grocery stores. More natural resources were used to make the container (trees or fossil fuels).

- The milk had to be kept cool in a refrigerator, and refrigerators require electrical energy. Electricity is often produced by burning fossil fuels, which must be extracted from the earth, transported, and refined, and which release carbon dioxide when burned.

- Eventually you will throw away or recycle the cereal box and milk container, which will take up space in a landfill or be subject to more resource consumption at a recycling plant.

The many components in the life cycle of the bowl of cereal include the raw materials, the energy used, and land needed. All of the components require space on and resources from the earth. The ecological footprint of the bowl of cereal shows the land area it takes to sustain the entire life cycle of the bowl. In comparison, the ecological footprint of the bowl of cereal is likely to be larger than a bowl of fresh fruit from the same location that was not as heavily processed. This is because the fresh food requires fewer raw materials, less processing, and less energy.

Challenge

▶ Can the earth's ecosystems sustain our current use of resources?

MATERIALS

FOR EACH STUDENT
Student Sheet 4.1, "Ecological Footprint Homework"
computer with Internet access

Every day choices, such as whether to hang clothes or put them in the dryer, affect the size of a person's ecological footprint.

Procedure

1. Collect the necessary information listed on Student Sheet 4.1, "Ecological Footprint Survey Questions," with your family, and bring the information to class.

2. Go to the SEPUP *Science and Global Issues* website at *sepuplhs.org/sgi,* and follow the links to the ecological footprint survey. Answer the questions as accurately as you can.

3. After completing the survey, record your "footprint in global acres" and the "number of planets" in your science notebook.

4. Share your results with your group. Compare your ecological footprint to those of others in the group, to average Americans, and to average individuals in the other countries shown in the table below.

Ecological Footprint by Country		
COUNTRY	AVERAGE AREA NEEDED TO SUSTAIN ACTIVITY (ACRES/PERSON)	AREA NEEDED IF THE WORLD POPULATION LIVED LIKE THIS (NUMBER OF PLANETS)
Nigeria	8.8	0.2
India	16.4	0.4
Brazil	31.6	0.8
Japan	123.3	3.2
United States	246.4	6.3

5. Predict what would happen if you changed one quantity—the answer to one question—in the survey. Write your prediction in your science notebook.

6. Go back to the on-line survey, and test your prediction from Step 5. Once you make the change in your survey responses, the effect appears on the screen. Record the change you made and the result in your science notebook.

7. Repeat Step 6 until you have figured out what changes most reduced your ecological footprint.

8. As a group, discuss three ways in which you might significantly change your daily activities to lower your ecological footprint. Record these ideas in your science notebook.

Analysis

1. How did your ecological footprint compare to that of an average person in the United States? Explain why you think your ecological footprint is or is not different from the average person's.

2. Are the footprints of the average person in other countries consistent with what you investigated about life in other countries in previous activities? Support your answer with the indicator data presented in previous activities.

3. What are the characteristics of a lifestyle that is

   a. more ecologically sustainable?

   b. less ecologically sustainable?

4. a. What questions do you think are missing from the ecological footprint survey?

   b. Explain why they might not have been included.

5. What are the strengths and weaknesses of using "number of planets" as an indicator for measuring the environmental impact of someone's lifestyle?

6. When the ecological footprint of every person on earth is considered, it requires 1.5 earths to sustain the global community indefinitely at the current population and rate of consumption.

   a. Is the population of the world ecologically sustainable at the current rate of consumption?

   b. If the world's population continues this level of consumption, what do you think will happen in the future?

KEY VOCABULARY

ecological footprint   sustainability

5 Jaffrey City's Problem

JAFFREY CITY IS a sprawling community located on the shores of Jaffrey Lake. The area has grown considerably in the past 20 years, which has been good for the local economy. But recently Jaffrey residents have noticed that Jaffrey Lake, which used to be clean, full of wildlife, and a great place to swim, has changed. Slimy, green algae floats on the surface, and the water has turned murky. People are finding dead fish on the shore, and everyone is afraid they'll get sick if they swim in the lake. Preliminary water tests found higher-than-normal levels of two substances: phosphates and nitrates. The Jaffrey City Council decided that the lake is in danger, and it ordered more tests on the lake water.

In this activity, you will take the role of scientists testing water from Jaffrey Lake to determine the levels of phosphate and nitrate. This data will provide **evidence,** information used to refute or support a claim, about the water quality. Based on the evidence, you will identify the likely source or sources of the contamination.

Challenge

▶ How can phosphate and nitrate indicators help identify the contamination problem in Jaffrey Lake?

MATERIALS

FOR THE CLASS

40   dropper bottles of Jaffrey Lake water (locations 1–40)

FOR EACH GROUP OF FOUR STUDENTS

Chemplate®

dropper

set colored pencils

FOR EACH PAIR OF STUDENTS

12   phosphate- or nitrate-test strips

phosphate or nitrate color-comparison chart

cup with rinse water

paper towels

white scrap paper

FOR EACH STUDENT

Student Sheet 5.1, "Jaffrey Lake Water Testing"

safety goggles

Procedure

1. Of the 40 possible locations to test in the lake, your group was paid to conduct 12 tests for each substance. Create a data table in your science notebook where you will record the results of the tests. You will record the water location number, the Chemplate cup number, and the test results for nitrate and phosphate.

2. In your group, decide which pair of students will test for nitrate and which will test for phosphate.

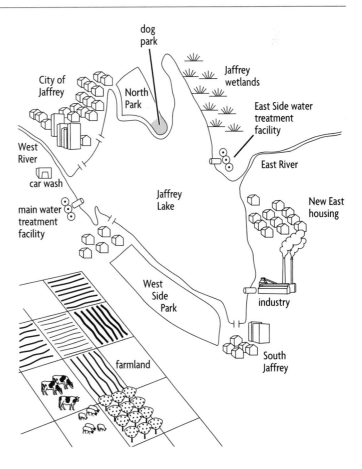

3. With your group, look at Student Sheet 5.1, "Jaffrey Lake Water Testing," and select three of the locations numbered 1–40 on the map to test first. Choose locations you think will most likely contain high concentrations of the substances. Record in your notebook why you predicted these locations.

4. To begin the testing, take your Chemplate to the "lake area" and find the three bottles with the matching location numbers. Place 5 drops from each location in separate Chemplate cups and bring it back to your table. Record the location numbers and the corresponding Chemplate cup numbers in your data table.

5. Test the three waters for your substance, as described in the testing procedure below. Record the data in your table.

   TESTING PROCEDURE:

   a. Place the white paper on top of the paper towel.

   b. Label the test strip with the location number.

   c. Put one drop of location water on the end of the test strip.

   d. For the phosphate test, compare the test strip to the color chart. For the nitrate test, wait one minute before comparing.

   e. Record the result in your table.

   f. Rinse out the dropper with water in the rinsing cup.

6. Using the results from your tests, begin to complete Student Sheet 5.1, "Jaffrey Lake Water Testing." Choose different colored pencils to represent the levels of each substance, and fill in the key using the scales shown on the color-comparison chart. Identify your map as either "nitrate" or "phosphate" concentrations, depending on the substance you are testing.

7. Share your data with the other pair in your group. As a group, choose three additional locations to test that are based on the results.

8. Repeat Steps 4–7 until you have tested 12 locations.

9. Compare maps and look for any patterns in the concentration levels and locations of the substances. Compare your data to the county standards shown below:

Phosphate in Jaffrey Lake	
NATURAL CONCENTRATION (PPM)	LOCAL LIMIT (PPM)
0.05	0.1

Nitrate in Jaffrey Lake	
NATURAL CONCENTRATION (PPM)	LOCAL LIMIT (PPM)
<2	10

10. Investigate both phosphate and nitrate and the environmental effects of these substances in high amounts.

11. Prepare a formal report for the Jaffrey City Council that includes the following:

    • A statement about the typical natural and man-made sources and amounts of phosphate and nitrate.

    • Information on the effects of high levels of phosphate and nitrate.

    • An explanation of the role of phosphate and nitrate in the eutrophication in the lake. **Eutrophication** is a dramatic increase of available nutrients in the water, resulting in an increase in plant growth.

    • Your group's test results and map.

    • Your group's conclusion about the likely source(s) and severity of the contamination.

    • A recommendation, if any, for future testing.

Analysis

1. What evidence is there that indicates Jaffrey Lake has a contamination problem?

2. It is estimated that nearly 50% of the lakes in North America have high phosphate or nitrate levels. Estimates for other regions of the world range from 30% (Africa) to 54% (Asia). How might these indicators inform decisions about our current and future water-treatment systems?

3. Suppose there is another lake in another city located farther down the East River.

    a. How might the city that is further down the river be affected by the contamination in Jaffrey Lake?

    b. If it is determined that the contamination in the other lake is partly a result of discharge from the East River, whose responsibility is it to clean that lake?

4. Look at the graph below, showing the average concentrations of four indicators in a lake over 60 years. Based on the graph data only, decide if you agree or disagree with the three statements below, and explain why. The following definitions may help you evaluate the claims:

A **correlation** is a relationship between one event or action and another. A positive correlation means that as one event or action becomes large, the other also becomes large, and vice versa. A negative correlation means that when one event or action becomes larger, the other becomes smaller, and vice versa.

A **causal relationship** between two correlated events is when one event (called the cause) directly produces another event (called the effect). In a causal relationship, the cause(s) alone produce the effect.

a. *There is a strong negative correlation between the phosphate concentration and the fish population. In other words, the phosphate concentration increased while the fish population decreased.*

b. *There is a strong positive correlation between the nitrate concentration and the algae concentration. In other words, after the nitrate concentration rose, the algae concentration increased in a similar way.*

c. *The increased nitrate concentration is causing the increased algae concentration. There is a causal relationship between the two.*

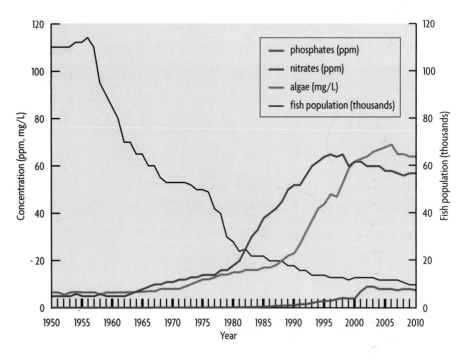

KEY VOCABULARY

correlation	**evidence**
causal relationship	indicator
eutrophication	

6 Jaffrey City's Master Plan

THE PEOPLE OF Jaffrey City have decided that in its current state Jaffrey Lake is not sustainable, and they are committed to reducing the contamination. There is some evidence that if no more phosphates are added to the lake, the affected ecosystem may recover. They want to stop the algae growth and reduce any health hazards from the nitrates. The City Council's goals to make the lake sustainable are to

- protect wildlife
- improve water quality
- prevent future pollution

Jaffrey City has a budget of $2 million per year to spend on cleaning up the lake.

In this activity, you will use the test results from the previous activity to create a master plan for Jaffrey Lake. When developing such a plan, it is important to consider the needs and interests of all of the stakeholders. **Stakeholders** are individuals or groups who are affected by or involved in a decision. To get enough stakeholders to support and implement a plan, **trade-offs,** or outcomes given up to gain other outcomes, may have to be made.

Protecting wildlife is one part of maintaining a sustainable ecosystem.

Storm drains often discharge run-off directly into lakes and streams.

Challenge

▶ How can a sustainability plan be developed for Jaffrey Lake that will balance the interests of all of the stakeholders?

MATERIALS

FOR EACH GROUP OF FOUR STUDENTS

    set of 9 Proposal Idea Cards

Procedure

Part A: Developing a Proposal

1. In your group, read the summary of the perspectives of each stakeholder on the next pages. Use the summaries to identify the priorities for each stakeholder in the community during the decision-making process.

2. Review each of the Proposal Idea Cards. Discuss the pros and cons of each suggestion with your group.

3. Keeping the $2 million budget per year and the stakeholders' interests in mind, create a sustainability proposal for Jaffrey Lake. Your group's solution should include:

- The Jaffrey City idea(s) you would adopt and the evidence from the previous activity that supports your choice.

- Indicators that will measure the success of your proposal in the future.

- A three-part explanation of the likely impact of your proposal:

  · Economic—explain what money will be spent, and when, in the next 5–10 years.

  · Environmental—predict what will happen to the phosphate and nitrate levels in Jaffrey Lake, and how any changes will affect the lake environment.

  · Social—explain how the community will be affected and predict which stakeholders will support your proposal.

4. Present your group's proposal to the class with the goal of convincing your classmates to choose your plan over the other proposals.

5. As a class, discuss the strengths and weaknesses of each proposal.

Part B: Voting for a Master Plan

6. Your teacher will assign you a role as one of the stakeholders. Cast your vote on which proposal should be implemented in Jaffrey Lake *as you believe the stakeholder would vote.*

7. Tally the votes of the stakeholders to see which proposal will become the Master Plan for Jaffrey Lake.

Jaffrey Lake Stakeholders

Jaffrey City resident

- Does not spend time at the lake or depend on it
- Doesn't want to pay more in taxes or fees
- Is concerned about industry discharging pollutants into the lake

SUPPORTED PROPOSAL IDEAS

Awareness Campaign, Phosphate and Nitrate Ban

OPPOSED PROPOSAL IDEAS

New Main Water-treatment Plant, Septic-tank Upgrades

Car-wash Owner

- Upgraded discharge system in the past five years and is still in debt for it
- Feels he has already done his part, and so the City needs to clean up the lake without raising his cost of doing business
- Does not want to be blamed for contamination problem in the lake

SUPPORTED PROPOSAL IDEAS

Awareness Campaign, Agricultural Incentives

OPPOSED PROPOSAL IDEAS

Phosphate and Nitrate Ban, New Main Water-treatment Plant

New East Housing Representative

- Spent a lot of money to put in a local sewage-treatment system
- Wants to continue to be steward of the lake
- Wants to maintain property values
- Cannot carry additional cost of new city treatment plant

SUPPORTED PROPOSAL IDEAS

Lakefront-protection Plan, Phosphate and Nitrate Ban, Awareness Campaign, Septic-tank Upgrades, Agricultural Incentives, Lake Research

OPPOSED PROPOSAL IDEAS

New Main Water-treatment Plant

Farmer

- Has always used fertilizer to grow strong crops
- Feels that his farming practice can improve with better technology
- Has applied to get some federal money to improve his farming but application is stalled
- More costs are likely to put the farm out of business

SUPPORTED PROPOSAL IDEAS

Lakefront-protection Plan

OPPOSED PROPOSAL IDEAS

Agricultural Incentive, Phosphate and Nitrate Ban, New Main Water-treatment Plant

Environmentalist

- Wants to act now before it is too late to restore the lake ecosystem
- Willing to spend whatever money it takes
- Wants stricter regulations and better enforcement for protecting the marsh area and wildlife

SUPPORTED PROPOSAL IDEAS

Lake Research, Lakefront Protection Plan, Agricultural Incentives, New Main Water-treatment Plant with phosphate and nitrate removal, Septic-tank Upgrades

OPPOSED PROPOSAL IDEAS

none

Fertilizer-plant Owner

- Pleased that demand continues to rise and business is doing very well
- Uses nitrate and phosphate sources that are reclaimed from nature when possible
- Interested in cheaper and quicker ways to reclaim material rich in nutrients from water
- Is aware that people think she is discharging into the lake and wants to convince them that her plant is clean

SUPPORTED PROPOSAL IDEAS

New Main Water-treatment Plant with phosphate and nitrate removal, Agricultural Incentives, Lake Research

OPPOSED PROPOSAL IDEAS

Phosphate and Nitrate Ban

Fisherman

- Fifth-generation fisherman and very proud of work
- Worried about the future of his profession since fish population has significantly declined
- Worried about the decline in cleanliness of the lake
- Has low profit and cannot pay additional fees or taxes

SUPPORTED PROPOSAL IDEAS

New Main Water-treatment Plant with phosphate removal, Lake Research

OPPOSED PROPOSAL IDEAS

Lakefront Protection Plan

City Councilor

- Wants to please as many stakeholders as possible so as to ensure re-election
- Needs a legal and fair solution
- Doesn't want to raise taxes or fees
- Doesn't want to put the city into debt

SUPPORTED PROPOSAL IDEAS

New Main Water-treatment Plant, Agricultural Incentives, Phosphate and Nitrate Ban, Awareness Campaign

OPPOSED PROPOSAL IDEAS

Lakefront Protection Plan

Land Developer

- Developed New East Housing area and wants to develop the marsh area
- Wants fewer regulations on building
- Has a history of being a responsible builder who is a good leader for businesses
- Wants cost of doing business to be as low as possible

SUPPORTED PROPOSAL IDEAS

Phosphate and Nitrate Ban, Awareness Campaign

OPPOSED PROPOSAL IDEAS

Lakefront Protection Plan

Wastewater Plant Manager

- Knows that wastewater can be completely cleaned, for a price and with proper equipment
- Wants clean water standards to be met
- Wants to upgrade the plant but doesn't have the money to do so
- Doesn't want liability for poor plant because City has thus far not supported improving it

SUPPORTED PROPOSAL IDEAS

New Main Water-treatment Plant with phosphate and nitrate removal, Septic-tank Upgrades, Lake Research

OPPOSED PROPOSAL IDEAS

Lakefront Protection Plan

Analysis

1. Describe the Proposal Idea you voted for in Procedure Step 6 and state the major evidence that most influenced your choice. Then describe the trade-offs of the proposal. The trade-offs should include the social, economic, and environmental impacts on the community.

2. Which stakeholder is most likely to

   a. support your proposal?

   b. oppose your proposal?

   Explain why he or she would support or oppose your proposal.

3. Should each stakeholder's interests have equal weight in the City Council's decision? Why or why not?

4. What could the residents of Jaffrey City do if the indicators from the Master Plan showed the health of Jaffrey Lake had not improved five years after your Master Plan was implemented?

5. Assume that many residents of Jaffrey City were aware of the dangers of phosphate and nitrate in the lake. For many years, the community knew of the likely sources of the contaminants. What are some of the possible reasons action was not taken to improve the lake before now?

6. How do you think a local situation like the one at Jaffrey City might be similar and different from what might happen

   a. in other countries around the world?

   b. in a lake that shares boundaries with more than one country?

7. There are many places in the world where sewage receives minimal treatment or is discharged directly into the environment. This has an effect on the water, soil, and the health of the nearby population. In the statistics shown below, "basic sanitation" means those who live in a structure with a connection to a sewer, septic system, or improved pit latrines. Basic sanitation does not necessarily include removal of phosphates, nitrates, or other contaminants.

Basic Sanitation					
INDICATOR	USA	JAPAN	INDIA	BRAZIL	NIGERIA
Basic sanitation (% population)	100	100	72	50	33

   a. For the countries above that do not have basic sanitation, what are some of the economic, social, and environmental challenges to overcoming this sustainability problem?

   b. What ideas do you have that could help overcome these challenges?

8. How do you think each of the following are involved in sustainable decision-making:

   a. science and technology

   b. individuals

   c. government

9. Identify a problem(s) in your own community that relates to the sustainability of the environment. Then identify what scientific knowledge would be needed for developing a plan to improve the situation.

KEY VOCABULARY

evidence	sustainability
indicator	**trade-off**
stakeholder	

Unit Review: Sustainability

Sustainability

A community is sustainable if it meets its present needs without compromising the ability of future communities to meet their own needs. Sustainability problems have adverse environmental, economical, and social impacts on communities. The consequences of unsustainable practices affect us at all levels—individually, locally, and globally.

To evaluate the sustainability of a human activity scientists identify the kinds of data that indicate problems or absence of problems. Some of these indicators reveal information on the quality of life in relation to natural resources consumption in a community. Measured nutrient levels in lake water, for example, identify contaminants that are having an effect on water quality and the ecosystem.

KEY VOCABULARY

sustainability

indicator

Natural Resources

One of the challenges for our global community is to agree on ways to sustain our planet's finite natural resources and, where necessary, to change the way we now live. Human activities that severely degrade land and water quality are usually a result of international, national, local, or individual choices. A community's policies can encourage or mandate individuals and industries to alter their practices to prevent further abuse of resources.

One tool for estimating an individual's role in the depletion of resources is the ecological footprint calculator. This is a computer model that estimates the area of the earth that is required to sustain an activity. An ecological footprint calculator helps an individual voluntarily take action to reduce his or her own ecological impact. Another way to analyze the environmental impact of daily life is to outline the life cycles of the products we each use. The product life cycle describes the resources and energy involved in making the product, the length of its usefulness, the environmental impact of the product, and how it is disposed of, recycled, or reclaimed when it is no longer useful.

KEY VOCABULARY	
ecological footprint	land degradation
eutrophication	product life cycle

Making sustainable decisions

Successful decision-making takes into account evidence and the interests of all stakeholders. Solutions to sustainability challenges are technologically, environmentally, economically, and socially viable. However, a community often must accept some trade-offs when seeking a sustainable response to a community problem.

KEY VOCABULARY	
evidence	stakeholder
trade-off	

Inquiry and the Nature of Science

Collecting and analyzing relevant data allows scientists to identify relationships between human activity and the resulting ecological, environmental and social impacts. Further research can determine if there is a causal relationship between two correlated events.

Models are useful for representing complex environmental phenomena. Information from models, and other types of evidence, inform decision-making that affects sustainability.

KEY VOCABULARY
correlation
causal relationship

Ecology: Living on Earth

OUR WORLD HOLDS an amazing variety of organisms living in all sorts of environments. Organisms affect their environments, and in turn the environment affects them. Understanding the complex web of relationships within ecosystems is essential to understanding their sustainability.

Humans interact with ecosystems in many ways. We rely on ecosystems to supply us food, shelter, energy, and the oxygen we breathe. As we consume resources and discard our wastes, however, we change ecosystems and sometimes threaten their sustainability.

In this unit you will examine a variety of ecological issues including the impact of human activities on ecosystems. You will see what can happen when people cause pollution in an area vital to nonhuman and human organisms. You will learn about invasive species and their impacts on established ecosystems. You will also investigate how different management strategies affect the sustainability of fisheries. Finally, you will suggest actions humans can take to help sustain ecosystems for the future.

1 Ecosystems and Change

ECOLOGY is the study of how organisms interact with one another and the environment. With an understanding of ecology, people can make informed decisions about environmental issues. Take, for example, a gardener who is considering how to deal with an insect that is destroying her tomatoes. To apply an insecticide she would need to know how that chemical would affect other organisms in the yard and what would happen if the insecticide got into the water or the soil.

A community of various organisms interacting with each other within a particular physical environment is known as an **ecosystem.** Ecosystems are constantly changing—sometimes in gradual and hardly noticeable ways and sometimes rapidly and dramatically. Change that occurs in one part of an ecosystem will affect other parts of the ecosystem. One of the most critical aspects of any change that occurs in an ecosystem is how it affects the ecosystem's **sustainability.** An ecosystem is **sustainable** if it can support its diversity and ecological processes through time.

Challenge

▶ How does change affect ecosystems?

Wildlife and humans live together in many ecosystems.

b

a

Some examples of the diverse ecosystems found on the earth include islands and atolls (a) and hot springs (b).

MATERIALS

FOR EACH STUDENT

3 sticky notes

Student Sheet 1.1, "Case Study Comparison"

Procedure

1. In your group, assign one student to each case study in this activity.

2. Following your teacher's directions, partner with someone from another group who is reading the same case study.

3. You and your partner will silently read your assigned case study. As you read, use the "Read, Think, and Take Note" strategy. To do this:

   • Stop at least three times during the reading to mark on a sticky note your thoughts and questions about the reading. Use the list of guidelines below to start your thinking.

Read, Think, and Take Note: Guidelines

As you read, from time to time, write one of the following on a sticky note:

• Explain a thought or reaction to something you read.

• Note something in the reading that is confusing or unfamiliar.

• List a word that you do not know.

• Describe a connection to something you learned or read previously.

• Make a statement about the reading.

• Pose a question about the reading.

• Draw a diagram or picture of an idea or connection.

- After writing a thought or question on a sticky note, place it next to the word, phrase, sentence, or paragraph in the reading that prompted your note.

4. Discuss with your partner the thoughts and questions you had while reading.

5. Discuss with your partner the causes of ecosystem changes in your study, and each fill in the column on your case study on Student Sheet 1.1, "Case Study Comparison."

6. Follow your teacher's directions to complete a diagram that shows the connections between the events described in the case study you read.

7. Return to your original group and summarize for the other members of your group what you have learned from the case study. Show the diagram you drew and Student Sheet 1.1, "Case Study Comparison," to help you with your summary.

8. Use the information provided by your group to complete the remaining columns on Student Sheet 1.1, "Case Study Comparison."

9. For each of the case studies, develop a prediction of what might happen in 50 years if nothing is done to further influence the situation described. Write your prediction in your science notebook. Include the reasoning behind your prediction.

10. Follow your teacher's directions in sharing your prediction with the rest of the class.

Analysis

1. For each case study, write one to three sentences that summarize the changes that occurred in each ecosystem.

2. Group the causes of the changes you listed in Question 1 as "naturally occurring" or "human-caused."

3. According to the information the case studies provide, what types of changes seem to make an ecosystem less sustainable? Explain your answer.

4. Use the predictions that were developed in Procedure Step 9 to infer how the diversity of organisms might change over the next 50 years in the locations described in each case study. Explain your answer.

KEY VOCABULARY	
ecology	sustainability
ecosystem	sustainable

CASE STUDY 1

The Crab Jubilee

IMAGINE WALKING ALONG the Chesapeake Bay shoreline in Maryland or Virginia and looking for crabs to catch. To your surprise you come across hundreds, maybe thousands, of crabs crowded together in shallow water and on the shore.

You will eat well tonight! Locals call this a "crab jubilee," and it is an event that people have witnessed many times in the past. Probably Native Americans saw this phenomenon thousands of years ago. As the human population of the region has increased, so has the frequency of the "crab jubilees." This may sound good if you like to eat crab, but in fact, it is a sign of problems in Chesapeake Bay.

The name Chesapeake is derived from a Native American word meaning "great shellfish bay," and shellfish have always been an important food source for the people in the area. The blue crab *(Callinectes sapidus)* has been harvested commercially in the bay

A "crab jubilee" on the shore of Chesapeake Bay

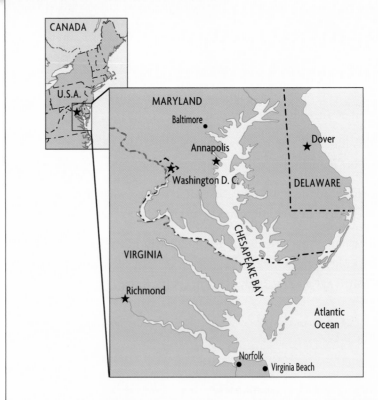

since the mid-1800s. Over the years more and more crabs have been harvested, with 1993 having a record catch—347 million crabs worth $107 million. Since that time, however, the number of crabs harvested has declined. In 2007 the number had dropped to 132 million, with a value of $52 million. In 1999, more than 11,000 people in the area had crab-related jobs, but in 2006, fewer than 7,000 were involved in the crab industry. The effect on the regional economy was so severe that in 2008 the U.S. Department of Commerce declared a commercial fishery failure.

One of the factors thought to have contributed to the failure of the blue crab fisheries is overfishing. To keep the crab populations stable a certain minimum number of egg-producing crabs must survive each year. Scientists have estimated that the crab population would not decline as long as the number of crabs harvested each year did not exceed 46% of the total crab population. However, over the past decade it is estimated that an average of 62% of all of the blue crabs in the bay were caught each year.

The other problem is pollution of the bay's waters from chemicals and sediment that have washed into the bay from such sources as farms, sewage treatment plants, suburban lawns, and golf courses. Nitrogen- and phosphorus-containing chemicals from these sources have increased the growth of algae in the bay. The algae and the sediment make the waters cloudy enough to limit the amount of sunlight that reaches the bottom and to impede the growth of underwater plants. Eelgrass, in particular, is crucial to crab populations because tiny crab larvae blend in with the grass and are less visible to predators. Without the grass fewer of the young crabs reach maturity.

Blue crab (Callinectes sapidus).

When the algae die they fall to the bottom of the bay. As bacteria decompose the dead algae, they remove much of the oxygen from the water. These oxygen-deprived areas cannot support life, and organisms that cannot move elsewhere die, creating dead zones. Crabs moving out of the dead zones may end up in great numbers on land where the oxygen levels are higher. This is the reason for the "crab jubilees." Although dead zones can develop as the result of natural phenomena, such as changes in ocean current patterns, scientists believe that dead zones indicate that human activities are increasing the frequency of "crab jubilees," and are ultimately affecting the sustainability of the crab population. ■

CASE STUDY 2

The March of the Toads

THEY DON'T BELONG in Australia, but there are already 200 million of them there. They can travel as far as 50 km (31 miles) a day and continue to spread across large areas of the country. They may feed as often as 200 times in a night, but almost everything that tries to eat them dies of heart failure. Who are these invaders? These are cane toads.

The cane toad *(Bufo marinus)* is a large and poisonous animal that is native to Central and South America. Because the toad had been introduced to various regions in the world in an attempt to control pests in cane fields, Australian authorities in 1935 approved the importation of cane toads to the Australian province of Queensland. About 100 were shipped in, allowed to breed in captivity, and were released into several sugar cane plantations where two types of beetles were ruining the crop.

Although the cane toads would certainly eat the beetles, it turned out that they didn't encounter the beetles frequently enough to eat many of them. One reason is that the beetles lived mainly in the higher parts of the sugar cane plants out of the toads' jumping range. Another reason is that the beetle only

Dozens of cane toads (Bufo marinus) pile on top of one another.

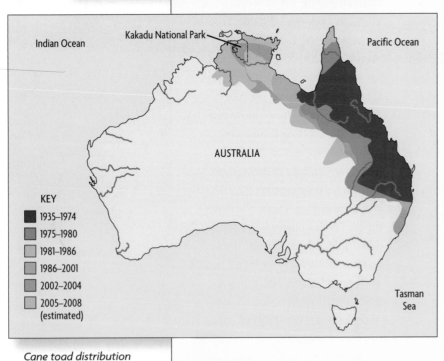

Cane toad distribution 1935–2008

Indian Ocean

Kakadu National Park

Pacific Ocean

AUSTRALIA

Tasman Sea

KEY
- 1935–1974
- 1975–1980
- 1981–1986
- 1986–2001
- 2002–2004
- 2005–2008 (estimated)

invaded the sugar cane fields at the time of year when the cane toads didn't go there because of the lack of protective plant cover. In addition, the beetles were most active during the day, but the cane toads fed mainly at night. The toads didn't go hungry though, as they ate pretty much anything that would fit into their mouths—including insects, frogs, small reptiles, mammals, and birds—eventually diminishing the biodiversity of the areas they were invading.

A female cane toad can produce around 35,000 eggs every time she mates, which can happen several times a year. They lay their eggs in almost any body of water, large or small, fresh or salt. Because cane toads can survive in a wide range of conditions, they adjusted well to the environment in Queensland and began to spread to other parts of Australia. Australia has no natural predator that can control the cane toad populations, but the cane toad has made its mark on populations of many other animals. The cane toad adult has poison glands in its skin, and the tadpoles are highly toxic to most animals. Most of the Australian predators that eat them die of heart failure. Even crocodiles are not immune, and since 2005, after cane toads invaded the Victoria River district of Australia's Northern Territory, there has been a 77% decline in the freshwater crocodile population.

Also, where cane toads are present, local populations of northern quoll have disappeared. Rabbit-sized marsupials that eat a wide variety of prey, quoll often die from eating cane toads. The population of northern quoll is particularly vulnerable to extinction because the males die after mating when they are one year old. When this natural loss is accelerated by the losses caused by the cane toads, quoll populations quickly become unsustainable.

Cane toads are causing yet other problems. They are suspected in reducing the numbers of animals that aboriginal bushmen traditionally rely on as food sources. The toads are known to eat pet food and feces, the latter leading them to carry diseases, such as salmonella. In 2001 the cane toads reached the carefully conserved Kakadu National Park, raising fears that the toads will disturb the delicate balance of species in the park and reduce its biodiversity. Local economies may be affected if tourism suffers as a result of changes to the park. ■

Northern quoll (Dasyurus hallucatus) (left) often die from eating poisonous cane toads. This crocodile (below) will likely die from the poison in the cane toad it is eating.

CASE STUDY 3

The Bleaching of the Reefs

CORAL REEFS OCCUPY a small fraction, about 0.2%, of the earth's ocean floor. Yet it is estimated that 25% of all marine organisms live in or around coral reefs and that nearly one million different species can be found there. Coral reefs support fishing and provide building materials for local communities. They also act as natural breakwaters, protecting coastal areas. They have great potential in providing ingredients for new medicines and are a major attraction for tourists. These benefits, however, also mean that coral reefs around the world are under threat.

Coral reefs are made up of millions of small animals called polyps. Polyps are invertebrates that flourish in warm and shallow parts of oceans. These tiny animals rely on even smaller organisms—algae— for their survival. These algae are single-celled, photosynthesize in the presence of sunlight, and live in the tissues of the polyps. Most polyps themselves live inside a hard external framework that they have made from minerals in the seawater. Large colonies of polyps and their limestone skeletons form the coral reefs, some of which are so large that they can be seen from space.

Scientists estimate that in the past 50 years more than a quarter of the world's reefs have been destroyed. Today there are no signs that this

Coral reef with a diversity of fish

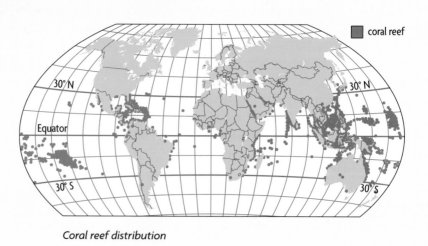

Coral reef distribution

destruction is slowing down. One source of coral reef damage is human-generated—in the form of unsustainable and illegal fishing practices, such as when fishermen drop dynamite onto the reefs to help them kill and catch fish.

Fishing can also harm coral indirectly. For example, it plays a role in increasing populations of the coral-eating sea star called the crown of thorns. Normally the number of sea stars living in a reef is low, as several species of reef organisms prey on the young sea stars. However, when too many of these predators are caught by fishermen, many more sea stars survive to become adults and eat up much more of the reef—up to 90% in some cases.

Another major threat to coral reefs is climate change, which is a global problem. Coral reefs are sensitive to changes in ocean temperatures, and many are in areas where the temperature is already close to the upper limit in which a reef can survive. A water temperature increase of as little as 1°C can decrease the ability of the coral algae to photosynthesize. It can sometimes cause the polyps to expel the algae. In both situations the coral loses its color and looks "bleached" or white, indicating that it is under stress.

Warmer ocean temperatures also favor the growth of bacteria that cause diseases in the coral reefs. Compounding those problems, the increase of carbon dioxide gas in the atmosphere is making the world's oceans more acidic. This reduces the concentration of some of the chemicals that the polyps use to build the limestone skeletons and further weakens the coral reefs.

In 1997 and 1998, coral reefs all over the world suffered extensive bleaching. More than 50% of the Great Barrier Reef in Australia was affected and at least 50% of the reefs in Palau in the South Pacific were killed. The following year tourism in Palau was down 10%. Coral reefs hold the largest biodiversity in the oceans and are estimated to contribute more than $20 billion to local economies around the world. All ecosystems, fortunately, have a certain level of resiliency, and, provided the tipping point isn't reached, change does not always have to have permanent negative effects. Should the ocean temperature go back down, some of the coral might recover. However, to reverse the ocean warming will require tremendous human effort, and it will be expensive. Can the world, however, afford to continue losing its coral reefs and the biodiversity within them? ■

Crown of thorns (Acanthaster planci) sea stars (top) can severely damage coral reefs.

This coral (above) has "bleached," likely due to fluctuation in water temperature.

The Yellowstone Fires of 1988

Fires sweep through Yellowstone in 1988.

OVER SEVERAL DAYS in August 1988, many towns close to Yellowstone National Park experienced smoke so thick that drivers had to turn on their head-lights in the middle of the day. People were advised to stay indoors to avoid breathing the smoke-filled air. Some communities in and around the park were temporarily evacuated as the worst fires ever recorded in Yellowstone burned out of control. By the fall of 1988, more than

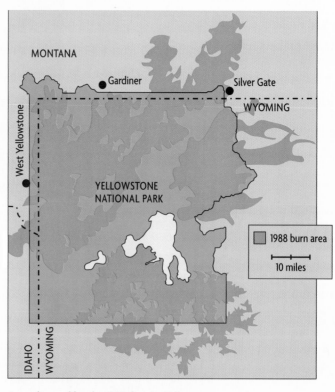

Areas burned by the 1988 fires in Yellowstone

25,000 firefighters had worked on controlling the fires and over one third of Yellowstone National Park had burned.

Yet at the start of the summer of that year there were few indications of the scale of what was to come. The previous six summers and the spring of 1988 had all been wetter than normal, and fire activity had been low. The lack of fire had led to a buildup of old trees and under-brush in the forests of Yellowstone. This was fuel that was ready to burn if the conditions were right. The summer of 1988 turned out to be the driest in the park's history. By the middle of July, 8,500 acres of the area had burned.

Within two weeks the area affected by fire had increased by a factor of 10 and on August 20 winds of about 130 km/h (80 mph) helped to double the size of the fires in a single day. Lightning caused most of the fires, but humans caused three of the largest. The first snows in September significantly dampened the fires, and they were all extin-guished before winter arrived. Concern was expressed across the country about the impacts of the fires on wildlife, vegetation, tourism, and local econo-mies. There was much discussion about whether the fires should have been put out earlier when they were still small.

Nearly all of Yellowstone's plant communities have burned at some time in the past. Scientists think that fires in Yellowstone naturally burn at intervals varying from 20 to 300 years, depending on the location and type of vegetation. While fire can be a destructive force, it also stimulates growth in the park. Soil receives nutrients from burned plant materials, and when forests burn, more sunlight reaches the ground. Both of these processes help plants to grow. Studying the Yellowstone fires and other fires has provided scien-tists with evidence that allowing periodic fires, instead of always preventing them, can benefit eco-systems. Periodic fires both prevent the build up of woody debris that can make fires much larger and stimulates growth in the forest.

Over hundreds of years the burned areas will progress through a variety of stages as they recover.

(Continued on next page)

This area is beginning to recover after the Yellowstone fires.

(Continued from previous page)

This process is called succession. Wildflowers, grasses, and sagebrush may be the first to grow, but soon aspen trees will begin to sprout. Aspen has a thin bark and burns readily in a fire. But while the part of the tree aboveground is damaged or destroyed, the extensive underground network of roots is protected from the heat of the flames by the soil, so it isn't long after the fire is out before shoots begin to grow. Unlike the aspen, Douglas fir trees have very thick bark that insulates most of the tree from the heat. Such trees are very resilient and can often survive fires. Lodgepole pine, which makes up 80% of the forests of Yellowstone, has thin bark and the trees burn readily in fires, but it also benefits from fire. This tree produces cones that are glued shut by resin. Only the heat of a fire is enough to melt the resin and allow the cone to open for the seeds inside to disperse. Since the seeds will be produced after the ground has been cleared and enriched by fire, they are more likely to grow.

Scientists found that 345 elk died as a direct result of the fires, which is less than 1% of the elk population. During the winter following the fire, thousands of elk died from lack of food, but the numbers of elk had recovered completely within five years. The fires also killed some fish, 36 deer, 12 moose, 6 black bears, 9 bison, and possibly 1 grizzly bear. The carcasses of these animals provided food for other animals, such as coyotes, bears, and some birds. Dead trees provided more places for birds like woodpeckers and bluebirds to find holes in which to build their nests. Overall there does not seem to have been a significant long-term negative effect on animal populations. The fires did have an effect on tourism while they were occurring, but the influx of firefighters and the media made up for this to some degree. There was no decrease in the number of tourists who visited the region the following year. ∎

—*Adapted from National Park Service,*
"Wildland Fire in Yellowstone."

2 A Population of Duckweed

THROUGHOUT THIS UNIT you will be studying populations of organisms. A **population** is a group of individuals of the same species that live in the same general area and are able to reproduce. For example, all of the rainbow trout living in one stream would be a population, if they were able to mate and have live offspring. Studying species' populations in an ecosystem helps scientists determine the stability of that ecosystem.

The population of bannerfish (Heniochus diphreutes), shown at left, lives near a coral reef.

In the community shown below, bannerfish, several species of coral, and other fish species all live near a coral reef.

You will also study the interactions of several species. Ecologists, scientists who study ecology, describe populations of multiple species living in the same area as a **community**. In a stream the biological community might include populations of rainbow trout, mosquitoes, aquatic plants, snails, and tadpoles. As you saw in the previous activity, it is communities of organisms, along with nonliving factors, that make up an ecosystem.

The plant you will study in this activity, duckweed *(Lemna minor)*, grows well in a range of conditions. While it flowers and reproduces sexually, it can also reproduce without flowering, via asexual reproduction. In some regions, duckweed is considered an invasive species, much like the cane toads are invasive in Australia. If enough duckweed grows on the surface of a pond, it uses up the dissolved carbon dioxide in the pond, preventing the native aquatic plants from obtaining carbon dioxide. This decreases the aquatic plants' oxygen production. Without enough oxygen the fish and other organisms living in the pond will die.

In this activity, you will collect data from a growing population of duckweed over several weeks to learn about populations and how they grow.

Challenge

▶ How quickly can a population grow? How does the size of a population change through time?

MATERIALS

FOR EACH GROUP OF FOUR STUDENTS
  permanent marker

FOR EACH PAIR OF STUDENTS
  clear plastic cup
  piece of masking tape
  bacteriological loop
  source of spring water
  duckweed plants

FOR EACH STUDENT
  Student Sheet 2.1, "Class Duckweed Population Data"
2 sheets of graph paper

A whole duckweed plant resembles the plant in this picture. Be sure you are only counting whole plants in your data collection.

Procedure

Part A: Establishing a Baseline

To track the growth of your duckweed population you need to set a baseline, or starting point, for your population. Having a baseline allows you to monitor population changes.

1. Write your names and the date on the masking tape, and affix it to the plastic cup.

2. In your science notebook, create a data table to record and track your population two times each week for eight weeks. Count and record how many plants your teacher has given you.

3. In your science notebook, sketch a graph predicting what will happen to the number of plants in your duckweed population over the next eight weeks. Beneath the graph explain how you made your prediction.

4. Fill your plastic cup to approximately two-thirds full with spring water.

5. Carefully transfer your duckweed plants into your plastic cup using the bacteriological loop. Make sure the plants are completely in the water.

   Caution: Duckweed plants are fragile. Be sure to handle them gently when transferring them with the loop so that you do not break the leaves or roots.

6. Place your duckweed population in the location designated by your teacher.

Safety

Because duckweed is invasive, be careful not to pour any down the drain. Your teacher will provide disposal instructions at the end of the experiment. Check your hands and equipment for pieces of duckweed plants before using the sink.

Part B: Tracking the Population

(To be done over several weeks)

7. Carefully count the number of live plants present in your population, and update your data table. Do not count plants that have turned completely brown or white.

8. Add water to your population as necessary or according to your teacher's instructions. If the water in your cup is evaporating too quickly, you may need to add water between data-collection points. Check with your teacher for instructions on how and when to do this.

9. At the end of the data-collection period, use graph paper to plot a line graph of population size versus time lapsed for your duckweed population.

Analysis

1. Interpret your graph by answering the following questions.

   a. What happened to your duckweed population over the study period?

   b. Why do you think your population changed the way it did?

2. Do the data you collected agree with your prediction from Procedure Step 3? Explain.

3. How is your graph different from other students' population graphs? Why do you think the graphs are different?

Duckweed overtakes a lake in Iowa.

4. What environmental limiting factor do you think is most important in setting the carrying capacity for duckweed in this activity? Explain your reasoning.

5. What effect do you think each of the following would have on the population:

   a. placing the population in a lake where other duckweed is already present

   b. introducing an organism that eats duckweed

   c. introducing a duckweed disease

   d. adding fertilizer to the duckweed habitat

6. The graph below shows the global human population growth over the past 2,000 years. Compare this graph to the graph of your duckweed population. What similarities and what differences are there?

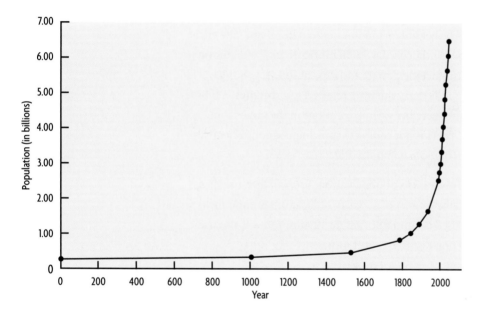

7. How does what you have learned about population growth and carrying capacity relate to sustainability?

KEY VOCABULARY	
carrying capacity	limiting factor
community	organism
ecosystem	**population**
invasive species	population growth rate

3 Biomes

As you saw in Activity 1, "Ecosystems and Change," around 100 cane toads were introduced in the 1930s to Queensland in Australia. The current number of cane toads in Australia is more than 200 million. Would such a dramatic increase have occurred if the cane toad had been introduced to Anchorage, Alaska, or Las Vegas, Nevada?

For an organism to exist in an ecosystem it has specific traits that permit it to survive in that ecosystem. If an organism moves to a location that is similar to its native environment, it is more likely to survive than if it moved to a place entirely different, because its traits are likely to still be helpful to it in this new environment. The environment where an organism lives is influenced by both **biotic** (living) and **abiotic** (nonliving) factors. Abiotic factors include climate and type of soil. Across the world are regions with similar abiotic conditions, which are referred to as **biomes**. A biome features a range of conditions, and therefore various locations in the same biome will be similar but not identical. There is not complete agreement among scientists as to the exact number and types of biomes in the world.

In this activity you will examine several sets of information. You will then use these as evidence to identify the particular biomes of a variety of locations around the world. **Evidence** is information used to support or refute a claim. You will also use evidence to match a selection of organisms to these biomes.

Hungarian steppes (left) and Montana prairie (above) have very similar biotic and abiotic factors, even though they are on two separate continents.

Challenge

▶ How do the characteristics of a biome determine the types of organisms found there?

MATERIALS

FOR EACH PAIR OF STUDENTS

    set of 8 Organism Cards

    pair of scissors

    container of glue or roll of transparent tape

FOR EACH STUDENT

    Student Sheet 3.1, "Climate Information for Locations"

    Student Sheet 3.2, "Biomes Match"

Procedure

1. Student Sheet 3.1 shows climate information for 16 locations around the world. Each graph contains two sets of data, average temperature and average precipitation per month. Cut the sheet into 16 separate climate graphs.

2. With your partner organize the climate graphs into eight groups by pairing each location with the one that has the most similar climate.

3. Read the descriptions of types of terrestrial biomes on the following pages. Write a short summary of each biome in your science notebook, leaving enough room between them to paste in the climate graphs when you are finished.

4. From the climate descriptions match each biome to one of the pairs of locations that you created in Step 2.

5. In your science notebook, paste each climate graph next to your summary of its corresponding biomes.

6. Using the information on the Organism Cards, match each organism to the biome in which the organism might be found. Match each organism to only one biome. Record your matches on Student Sheet 3.2, "Biomes Match," and make sure that all biomes are matched with one organism.

7. In your science notebook include your reasons for matching each organism with the particular biome you chose.

Tropical Rain Forest

A tropical rain forest is warm and humid all year. Temperatures are fairly constant in the 20°C–30°C (68°F–86°F) range. Total rainfall per year can vary from 2,000–4,000 mm (about 80–160 inches). In many tropical rain forests there is no dry season. The soil has limited nutrients, but the warm temperatures and abundant water support a wide variety of organisms. Plants can grow quickly, and dead matter decays rapidly. Trees can become very tall, and many are evergreen and do not shed their leaves. Plants compete for light. Many of these

forests are found near the equator where daylight length is about 12 hours throughout the year. ■

Desert

Deserts have low precipitation of 15–300 mm (about 0.5–12 inches) per year. The low humidity allows temperatures to become cold

at night. Hot deserts experience temperature variations from an average of about 10°C (50°F) in winter to 35°C (95°F) or more in the summer. The soil is often poor in nutrients but rich in minerals. To survive in the desert, plants and animals must be able to conserve water. Desert plants generally provide very little shade, and there are very few trees. ■

Savanna

The savanna has warm temperatures, generally around 25°C–35°C (77°F–95°F) year round. Temperatures are not as constant throughout the year as are those in the tropical rain forest. Total rainfall varies from 500–1,500 mm (about 20–60 inches) per year but is not evenly distributed. There is a long dry season and a rainy season. Trees are scattered, and grasses grow quickly when it rains. The soil is shallow and drains quickly. Fires can occur during the dry season and are important in maintaining biodiversity. When the fires kill small animals, the bodies of the dead animals provide food for other animals, such as birds. Other organisms survive the fires by running away, burrowing underground, or having deep roots. The parts of the plants that burn above ground nourish the soil. ■

Chaparral

The chaparral receives most of its precipitation as rain during the winter months. Rainfall totals vary from about 200–700 mm (about 8–28 inches) per year. Winter, spring, and fall are generally cool and mild with average temperatures between 10°C and 15°C (50°F–59°F). Summers are warm with average temperatures around 25°C (77°F) although on some days the temperature may rise as high as 40°C (104°F). Some areas of chaparral experience frost at certain times of the year, but there are usually six months or more of frost-free days. The dry summers often cause drought conditions and increase the chance of fires. Vegetation is diverse

and sometimes dense. Shrubs, wildflowers, and grasses are common. There are a wide variety of small animals, including amphibians, birds, reptiles, insects, and small mammals. ■

Temperate Grassland

Temperate grassland experiences a wide range of temperature and precipitation through the year. Precipitation is moderate with a yearly average of 500–900 mm (about 20–35 inches). Most rain falls in late spring and in summer. The winter is cold, with average temperatures well below freezing, while summer temperatures average around 25°C (77°F). Five to six months of the year are frost-free. The soil is often fertile and dominated by tall grasses that have adapted to the cold winter temperatures, occasional summer droughts, and periodic fires. The

roots of these grasses help to hold the soil together. Many large mammals graze in these grasslands. ■

Taiga

Taiga is an area of extensive forests where the ground is frozen for much of the year. The winters are long and cold with average temperatures around –15°C (5°F). Precipitation ranges from 300–850 mm

(about 12–34 inches) per year. Summers are short, moist, and generally mild enough that the ground thaws. Average temperatures in the summer are around 15°C (59°F), but daily maximum temperatures occasionally rise as high as 30°C (86°F). About three months of the year are frost-free. The range of types of plants that grow here is quite narrow because many plants cannot access the nutrients in the frozen soil. Most of the trees are evergreen conifers. Many different types of mammals live in the taiga, including some very large ones. ■

Temperate Deciduous Forest

Temperate deciduous forests experience four distinct seasons with a total annual precipitation of 700–2,000 mm (about 28–80 inches) that is spread throughout the year. Temperatures vary a lot over the year and between locations. There are about 140–200 frost-free days each year, depending on the location. Average winter temperatures usually fall to below freezing, and summer averages are around 25°C (77°F). The generally fertile soil, year-round precipitation, and approximately six-month growing period support a wide diversity of plants. Most trees lose their leaves before winter, and some animals hibernate or migrate during the winter months. ∎

Tundra

Very cold temperatures and low precipitation, with yearly totals between 120 and 250 mm (about 5–10 inches), are characteristic of tundra. Winters are long with average temperatures of –30°C (–22°F) or lower. The soil is thin and covers a permanently frozen layer of subsoil called permafrost. The permafrost makes it difficult for plants to extend roots deep into the ground. The permafrost also prevents water from seeping deep into the ground during the short summer when the soil at the surface thaws. Animals usually have fat and fur to help cope with the cold temperatures. Some animals hibernate to survive the harsh winters, and some migrate. Average summer temperatures can reach 10°C (50°F). The growing season for plants is very short with only about two months of the year being frost-free. Plants that do well in tundra tend to grow close to the ground. ∎

Analysis

1. Which biome has the most extreme conditions? Explain your answer.

2. Which biome has the most constant conditions over the course of the year? Explain your answer.

3. Make a climate graph using the data in the table below.

Climate Data for Location Q		
MONTH	AVG. TEMP. (°C)	AVG. PRECIP. (mm)
January	29	37
February	28	41
March	25	31
April	20	17
May	16	19
June	12	14
July	12	14
August	14	9
September	19	8
October	23	21
November	26	29
December	28	38

   a. Which biome is Location Q likely to be in? Explain your choice of biome.

   b. What else do the climate data indicate about where Q might be? Explain your answer.

4. **Biodiversity** is the number of species found in a given ecosystem or area. Based on what you learned in this activity, why do you think levels of biodiversity differ from biome to biome?

5. Review the description of *Monarda fistulosa* from Procedure Steps 6 and 7 in your student notebook. In which other biome could *Monarda fistulosa* most likely be found? Explain your answer.

6. *Cyclorana platycephala* is a frog that is found in Australia. Like all frogs, it needs to keep its skin moist. During periods of drought it digs a chamber in the ground and lines it with mucous, which hardens and seals the chamber from water loss. The frog settles into the chamber, its metabolism slows down, and it becomes inactive. The frog can survive in this state for up to five years. Describe how this trait will determine the types of biome that the frog might live in.

7. How might ecologists use the frog described in Question 6 as an indicator for change within a biome?

8. What might be two of the reasons that scientists do not agree about the number and types of biomes that exist in the world?

KEY VOCABULARY	
abiotic	**biotic**
biodiversity	ecosystem
biomes	**evidence**

4 Invasive Species

SPECIES ENTER NEW areas in several ways. In the case of the cane toads, people intentionally introduced them to Australia for pest control. In some cases an organism is carried accidentally with cargo that is being transported from one place to another. In other cases, organisms are carried on the wind and on currents in rivers, lakes, and oceans. If a species is introduced to an area where it is not naturally found, it is referred to as **nonnative**, and is also known as *exotic* or *non-indigenous*. The specific location where an organism lives within an ecosystem is its **habitat**. This is different from an ecosystem, which refers to all of the biotic and abiotic factors interacting in one location. Within an ecosystem, the population of a native species may decline, and even become locally extinct when an introduced species begins to take over the same role in a habitat. This, in turn, decreases the native biodiversity of the area.

Many crops and animals currently found in the United States are nonnative, including wheat, potatoes, soybeans, honeybees, cows, sheep, and goats. In fact there are approximately 50,000 nonnative species of organisms in the United

a

b

d

c

Many species commonly found in the United States are non-native and invasive, such as the brown tree snake (a), honey bees (b), ice plant (c), and eucalyptus trees (d).

States today, of which about 4,300 are regarded as invasive. For a nonnative species to be considered **invasive,** it must cause harm to the economy, the environment, or human health. Invasive species often diminish the sustainability of an ecosystem by consuming resources and upsetting the typical interactions between species.

Challenge

▶ How do certain characteristics increase the likelihood that a nonnative species becomes an invasive species?

MATERIALS

FOR EACH STUDENT

Student Sheet 4.1, "Invasive Species Information"

Literacy Student Sheet 6, "Discussion Web"

Procedure

Part A

1. On the following pages are four case studies of particular invasive species. Decide in your group who will read each case study.

2. Use the information from the case studies to complete Student Sheet 4.1, "Invasive Species Information," as you read about your assigned species.

3. Compare your results with those of the members in your group who studied the other three invasive species. In your science notebook, write down any similarities that you see among the case studies.

4. As a group, use these similarities to develop a list of characteristics that you think increase the potential of a nonnative species to become invasive. Write the list in your science notebook.

5. Follow your teacher's directions on when and how to share your group's thinking with the rest of the class. As a class, decide on the characteristics that increase the likelihood that a nonnative species will become invasive.

CASE STUDY 1

The Round Goby

THE ROUND GOBY is a freshwater fish that grows to between 10 and 25 cm in length. Originally from central parts of Eurasia, it was discovered in the Great Lakes in the 1990s and is thought to have been accidentally discharged in the ballast water from oceangoing cargo ships visiting ports in the Great Lakes. The goby is no longer limited to the Great Lakes and is spreading throughout the region's rivers and canals.

Round goby (Neogobius melanostromus)

The round goby is an aggressive fish, especially when protecting its spawning grounds. It consumes great quantities of food and can eat clams, mussels, plankton, large invertebrates, fish eggs, small fish, and insect larvae. The round goby can feed in total darkness due to a well-developed sensory system that allows it to detect water movement.

It can also feed in fast-moving water by attaching itself to the bottom of a stream or river with a suction-like disk on its underside.

The round goby is capable of rapid population growth and spawns repeatedly during the summer months, with the female producing up to 5,000 eggs each time. It can live in a variety of habitats and compete with native species for food and space. Often the round goby is the only fish that fishermen see in a section of water. This can make many riverbank or lake-front towns less appealing to visiting sport fishermen, who are trying to catch such fish as trout and salmon. One positive side effect is that the round goby eats another invasive species, the zebra mussel. Native predatory fish, such as the walleye, eat round gobies. ∎

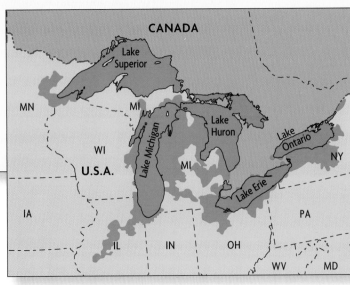

The top map shows locations where the round goby was documented in 2000. The bottom map shows data from 2009.

CASE STUDY 2

The Indian Mongoose

Indian Mongoose (Herpestes javanicus)

THE INDIAN MONGOOSE grows to around 60 cm (24 inches) and lives as long as 13 years, although 3–4 years is more common in the wild. It is fast moving, and although it mainly eats insects, it will also eat crops, fruits, seeds, birds, eggs, small cats, snakes, frogs, and crabs. Usually solitary creatures, they sometimes live in groups, and their habitat ranges from scrubland to different types of forest to areas where humans live. They breed rapidly, with males able to father offspring when they are only four months old. Each female can produce two to five pups every year.

Seventy-three Indian Mongooses were intentionally introduced to the Hawaiian Islands in 1883. They were imported to eat rats that were destroying the sugar cane crops. However, rats tend to be most active during the night, whereas mongooses are most active during the day, so the plan did not work very well. The Indian Mongoose is suspected in causing the extinction of at least one species of bird in Hawaii, and it has killed significant numbers of other native species. As do many other animals, mongooses can carry rabies and leptospirosis. Leptospirosis is a bacterial disease that causes symptoms ranging from rashes to kidney and liver failure. Mongooses may transfer it to humans if the animals' urine mixes with water supplies. ■

Leptospirosis can be passed on to humans.

CASE STUDY 3

Zebra Mussel

ZEBRA MUSSELS are native to Eastern Europe. They generally live for four to five years and grow to 5 cm (about 2 inches) in length. The females can reproduce at around two years old and are capable of producing up to one million eggs per year. Adults survive out of water for several days if the temperature is low and humidity is high. Young zebra mussels swim freely and are spread easily by water currents. Adult mussels spread when they attach themselves to objects that have hard surfaces, such as hulls of boats. When the object is moved to a different location, the zebra mussels move with it.

Zebra mussels first appeared in the Great Lakes in 1988, most likely having been flushed into the lakes when ocean going cargo ships discharged ballast water. Zebra mussels feed by filtering algae and plankton from water, with each mussel filtering up to one liter per day. In areas where there are millions of zebra mussels, two major changes to the ecosystem have occurred: the water has become clearer, which is beneficial for some organisms but not others; and the food for native larval fish has decreased. The clearer water can benefit plants that live on the bottom of the lakes because they

Zebra mussels (Dreissena polymorpha) can clog the insides of pipes.

have more access to light and thus grow more. Fish that prefer this type of habitat have actually increased in the Great Lakes. The decrease in food for native larval fish causes fewer of the larval fish to survive, creating a food shortage for the animals that feed on these fish. Zebra mussels also attach themselves to native mussels, clams, crayfish, and turtles, sometimes in such great numbers that these organisms have trouble functioning. Several native species of fish eat zebra mussels, but not enough of them to keep the mussel populations down. Sometimes the colonies block water-intake pipes, restricting water flow and causing problems at power plants and water-supply facilities. ■

CASE STUDY 4

Giant Salvinia

*Giant salvinia
(Salvinia molesta)*

GIANT SALVINIA IS an aquatic plant native to South America that was first found in the United States in 1995. It forms mats as it floats freely on the surface of slow-moving or still freshwater and reproduces asexually when fragments break off to form clones. The plant can double in size in as little as two days, and its mass can double in a week. As the mats grow they form layers as much as a meter thick. The buds of giant salvinia can withstand dry conditions, and the plants can tolerate freezing air temperatures—but not ice—on the surface of the water where they grow.

Giant salvinia can spread on moving water or by clinging to boats and other recreational craft. A single plant can spread over an area of more than 100 sq km (about 40 sq mi) within a three-month period.

The floating mat formed by giant salvinia blocks sunlight from the water and prevents oxygen mixing at the surface. This change in conditions reduces the number and variety of microorganisms living in the water, which in turn means less food for the organisms that feed on them. The rapid spread of giant salvinia can threaten crops, such as rice, and clog irrigation and drinking-water lines. The thick mats can clog waters to the extent that swimming, boating, and fishing become impossible. The mats are also breeding grounds for mosquitoes. ■

This pond has been taken over by a population of giant salvinia.

Part B

In this section you will read about the benefits and risks of the possible introduction of a nonnative species to try to replenish a fishery. The balance between these benefits and risks is known as a trade-off. A **trade-off** is an exchange of one thing in return for another, giving up something that is a benefit or an advantage, in exchange for something that may be more desirable.

6. Read the summary of a report about the possible introduction of nonnative oysters into Chesapeake Bay.

7. Use a Discussion Web to analyze the statement "nonnative oysters should be introduced into Chesapeake Bay as soon as possible." In the Discussion Web, make sure to discuss the characteristics of invasive species the class listed in Step 5. For the Discussion Web, have two members of your group take the role of fishermen who make their living from harvesting oysters in the Bay, and two should act as conservationists who wish to return the Bay to its original state.

8. When you have completed the Discussion Web, with your same-role partner, compare your comments and conclusions with the members of your group who took the other role. In your science notebook, write down any questions that you would want answered before making a final decision on whether to introduce the nonnative oyster species into the Bay.

9. Under your teacher's direction, discuss as a class the questions that you recorded for Step 8.

Oysters are growing on floats in a creek near Chesapeake Bay as part of an aquaculture education project.

Analysis

1. What characteristics increase the likelihood that a nonnative species will become an invasive species?

2. What conditions in an ecosystem are likely to allow a species to become invasive there? How might scientists use biomes to study this?

3. Biological control involves the introduction of a natural enemy to control the spread of an organism that is considered a pest. What are the trade-offs in introducing a nonnative species to control an established invasive species?

4. Summarize the position taken by either the fishermen or the conservationists about the oysters in Chesapeake Bay. Include the evidence that supports that position. Weigh the evidence to make a recommendation for or against the introduction of the nonnative oysters into Chesapeake Bay. Include at least two trade-offs associated with your recommendation.

KEY VOCABULARY	
ecosystem	**invasive species**
evidence	**nonnative species**
habitat	**trade-off**

REPORT SUMMARY

Chesapeake Bay Oysters

ONE HUNDRED YEARS ago Chesapeake Bay was the world's largest oyster-producing region, with fishermen harvesting more oysters than all other countries combined. Slowly but surely the oyster catch has declined and is now only 1% of what it was at the start of the 20th century. Among the factors causing this huge drop are destruction of habitat, reduction in water quality, disease, and overharvesting. The decrease in oysters has had a devastating effect on both the environment and the local economy. Without large numbers of oysters, the water in the bay is not filtered sufficiently. This, along with increased runoff rich in nitrogen and phosphorous, has allowed more algae to grow in the waters of the bay. As a result the oxygen levels in the bay are lower. "Dead zones" sometimes form as a result of eutrophication, with lethal consequences for many organisms, including the oysters. More and more families that have traditionally made a living from the oyster and fishing industries are leaving the area every year or having to find a different form of employment.

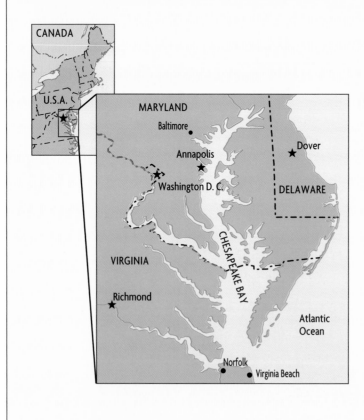

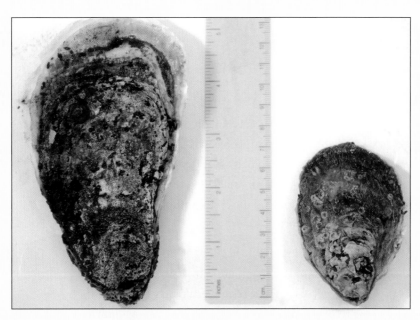

Nonnative oysters, Crassostrea ariakensis *(left), are much larger than the native oysters,* Crassostrea virginica *(right).*

Numerous efforts have been made to improve the Chesapeake Bay ecosystem and to restore the oyster resources of the bay. One proposal made in the early years of this century involved the potential introduction of a species of oyster that is native to the coasts of Asia, *Crassostrea ariakensis*. The hope was that this species would thrive, and filter the polluting algae from the bay's waters, improving conditions sufficiently for native oyster populations to begin to recover.

Crassostrea ariakensis is larger and tends to reproduce more quickly than the native oysters *(Crassostrea virginica)*. It also grows much more rapidly than native oysters during the winter months. It can be harvested and sold and would provide a much-needed economic boost to the oyster fishing industry.

Crassostrea ariakensis can survive in a wide range of conditions, including those currently encountered in Chesapeake Bay. However, recent research has indicated that the nonnative species does not reproduce or grow as well when space is limited, for example when it has to compete with other species. *Crassostrea ariakensis* has been shown to have some resistance to the diseases that killed many of the native oysters, but they are susceptible to, and may carry, other diseases and parasites. These diseases, however, are not currently common in the Chesapeake Bay. The nonnative Asian oysters that would be introduced to the bay through the proposal would come from oyster farms in Oregon. ■

5 The Tragedy of the Commons

ONE MAJOR CAUSE of ecosystem disruption is human activity. One of the things you will study in this unit is how people make decisions about the resources we use and rely on for our survival. Ecologists refer to these resources as **ecosystem services**. Ecosystem services include air, water, and food, which we benefit from directly, but also climate regulation and the cycling of nutrients, which are more indirectly beneficial.

In this activity, you will explore a theory known as the "Tragedy of the Commons." According to the **Tragedy of the Commons**, if people are allowed to use a common resource however they want, they will overuse the resource and eventually cause its destruction. Preventing the resource from being overused is not always easy, and can involve many trade-offs.

In the second half of this activity, you will decide which indicators to use to measure the health of a particular community common, Blue Lake. An **indicator** is an observation or calculation that shows the presence or state of a condition or trend. In this game-type model, the lake will be considered successful if the ecosystem services are maintained—namely, if it has the same or more fish than it started with by the end of the game.

Humans rely on many ecosystem services, such as fish or other food, for our survival.

Challenge

▶ How can the overuse of an ecosystem service be prevented?

MATERIALS

FOR EACH GROUP OF FOUR STUDENTS

100   fish crackers (orange)

30   fish crackers (yellow or color other than orange)

tray or dish

set of 12 Character Cards

timer that beeps

FOR EACH STUDENT

Student Sheet 5.1, "Tragedy of the Commons"

pair of chopsticks

cup

paper towel

Safety

Don't eat the crackers; many people have handled them. If you have any severe food allergies, such as a nut allergy, alert your teacher before handling the materials to ensure the materials will not harm you.

Procedure

Part A

1. Place 25 orange fish and 5 yellow fish in the tray in the center of your table. This represents Blue Lake and the fish in it. Each person will use a set of chopsticks to fish in the lake.

2. Read the following rules of the game:

   a. Each person is assigned a fishing limit by picking a Character Card from the cards labeled Game A. These are the instructions for you for this round. Tell your group what is on your card, so that everyone knows the others' fishing limits.

   b. You have 15 seconds for each round, and you will play four rounds per game. Each of you can take as many fish as your fishing limit allows within the 15-second round, but you must use the chopsticks to pick them up, and you must put them in your cup. You may pick up just one fish at a time.

   c. You need to catch at least two fish to continue fishing in the next round. If you catch more than two, score for yourself one dollar per extra orange fish and two dollars per extra yellow fish.

   d. Every fish left on the tray at the end of the round will reproduce one more fish of the same color. And so, add an equal number of fish to the existing population.

   e. During any round of any game, your teacher may hand your group an Incident Card. Follow the instructions on that card for the next full round.

3. Begin playing. At the end of each round record your data for Game A on Student Sheet 5.1, "Tragedy of the Commons," and then empty your cup onto your paper towel. After four rounds, stop, and finish recording the data for Game A on your student sheet.

4. After the fourth round, discuss, as a group, what happened in Game A. Record your responses in your science notebook. Be sure to answer the following questions:

> How did your fishing limit affect your behavior?
>
> How did it affect what happened to Blue Lake?
>
> How did each person do (did they catch enough to survive, did they earn extra money)?
>
> What is the condition of the fishing community (did everyone catch enough to survive, did everyone earn some extra money)?
>
> What is the condition of Blue Lake (are there fish left, will there be enough for the next generation)? Is this fishing practice sustainable?

Part B

5. Return all your fish from the previous game to the fish bag. Reset the game by adding or subtracting fish from the tray so that the lake again contains 30 fish (25 orange, 5 yellow).

6. Follow the same rules as for Game A. Repeat Steps 3 and 4, using Character Cards for Game B.

Part C

7. Play the game again, following the same rules as before. Repeat Steps 3 and 4, using Character Cards for Game C.

Part D

8. As a group, create a plan for a revised game that you think will continue to keep a population of fish in Blue Lake. Decide what each fisherman's catch limit will be. What will be your indicators that the Blue Lake fishery is continuing to survive? Are there any trade-offs you need to make to keep Blue Lake's fishery going? Record your plan in your science notebook.

9. Play four rounds according to your plan, but keep all of the rules the same as for Game A, and start with the same number of fish. Continue to record your data on Student Sheet 5.1, "Tragedy of the Commons," after each round.

10. As a group, discuss what happened in your game. Record your responses in your science notebook. Be sure to include the following questions:

    Did your new fishing limits change the results of the game as compared to Games A, B, and C?

    How did each person do (did they catch enough to survive, did they earn extra money)?

    What is the condition of the fishing community (did everyone catch enough to continue fishing, did everyone earn some extra money)?

    What is the condition of Blue Lake (are there fish left, will there be enough for the next generation)? Is this fishing practice sustainable?

Analysis

1. What differences did you notice in your results from games A, B, C, and D?

2. What might the results of each game mean in terms of the sustainability of Blue Lake?

3. Were both the orange and yellow fish populations successful? Why or why not?

4. Who was making decisions about the success of Blue Lake each round? What impact did those decisions have on the lake and on the other fishermen?

5. How did each individual affect the success of Blue Lake in the different games? Did this differ from how the group as a whole affected the success of Blue Lake?

6. How does this game model the idea of the Tragedy of the Commons?

7. How do you think this model compares to a real situation? Explain your reasoning.

8. What factors other than fishing might affect the success of Blue Lake?

9. What role can each of the following play in preventing overuse of common resources?

    a. scientists

    b. individuals

    c. society

10. The air we breathe is considered a global commons because the entire planet shares it. Many places have severe air pollution. Who should determine how the air is managed in those places and if it is being managed successfully? Why should they be the one(s) to decide?

11. Think about the community you live in.

    a. What are some commons there?

    b. Imagine you are asked to be in charge of a committee that manages your community's commons. What management plan would you suggest to the committee? What indicators would you use to measure how well you were managing the commons? What evidence would you look for to show that you were successful? What trade-offs would you have to make to accomplish this?

KEY VOCABULARY	
ecosystem services	population
evidence	trade-off
indicator	**Tragedy of the Commons**

6 Producers and Consumers

I N KELP FORESTS or coral reefs near the shore of the ocean it is easy for us to see the various parts of an ecosystem, especially because the near-shore ecosystems tend to be particularly productive and have a high level of biodiversity. The level of biodiversity in an ecosystem, however, is not always obvious. For example, consider the open ocean: huge and deep bodies of waters away from coasts and continental shelves. The open ocean is an ecosystem that supports populations of fish, whales, and other animals. Think about a tuna or a whale in the middle of the ocean, far from any land, reef, or kelp forest. What does it eat? Where does its oxygen come from?

Much of the life in the open ocean consists of free-floating organisms called plankton. **Plankton** are drifting organisms that live for at least part of their life in the open ocean or other body of water. The majority of plankton are minuscule; in fact, one drop of ocean water can contain thousands of plankton. Most plankton inhabit the top 20 m (about 66 feet) of the water. Those are concentrated in this narrow layer of the ocean because that is as deep as sunlight penetrates water fairly easily. This light allows plankton that are capable of photosynthesis—phytoplankton—to survive. Phytoplankton are responsible for nearly half of the oxygen production on Earth! Other plankton, called zooplankton, are consumers that feed on phyto-plankton or other zooplankton. Plankton are the sole food source for most larval fish and many open-ocean consumers. The blue whale is the largest living organism in the world. It's a consumer, and its diet consists entirely of plankton, which it strains from the water with the baleen plates in its mouth.

One blue whale (Balaenoptera musculus) *consumes up to 4,100 kg of plankton, consisting of more than 300 different species every day.*

Challenge

▶ How do plankton populations affect the sustainability of a fishery?

MATERIALS

FOR EACH GROUP OF FOUR STUDENTS

8   prepared sides of plankton
(closterium, copepods, diatoms, euglena, rotifers, oscillatria, stentor, volvox)

dropper

15-mL dropper bottle of methyl cellulose

graduated cup of water containing live plankton

FOR EACH PAIR OF STUDENTS

microscope

microscope slide with a well

coverslip

Procedure

Part A: Observing Prepared Slides

Safety

Always carry a micro-scope properly with both hands—one hand underneath and one holding the microscope arm. Because you are working with live organisms, wash your hands thoroughly after you are finished.

1. You and your partner will observe eight prepared slides of plankton. Choose one slide, and place it on your microscope stage.

    Hint: Most of the plankton you will see are multicellular creatures similar to the ones shown in the image at the end of Part B. You might also see some single-celled plankton on your slide.

2. Use the information on the next page, "Focusing a Microscope," as guidelines for how to use your microscope.

3. Begin by observing the specimen at the lowest level of magnification, and draw what you see.

4. Observe the specimen at each of the higher levels of magnification, and draw what you see at each level. **Note:** Use only the fine-focus knob for a middle- or high-magnification setting to avoid breaking the slide.

5. In your science notebook, sketch what you observe on the slides, as directed by your teacher. Label your sketch with the name of the plankton on the slide. Make notes on any features you see that help you to decide whether it is a phytoplankton or a zooplankton.

6. Repeat Steps 3–5 with each prepared slide.

Focusing a Microscope

Be sure that your microscope is set on the lowest power before placing your slide onto the microscope stage. Place the slide on the microscope stage. Center the slide so that the sample is directly over the light opening, and adjust the microscope settings as necessary. If the microscope has stage clips, secure the slide in position so that it does not move.

Observe the sample. Focus first with the coarse-focus knob, and then adjust the fine-focus knob.

After switching to a higher power magnification, be careful to adjust the focus with the fine-focus knob only.

Return to low power before removing the slide from the microscope stage.

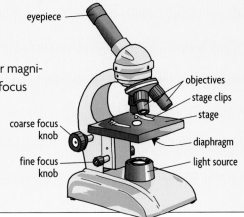

Part B: Searching for Plankton

7. Use the dropper to place a drop of water containing live plankton into the well of a microscope slide.

8. If your teacher directs you to, add one drop of methyl cellulose to the drop on the slide.

9. Carefully touch one edge of the coverslip to the water, at an angle. Slowly allow the coverslip to fall into place. This should prevent trapping of air bubbles under the coverslip.

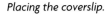

Placing the coverslip.

10. Center the slide so that the well is directly over the light opening, and adjust the microscope settings as necessary.

11. Begin by observing the sample on the lowest objective lens. You may need to search the slide to find specimens, and they may move across your field of view.

12. Draw at least two different organisms that you observe. For each drawing be sure to record the level of magnification. Refer to the drawings on the next page to help you identify the organisms in your drawings.

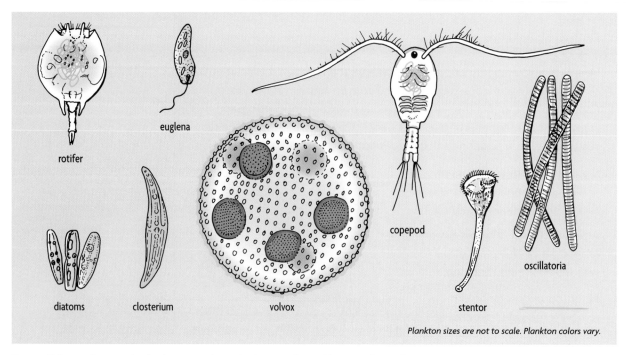

rotifer

euglena

copepod

oscillatoria

diatoms

closterium

volvox

stentor

Plankton sizes are not to scale. Plankton colors vary.

Some of these microscopic plankton are phytoplankton and are able to perform photosynthesis. Others are zooplankton that consume the phytoplankton.

Part C: Calculating Plankton Biomass

The plankton you have been examining are only a few examples of the thousands of species of plankton found in the oceans and freshwater bodies around the world. The Atlantic herring *(Clupea harengus)* fishery is one of the largest commercial fisheries on the east coast of the United States. A **fishery** is an industry that catches or raises a specific type of fish or shellfish to be processed or sold. To better understand the link between plankton and this fishery, complete the calculations below in your science notebook.

13. It is estimated that the mature Atlantic herring population today has a biomass (total weight of the population) of approximately 2 million metric tonnes (2 billion kg). If an average adult Atlantic herring weighs 0.125 kg, how many adult Atlantic herring are there in the entire population?

   Hint: $\dfrac{kg}{0.125 \text{ kg per fish}} =$ _____ fish

14. An adult Atlantic herring consumes, on average, 10 g of plankton per day. How much plankton would the adult Atlantic herring population consume in a day?

15. In some places, human impacts on the marine environment, such as coastal erosion, global warming, and pollution, have caused up to a 70% decrease in the biomass of plankton. If there were a severe reduction of plankton available to the Atlantic herring population, and therefore a 55% decrease in the herring, how many mature Atlantic herring would be supported by the ecosystem? How many kilograms?

Analysis

1. Identify at least two similarities and two differences between phytoplankton and zooplankton.

2. What is the role of phytoplankton in an aquatic ecosystem?

3. Did you observe evidence of the roles of phytoplankton or zooplankton in your sample of live plankton? Explain.

4. How might changes in the amount of plankton in the ocean affect the ocean's ability to provide a sustainable source of food for the world's human population? Explain.

5. Strict fishing limits were set on the Atlantic herring fishery in the 1970s and 1980s because the population had dropped to about 75,000 metric tons. There was alarm that the population was so small that it was not sustainable if unlimited fishing continued. By the early 1990s the population returned to historically normal levels, and the yearly catch limit now ranges from 80,000 to 124,000 metric tons to keep the fishery sustainable.

    a. If the scenario in Procedure Step 15 were to occur, would the Atlantic herring fishery still be sustainable? Explain what indicator(s) you would use to monitor this.

       Hint: The biomass of the Atlantic Herring can be found in Procedure Step 13.

    b. What do you think would happen to the sustainability of the plankton population if this scenario occurred? Explain.

KEY VOCABULARY	
biodiversity	phytoplankton
consumers	**plankton**
fishery	producers
organism	zooplankton

7 Energy Flow Through an Ecosystem

Now that you are familiar with producers and consumers, you are going to learn about how these organisms interact within an ecosystem. Picture a seal swimming in the Pacific Ocean just off the coast of California. Chances are this seal is among a forest of seaweed including a species called giant kelp. Giant kelp *(Macrocystis pyrifera)* is a type of algae that grows up to two-thirds of a meter a day, and over 45 m (about 148 feet) in height. At its base is a woven knot of rootlike branches called a holdfast that attaches to rocks on the ocean floor. The kelp grows in clusters with each plant shooting upward to the surface, then spreading out and sheltering thousands of organisms in a complex ecosystem.

The kelp forest ecosystem is often compared to an underwater tropical rainforest, in part because of its high levels of biodiversity. The kelp are tall, with long leaf-like structures that create a canopy that blocks the light at lower ocean depths, providing habitat and nourishment for organisms that thrive in limited light conditions. Many species of aquatic organisms, such as sea urchins and anchovies, live and reproduce on and among the long strands.

When organisms in the kelp ecosystem die, other organisms, including specialized bacteria, consume their remains, keeping the nutrients flowing through the ecosystem. These essential organisms are called **decomposers.**

This harbor seal (Phoca vitulina) *is swimming in a forest of giant kelp.*

One way to show these interrelationships between the organisms in an ecosystem is by creating a **food web,** mapping what each organism eats and how the energy flows through an ecosystem. In the last activity the food web included plankton, herring, and whales. In this activity you will construct a food web for a kelp forest ecosystem and from it predict what will happen to the ecosystem in various circumstances.

Challenge

▶ How can we use food webs to predict the short- and long-term effects of particular events on an ecosystem?

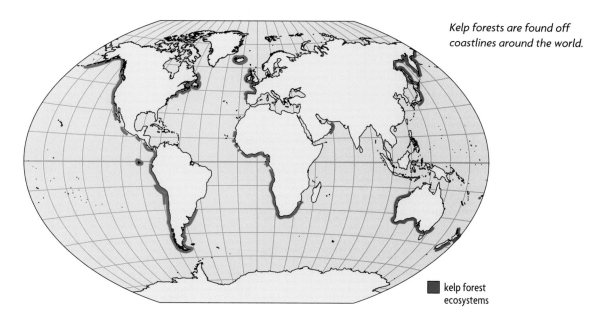

Kelp forests are found off coastlines around the world.

■ kelp forest
ecosystems

MATERIALS

FOR EACH GROUP OF STUDENTS
  sheet of chart paper
  set of colored pencils

FOR EACH PAIR OF STUDENTS
  set of 12 Kelp Forest Organism cards
  set of 4 Ecosystem Event cards

Procedure

Part A: Construct a Food Web

1. With your group, read each Kelp Forest Organism card, noting the similarities and the differences in what substances are going into and coming out of each organism.

2. Sort the organism cards into at least two sets of cards based on similarities in the information about the organisms.

3. As a group, develop a system for further sorting the organisms within each set of cards. When your group comes to agreement, record in your science notebook the organisms in each set of cards and the feature(s) they have in common.

4. Construct an ecosystem food web to show the direction of energy transfer from one organism to another. Begin by laying the giant kelp card on the table in front of your group.

5. Look through the cards and identify all of the organisms that feed on giant kelp. Place these above the giant kelp card.

6. Continue placing cards on the table based on the organisms they feed on, forming a food web. When you have placed all of the cards, show your teacher your work.

7. With your group, record the food web on a piece of chart paper.

8. Draw arrows from one organism to the next to show how energy passes from one organism to another.

   Hint: Remember that arrows in a food web point in the direction of energy flow—*toward* the organism that is doing the "eating," as shown in the food web below.

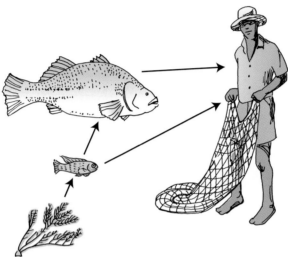

9. One way scientists classify organisms in an ecosystem is by describing how the organisms obtain energy. This is known as the organism's trophic role in the food web. Read about these trophic roles in the table below.

Trophic Roles of Organisms in an Ecosystem	
TYPE OF ORGANISM	**HOW ORGANISM GETS ENERGY TO SUSTAIN LIFE**
Producer	Transforms light energy or other energy sources into chemical energy The chemical energy is stored in carbon-containing molecules, such as simple sugars or starch.
Consumer	Feeds on other organisms to obtain energy
Decomposer	Feeds on other organisms and dead and decaying biological material and wastes to obtain energy

10. Select a colored pencil to represent each of the trophic roles shown in the table above. Make a key on the side of your chart paper to indicate which color indicates which role.

11. With your group, color-code each of the organisms in the food web to indicate its role in the ecosystem.

Part B: Use a Food Web to Predict the Impact of Actions and Events on an Ecosystem

12. Obtain a set of Ecosystem Event Cards from your teacher. With a partner, select and read one of the cards.

13. Using the information provided by your kelp forest food web, discuss how the event described on the card affects the ecosystem.

    Hint: Choose one organism or factor in the web that is affected, and think of the chain of events that will then occur throughout the ecosystem. Scientists call this type of chain of events a trophic cascade.

14. Record the following for each event card in your science notebook:

    a. summary of the event

    b. what effect the event will have on the ecosystem in the

      i. short term

      ii. long term

    c. what effect the event will have on the flow of energy through the kelp forest ecosystem

Part C: Construct an Energy Pyramid

An energy pyramid is a diagram of the amount of the sun's energy that is stored in each level of organisms in a food web. The organisms use part of this energy, part of it is lost as heat, and part of it is stored and therefore available to other organisms.

15. With your group use the information from the kelp forest food web to place the name of each organism on the energy pyramid on Student Sheet 7.1, "Kelp Forest Energy Pyramid."

16. With the class discuss what the energy pyramid shows.

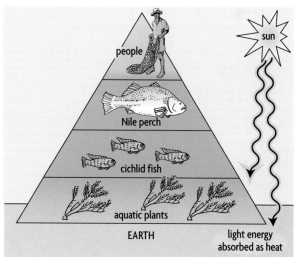

This energy pyramid shows how much energy is stored at each level of the food web.

Analysis

1. Name one organism from the kelp forest ecosystem that is:

   a producer

   a consumer

   a decomposer

2. What is the difference between the role of an organism that is a producer and one that is a consumer? How is a decomposer different from other consumers?

3. Explain the role of the sun in the kelp forest ecosystem.

4. Describe the flow of energy in the kelp forest ecosystem.

5. From the lake food web at right:

   a. predict what would happen if all of the walleye were fished out of the lake

   b. choose an organism other than the walleye, and predict what would happen if it disappeared from the lake

6. Explain why a pyramid is helpful for describing the amount of energy available in a food web.

7. Imagine you are an ecologist who studies kelp forest ecosystems. You have been asked by the federal government to evaluate two plans for managing the California sheephead fishery, which relies on kelp forests. A summary of two proposals follows. Read the proposals and determine:

   a. how the two proposals differ

   b. which proposal you think the government should implement

   In your recommendation include a discussion of the trade-offs you considered.

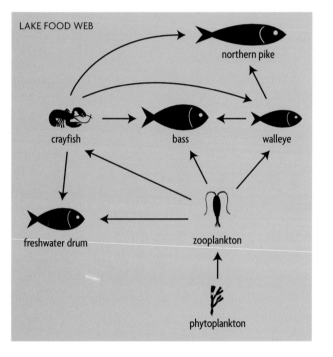

Proposals for Managing the California Sheephead Fishery

PROPOSAL A

Take population counts of California sheepheads once every three months.

If the fish population is below sustainable levels, decrease the size of the allowed sheephead catch. If the sheephead population is at or above sustainable levels, keep the catch limit at current levels.

Cost to implement this proposal: $750,000

PROPOSAL B

Take population counts of California sheepheads and sea urchins once every three months. Measure the density of the giant kelp population once every three months.

If the size of any population is below sustainable levels, decrease the size of the sheephead catch allowed. If the size of each population is at or above sustainable levels, keep the sheephead catch limit at current levels.

Cost to implement this proposal: $1,250,000

KEY VOCABULARY	
biodiversity	energy pyramid
consumers	**food web**
decomposers	producers

8 | Carbon Cycle

ESSENTIAL FOR LIFE on earth, carbon is an element that is found in many forms everywhere on earth. Coal, diamonds, limestone, and sugar, for example, all contain carbon. It is in organisms, the atmosphere, oceans and fresh water, soil on the earth's crust, and fossil fuels under the earth's surface. Each of these locations serves as a reservoir for carbon-containing molecules. As organisms interact in ecosystems and as geological changes occur, carbon flows from one reservoir to the next. A **carbon reservoir** is a natural feature, such as a rock, a pinch of soil, or an organism, that stores carbon-containing molecules and exchanges them with other carbon reservoirs. The movement of carbon between these reservoirs is known as the **carbon cycle.**

As you saw in Activity 7, "Energy Flow Through an Ecosystem," energy flows from one organism to another in a food web. This energy flow happens when one organism eats another and carbon-containing molecules pass from the eaten organism to the organism doing the eating. This flow of energy is just one of many paths carbon-containing molecules can follow in the carbon cycle.

In this activity you will model the pathways that carbon takes as it flows from one reservoir to another. You will consider how human activities alter the carbon cycle.

In the food web above, carbon flows from one organism into another.

Challenge

▶ How does human activity affect the movement of carbon through the carbon cycle?

MATERIALS

FOR EACH PAIR OF STUDENTS
   computer with Internet access

FOR EACH STUDENT
   Student Sheet 8.1, "Carbon Cycle"

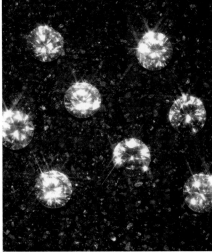

All of these materials contain carbon.

Procedure

1. With your partner, visit the *Science and Global Issues* page of the SEPUP website at *sepuplhs.org/sgi* and go to the carbon cycle simulation. Use your student sheet to guide you through the simulation.

Analysis

1. What happens to the total amount of carbon as it moves through the carbon cycle?

2. In what ways does human activity affect the carbon cycle? Support your answer with evidence.

3. Explain one possible path a carbon molecule might take if it began in a small fish and ended up in a blade of grass.

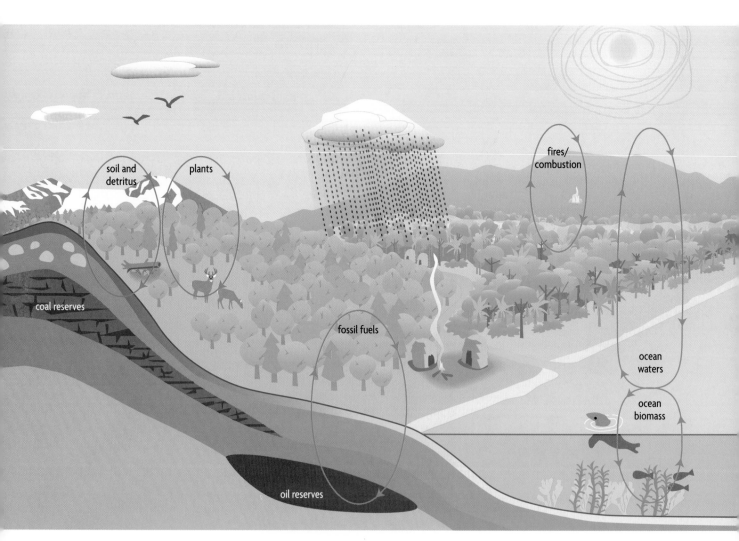

This diagram of the carbon cycle shows how carbon is exchanged between carbon reservoirs by processes that involve geological changes and organism interactions.

4. How has the burning of fossil fuels affected the global carbon cycle?

5. An algal bloom is an event in an aquatic ecosystem that occurs when the level of nutrients in an aquatic ecosystem rises. Higher nutrient levels increase the ecosystem's carrying capacity for algae, and the algae population multiplies dramatically. Describe how an algal bloom might alter the local carbon cycle in that ecosystem.

KEY VOCABULARY

carbon cycle   organisms

carbon reservoir   photosynthesis

cellular respiration

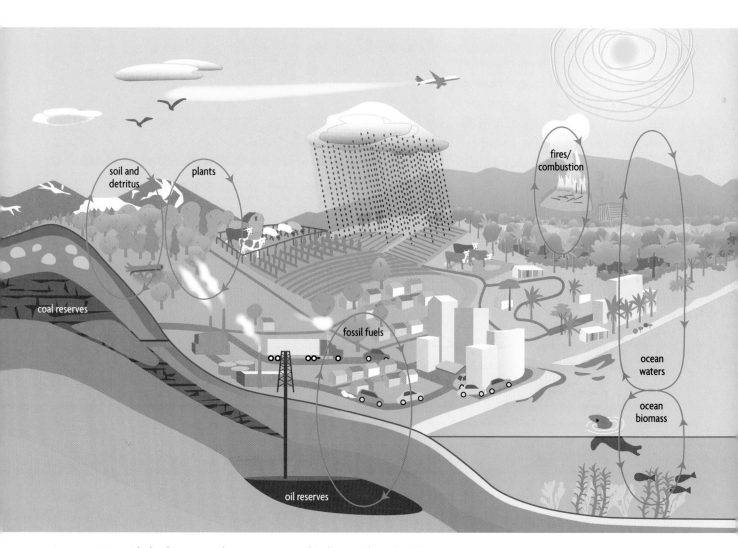

In comparison with the diagram on the previous page, this diagram shows how human population growth, use of technology, and burning of fossil fuels have altered the carbon cycle.

9 The Photosynthesis and Cellular Respiration Shuffle

IN THE PREVIOUS activity, "Moving Through the Carbon Cycle," you examined how carbon travels between reservoirs on earth. In this activity you will look more closely at how carbon and oxygen are continuously cycled by organisms and how these elements sustain both the organisms and ecosystems. You will examine what happens to carbon and oxygen at the cellular level.

Two fundamental cellular processes are cellular respiration and photosynthesis. **Cellular respiration** is the process by which cells release stored energy from sugars. **Photosynthesis** is the process in which producer cells use carbon dioxide, water, and nutrients to produce glucose and oxygen. Together these two processes make the carbon cycle possible, and move essential molecules through ecosystems.

All organisms in this community perform cellular respiration and some photosynthesize.

Challenge

▶ How do carbon and oxygen cycle through the environment?

MATERIALS

FOR EACH GROUP OF FOUR STUDENTS
   set of 12 Photosynthesis and Cellular Respiration Shuffle paper strips

FOR EACH PAIR OF STUDENTS
   computer with Internet access

FOR EACH STUDENT
   Student Sheet 9.1, "Photosynthesis and Cellular Respiration Diagram"

Procedure

1. Complete Student Sheet 9.1, "Photosynthesis and Cellular Respiration Diagram," as directed by your teacher.

2. Find the "Photosynthesis and Cellular Respiration Shuffle" animation on the *Science and Global Issues* page of the SEPUP website at *sepuplhs.org/sgi*. Sort the images based on what you already know about photosynthesis and cellular respiration, and on what you can see in the images.

3. When you have completed the animation, follow your teacher's instructions to record the results in your science notebook.

4. Obtain the Photosynthesis and Cellular Respiration Shuffle paper strips from your teacher.

5. With your group, lay all of the strips out on the table, and read each one aloud.

6. Sort the strips into two piles, one for cellular respiration and one for photosynthesis. If you are unsure about where any of the strips belong, lay them out next to where you will be working so that you can see them as you work.

7. Choose a stack to start with. Put the strips in the order in which you think the processes are happening.

8. Repeat Step 7 for the stack you have not ordered yet.

9. If you had any strips that you did not place, try to decide where they belong now that you have ordered the other strips.

10. Once you have all of the strips in order, compare your strips to the results from the animation, and make any adjustments in the order of the strips that you need to.

    Note: There are more strips than animation images, and so more than one strip may fit with a single image.

11. Based on what you see in the animation and on the strips, write in your science notebook a short paragraph describing cellular respiration and one describing photosynthesis. Be sure you write in your own words, and do not just copy the strips.

Analysis

1. What does a producer need for performing photosynthesis, and what does photosynthesis produce?

2. What does an organism need to perform cellular respiration, and what does cellular respiration produce?

3. What roles do photosynthesis and cellular respiration have in an ecosystem?

4. Go back to your diagram on Student Sheet 9.1, "Photosynthesis and Cellular Respiration Diagram," and revise it, or sketch a new one based on what you have learned in this activity. Be sure to show where enzymes are involved, as well as carbon dioxide, water, oxygen, and glucose.

5. If someone says, "Only organisms that breathe can perform cellular respiration," are they correct? Explain.

6. If the mitochondria of half the organisms in the ecosystem stopped functioning, what indicators in the ecosystem would change? Explain.

7. There are specialized producers that live in warm-water vents deep in the ocean. These producers do not perform photosynthesis, but instead perform a similar process with iron and other chemicals. Why do you think these producers use this process instead of photosynthesis?

KEY VOCABULARY	
cellular respiration	organisms
enzymes	**photosynthesis**

10 Respiring Beans

AS YOU LEARNED in the previous activity, photosynthesis is the chemical process that produces sugar molecules from carbon dioxide and water. Photosynthesis requires light and takes place in cells of green plants and other producer organisms. You have also learned that cellular respiration is a chemical process by which living cells, including plant cells, use oxygen to release energy from sugar molecules. During cellular respiration, sugars released in the breakdown of food react with oxygen to produce water and carbon dioxide and release energy. These are the two main reactions that cycle the carbon and oxygen needed to sustain an ecosystem and convert energy into usable forms. Without photosynthesis and cellular respiration ecosystems are not sustainable, as you saw in the case study about crabs in the Chesapeake Bay in Activity 1, "Ecosystems and Change."

In this activity you will use beans to investigate rates of cellular respiration. The beans have been germinated, which means they have sprouted and are starting to grow.

Germinated bean seeds have sprouted and started to grow.

In beans sugars are stored as starch, similar to starch stored in other plant structures, such as tree trunks. This stored starch provides the sugars that the new sprouting bean uses in cellular respiration. You will investigate the rate of cellular respiration with a chemical indicator called phenol red. Phenol red is red when a solution is basic and turns orange and then yellow if the solution becomes increasingly acidic. Because carbon dioxide makes water acidic, phenol red allows us to infer that cellular respiration is taking place. You will design your own experiment to test how one variable affects the rate of cellular respiration of sprouted beans.

Challenge

▶ How do various factors affect the rate of cellular respiration?

MATERIALS

FOR EACH GROUP OF STUDENTS

  4 transparent, sealable cups

  4 plastic disc inserts

     250-mL Erlenmeyer flask

     timer

     30-mL dropper bottle of phenol red indicator solution

     germinated beans

     dried beans

     masking tape

     permanent marker

     source of water

FOR EACH STUDENT

     Student Sheet 9.1, "Photosynthesis and Cellular Respiration Diagram" from Activity 9

Procedure

1. As a group, you will design an experiment that demonstrates how one variable affects the rate of cellular respiration in beans. Your teacher will explain to you the materials that are available, in addition to those listed above, and explain any other conditions your experiment must meet. As a group, brainstorm a list of variables you can test. Decide with your group which variable on your list you will test.

2. Use the guidelines below to determine the procedure you will follow:

   a. The cups should be set up so that the beans are not in the liquid. Place the plastic disc insert into the cup to keep the beans out of the liquid, as shown below.

> Safety
>
> The indicator used in this activity, phenol red, will stain skin and clothing. If you get it on your skin or clothing, immediately flush the area with water.

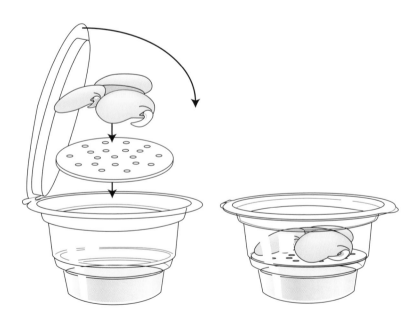

b. Use the indicator to track cellular respiration. Prepare your indicator solution by adding 25 drops of phenol red to 125 mL of water and swirling the solution to mix it.

c. Pour enough indicator solution into the bottom of each cup so that it is just below the plastic disc insert.

d. Set up a control. Determine with your group how you will set up your control and how you will set up your experimental variable. Use the masking tape to label each cup appropriately.

e. After your experiment is set up, you must fix the lids on the cups tightly to prevent any gas from escaping.

3. Write out your procedure in your science notebook. Have your teacher approve your procedure before you set up your experiment.

4. As a group, decide how you will collect your data. Set up an appropriate data table in your science notebook. In your science notebook predict what will happen, and explain why.

5. Set up your experiment. If your experiment will be left overnight, ask your teacher for further instructions.

6. Run your experiment, and collect and record your data.

7. Follow your teacher's instructions to clean up and dispose of your materials properly.

8. Follow your teacher's instructions on how you will share your results with the class.

9. Go back to your diagram on Student Sheet 9.1, "Photosynthesis and Cellular Respiration Diagram," and revise it or sketch a new one based on what you have learned in this activity. Be sure you have indicated where enzymes are involved, as well as carbon dioxide, water, oxygen, and glucose.

Analysis

1. What variable did you test? Explain your choice.

2. What did your variable show about rates of cellular respiration? Identify the conclusions you can draw from your data.

3. How did your experiment compare to those of the other groups? What variables did other groups test?

4. Summarize the conclusions that can be drawn based on the experiments performed by the class. Include all relevant data that supports your conclusions.

5. In Activity 1, "Ecosystems and Change," you read about dead zones and the crabs in Chesapeake Bay not having enough oxygen because of an increase in bacteria in the water. How could you use data from this experiment to explain what is happening in Chesapeake Bay?

6. In Activity 3, "Biomes," you read about the characteristics of the temperate deciduous forest. Some trees in this biome lose their leaves in the fall, and cannot perform photosynthesis without them. Explain, based on what you learned in this activity, why the trees do not die over the winter months.

KEY VOCABULARY

cellular respiration	photosynthesis
chemical indicator	variable

11 Respiration and Photosynthesis in Plants

As you have learned, plants and other producers perform cellular respiration as well as photosynthesis. Ecosystems need a balance between these two processes in order to be sustainable. If this balance is altered, for example in a bleached coral reef or a dead zone, the sustainability of the ecosystem may be threatened.

Simplified chemical equations for cellular respiration and photosynthesis are shown below. As you can see, these two equations have similar components: energy, oxygen, carbon dioxide, water, and sugar.

Chemical Equations for Cellular Respiration and Photosynthesis

CELLULAR RESPIRATION

$$C_6H_{12}O_6 + 6O_2 \rightarrow 6H_2O + 6CO_2 + \text{energy}$$

One molecule of glucose (a type of sugar) reacts with six molecules of oxygen to form six molecules of water, six molecules of carbon dioxide, and release energy.

PHOTOSYNTHESIS

$$6H_2O + 6CO_2 + \text{light energy} \rightarrow C_6H_{12}O_6 + 6O_2$$

In the presence of light energy, six molecules of water react with six molecules of carbon dioxide to form one molecule of glucose and six molecules of oxygen.

In this investigation you will further explore cellular respiration and photosynthesis in plants, and measure the production and consumption of carbon dioxide during respiration and photosynthesis. You will use the chemical indicator bromothymol blue (BTB), which is blue when a solution is basic and turns green and then yellow as the solution becomes more acidic. Because carbon dioxide makes water acidic, BTB allows us to infer when cellular respiration and photosynthesis are happening in a plant.

Challenge

▶ How does changing one variable affect photosynthesis and cellular respiration in plants?

MATERIALS

FOR EACH GROUP OF FOUR STUDENTS

6   transparent, sealable cups

4   sprigs of aquatic plant, each approximately 4–6 cm long

    30-mL dropper bottle of bromothymol blue (BTB)

    drinking straw

    250-mL Erlenmeyer flask

    beaker or other clear container, at least 1,000-mL capacity

    roll of masking tape

    permanent marker

    source of water

FOR EACH STUDENT
Student Sheet 9.1, "Photosynthesis and Cellular Respiration Diagram"

All plants respire and photosynthesize.

Procedure

1. As a group, brainstorm a list of variables you might test. Consult with your teacher to determine one variable that you can test in this activity. Follow your teacher's directions for setting up your experiment to test the variable. Remember that if it is to survive, the plant must be kept in water.

2. With your group determine your procedure to test your variable, record the procedure in your science notebook, and set up your data table for the investigation.

3. Fill the beaker with 600 mL of water. Add 60 drops of BTB to the water, and swirl the beaker until it is thoroughly mixed.

4. Have one person from your group slowly exhale through a straw into the beaker until the solution turns green. Be careful not to blow so much air through the straw that the solution turns yellow. Do not drink the solution!

5. Label your cups 1–6, and add one sprig of aquatic plant to cups 1 and 3.

6. Completely fill cups 1–4 with the green solution. With these cups you will test the effect of light on photosynthesis and cellular respiration.

7. Set up cups 5 and 6 to test the variable you chose in Step 1. They should be completely filled with solution.

8. Cap all six cups tightly so that no gas can escape. On your data table record the colors of the solutions in the six cups.

9. Place cups 1 and 2 in the sun or under fluorescent lights, according to your teacher's instructions. Place cups 3 and 4 in a dark location. Place cups 5 and 6 according to the experimental setup you designed.

10. In your science notebook, answer the following question: What was the purpose of preparing the solution of BTB, water, and a small amount of carbon dioxide? Predict if any of the vials will show a color change over the next few minutes or hours. Record and explain your prediction(s).

11. Check the cups every 15 minutes until the class period ends. Record your observations in your data table.

12. Make a final observation of the cups when you next return to class.

13. Go back to your diagram on Student Sheet 9.1, "Photosynthesis and Cellular Respiration Diagram," and revise it, or sketch a new one based on what you have learned in this activity. Be sure you have indicated where enzymes are involved, as well as carbon dioxide, water, oxygen, and glucose.

Safety

Use caution when preparing the BTB solution. While using the straw, exhale only. Wash your hands thoroughly after the activity.

Because certain aquatic plants are considered invasive species in many areas, be careful not to pour any down the drain. Your teacher will provide disposal instructions at the end of the experiment.

Analysis

1. Did you observe any color changes? Describe them.

2. Based on the color change(s) you observed, what can you infer about what gas was present in each tube at the start and at the end of the experiment?

3. What was the purpose of cups 2 and 4?

4. Describe the variable that you decided to test in cups 5 and 6. Describe your results, and explain what you concluded from them.

5. What evidence do you have from this activity that plants photosynthesize? Explain.

6. What evidence do you have from this activity that plants perform cellular respiration? Explain.

7. Did the color changes you observed occur at the same rate? What explanation can you provide for any similarities or differences in the rates?

8. You and your friend Danielle are talking about what you learned in class today. Danielle says, "I think plants photosynthesize during the day and respire at night." Do you agree with Danielle? What kind of experiment could you design to test her hypothesis?

9. How could the rate of plants' photosynthesis be an indicator for the overall health of an aquatic ecosystem?

   Hint: Think back to the case studies from Activity 1, "Ecosystems and Change."

KEY VOCABULARY

cellular respiration   photosynthesis

chemical indicator

---

12 Too Much Life

MOST UNDISTURBED ECOSYSTEMS have an approximate balance of producers and consumers, and energy and nutrients flow between them, primarily in the form of carbon-containing compounds. If that balance is disrupted, however, it can have a significant impact on the ecosystem and the organisms within it.

In this activity you will examine what happens to oxygen levels as the number of organisms in an environment increases. Modeling a marine ecosystem, you will work with yeast, a live organism, to represent the organisms in a marine environment. You will use methylene blue, a chemical indicator that shows the presence of oxygen. Methylene blue is blue but turns colorless when the oxygen in the solution is no longer present.

Challenge

▶ How does the rate of cellular respiration affect the oxygen levels available in an aquatic ecosystem?

MATERIALS

FOR EACH PAIR OF STUDENTS
- SEPUP tray
- stir stick
- 10-mL graduated cylinder
- graduated dropper
- timer
- piece of white paper
- 30-mL dropper bottle of 0.01% methylene blue
- 25 mL skim milk
- 14 mL yeast solution
- paper towels

FOR EACH STUDENT
- 3 sticky notes

Safety

Methylene blue will stain clothing and skin. Flush thoroughly with water if it comes in contact with clothing or skin. Milk and yeast solution are for laboratory use only.
Do not drink or eat these materials.

Background Information

In the 1970s, part of Chesapeake Bay, on the east coast of the United States, was identified as one of earth's first marine dead zones. A **dead zone** is an area in a body of water where the water at the bottom has little or no dissolved oxygen.

When a large amount of nutrient-rich water flows into an area, causing an increase in plant growth—an occurrence known as **eutrophication**—the conditions are prime for a dead zone to develop, as shown in the diagram below. Phytoplankton populations increase quickly in the nutrient-rich water. When the phytoplankton die and sink, they increase the amount of organic matter available for bacteria to feed on at the bottom of the ocean. As their population grows, the bacteria's combined cellular respiration increases, depleting the surrounding water of oxygen. Very few organisms can survive this lack of oxygen, and so they migrate or die.

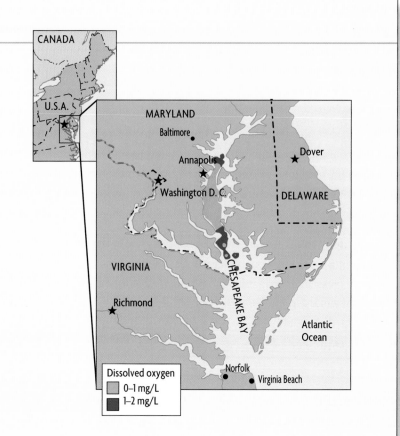

You learned in Activity 1, "Ecosystems and Change," about the crab jubilees that happen as a result of these dead zones in Chesapeake Bay.

Eutrophication can be caused by natural systems where nutrients are high, but increasingly it results from human-related activity, such as fertilizer run-off from agricultural areas or farms, sewage spills, vehicle exhaust, and storm water run-off that picks up sources of nitrogen, phosphorus, and other nutrients.

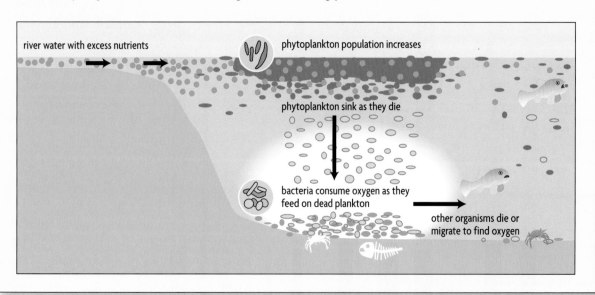

Since the 1960s, the number of dead zones in the world has doubled approximately every 10 years, and currently involves more than 245,000 sq km in more than 400 systems.

Many of these systems, including Chesapeake Bay, were once homes to important commercial and recreational fisheries. However, eutrophication combined with overfishing and other types of pollution has caused many of these fisheries to collapse or shrink considerably. Plans for healing these ecosystems seek to prevent eutrophication, while at the same time working to curb overfishing and pollution. ■

The brown plume is where water from rivers upstream flows into the Gulf of Mexico where large dead zones have been documented. This water contains high concentrations of fertilizer runoff (right).

The image at left, below, shows winter conditions in the Gulf of Mexico. The image to its right shows summer conditions. Red and orange represent the highest concentrations of phytoplankton and sediment in the water.

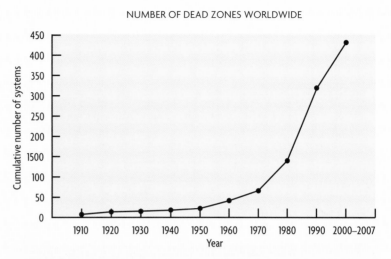

NUMBER OF DEAD ZONES WORLDWIDE

Procedure

1. Make a data table in your science notebook, like the one below.

Eutrophication Data

	Cup A 0 mL yeast	Cup B 2 mL yeast	Cup C 3 mL yeast	Cup D 4 mL yeast	Cup E 5 mL yeast
Start time					
Stop time					
Total time					

2. With your partner, predict the order in which the experimental setups will lose their blue color. Explain your reasoning in your science notebook.

   Hint: Methylene blue turns colorless when oxygen is no longer present in a solution.

3. Using the amounts specified in the table below, add the milk, methylene blue, and water to each large cup in your SEPUP tray (Cups A–E). Mix well with the stir stick.

Cup Contents					
	CUP A	CUP B	CUP C	CUP D	CUP E
Milk (mL)	5	5	5	5	5
Methylene blue (mL)	1	1	1	1	1
Water (mL)	5	3	2	1	0
Yeast solution (mL)	0	2	3	4	5

4. Place the tray on top of the white paper so you can compare the colors of the solutions. You may want to observe from the back side of the tray to see the solutions, as shown on the next page.

5. Start the timer for Cup A, and record the start time on your data table.

6. Add the yeast solution to Cup B, record the start time, and stir the contents. Be sure to record the start time as soon as you add the yeast to the cup.

7. Repeat Step 6 for each of the remaining cups, adding the amount of yeast solution indicated on the table.

8. Stir the contents of each cup approximately every 30 seconds, wiping off the stir stick between cups to avoid contamination.

9. Observe the large cups from the back side of the tray while continuing to stir the contents every 30 seconds. Record the times when the contents of each cup turn white.

10. Subtract the start time from the stop time to determine the total time it took the solution to turn white in each of your experimental setups.

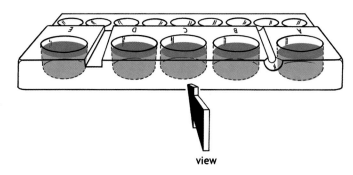

view

Analysis

1. In what order did the solutions lose their color? Did this match your predictions? Explain.

2. **a.** What do the different parts of the model (that is, yeast and milk) represent?

   b. If Cup B and Cup E represent different ecosystems, how are they different?

3. **a.** How does the concentration of organisms in a body of water affect the rate of oxygen consumption?

   b. How does your answer to 3a relate to eutrophication?

4. What effect would an increase in phytoplankton have on the food webs in the surrounding ecosystem? Explain, using evidence from your investigation.

5. How does eutrophication cause a dead zone to occur, and how does that differ from an area where there is no eutrophication?

6. What effects might eutrophication and dead zones have on nearby fisheries?

7. Using the evidence you gathered in your experiment, how could you explain the eutrophication and dead zones in Chesapeake Bay?

KEY VOCABULARY	
cellular respiration	organism
dead zone	population
eutrophication	

13 Symbiotic Relationships

IF YOU WERE asked to describe the interaction between two organisms in a marine ecosystem, you might think of a seal eating a fish, or a shore bird hunting for clams. As you have already learned, if an ecosystem and its food webs are examined closely, it turns out that many of the relationships between animals and plants are much more complex than "who eats whom." In this activity you will be examining the close relationships between many of the animals and plants that inhabit a kelp forest.

The close relationship of organisms in an ecosystem is known as **symbiosis.** As you learned in Activity 1, "Ecosystems and Change," coral polyps provide shelter for algae, and the algae perform photosynthesis, providing food for the coral. That symbiotic relationship is part of the balance required for an ecosystem to be sustainable. Ecologists study these relationships and their interactions within larger ecosystems in order to better understand how ecosystems function. In this activity you will categorize symbiotic relationships found in a kelp forest, and the advantages and disadvantages for the plants and animals involved.

Challenge

▶ How do organisms gain or lose from their interactions with each other?

This crab disguises itself by placing small anemones, algae, and other organisms on its carapace (shell) to make it blend in with the sea floor.

MATERIALS

FOR EACH GROUP OF FOUR STUDENTS

set of 16 Symbiotic Relationship Cards

set of 4 Interaction Description Cards

Procedure

1. With your group of four, read through the description on each of the Symbiotic Relationship Cards, noting the similarities and differences among the relationships.

2. Sort the cards into several sets according to the similarities in the symbiotic relationships.

3. In your science notebook, list the common features of each set of symbiotic relationships. Then write down the species pairs of each set.

4. According to your teacher's instructions, share with the class how your group classified the symbiotic relationships.

5. Get a set of Interaction Description Cards from your teacher. Each card represents a set of symbiotic relationships as classified by ecologists. Based on the information described on the Interaction Description Cards, place each Symbiotic Relationship Card under one of the Interaction Description categories.

6. In your science notebook, list the common features of each category of symbiotic relationships as described on the Interaction Description Cards. Then list the species pairs that belong to each set.

7. With your group, compare the two classification systems. Describe the similarities and differences of those systems.

8. Record your group's ideas in your science notebook.

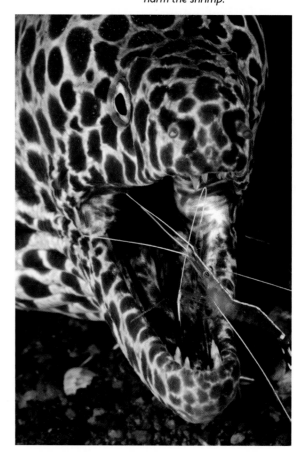

Cleaner shrimp eat small parasites and dead skin from the mouth of a moray eel. The eel remains still while the shrimp works, and will not harm the shrimp.

Analysis

1. Define each of the following, and cite an example:

   amensalism

   commensalism

   mutualism

   parasitism

2. Choose four of the symbiotic relationships you examined in this activity, one from each category. Describe the benefits and drawbacks within each relationship.

3. How would the food webs and the symbiotic relationships in the kelp forest be affected if the senorita fish were overfished and were no longer found in the kelp forest?

4. How are the mutualism examples you learned about in this activity similar to organisms in an ecosystem performing photosynthesis and cellular respiration?

KEY VOCABULARY	
amensalism	parasitism
commensalism	symbiosis
mutualism	

14 Investigating Population Growth Rates

THERE ARE LIMITS on the sizes of populations ecosystems can support. These limits—the **carrying capacities** for particular populations—are determined by the resources available and the other species present in the ecosystem. Carrying capacities of an ecosystem change as the resources in the ecosystem change. The graph below shows 25 years of population levels of zebra mussels in a lake.

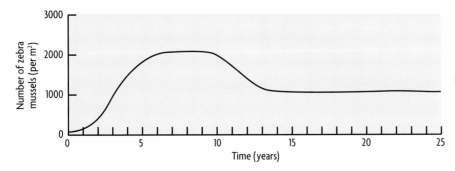

This population of zebra mussels reached its carrying capacity around Year 14.

Initially the zebra mussel population grew to a point where the lake could not sustain it, but by Year 14 the population had decreased to a level at which the ecosystem was able to sustain it over an extended period of time. What factors do you think might change the carrying capacity for this population?

As you learned in the previous activity, many organisms have interdependent relationships. In predator–prey relationships, the size and health of one population is frequently closely tied to the size and health of the other, as you learned in Activity 7, "Energy Flow Through an Ecosystem."

A change in a population level is one indicator that can reflect the health of an ecosystem. A population of a successful invasive species, such as duckweed, will increase rapidly in a new habitat, possibly causing the populations of other, native species to shrink. This can change both population and biodiversity levels. You saw several examples of this in the first few activities of this unit. The **population growth rate** describes the change in a population over specified intervals of time. A positive growth rate indicates that the population is

Anchor covered with zebra mussels.

growing, while a negative growth rate indicates the population is shrinking. A population that remains the same size has a zero-growth rate.

In this activity you will examine how different variables affect population growth rates of a fish population and the carrying capacity of the ecosystem the population lives in.

Challenge

▶ How do changing variables alter population growth rates and ecosystem carrying capacities?

MATERIALS

FOR EACH PAIR OF STUDENTS

computer with Internet access

colored pencils

FOR EACH STUDENT

Student Sheet 14.1, "Avril Seal Population"

Student Sheet 14.2, "Investigating Population Growth"

sheet of graph paper

Procedure

1. With your partner, visit the *Science and Global Issues* page of the SEPUP website at *sepuplhs.org/sgi* and go to the population simulation. Use your student sheet to guide you through the simulation.

Analysis

1. Describe the shapes of the graphs you created when working with the online simulation. Explain what the shape of the curve indicates about the population.

2. Based on your work in this activity, describe the relationship between birth and death rates and the growth rate of a population.

3. Based on your work in this activity, describe the relationship between carrying capacity and the size of a population.

4. How do the sizes of populations of other species relate to the sustainability of the human population? Think of at least two examples, and describe the relationship of each to the human population.

5. Some bacteria reproduce by doubling once every 20 minutes.

   a. If you started with one bacterium, how many would you have in three hours?

   b. Describe what would happen if the bacteria continued to reproduce for 24 hours (do not calculate an exact number).

   c. Suggest at least two limiting factors that will ultimately stop the increase of a bacteria population.

6. Scientists and policy makers often have to work together to set catch limits on fisheries. Imagine that a policy maker proposes to allow the fishing of a certain species to go on at current rates because, she says, "Fishing at current rates will not impact the ecosystem. We are removing fish at a rate lower than the birth rate of their population." Is this claim valid? What indicators would you look at to support or disprove this claim? Explain your reasoning.

7. Look at the population graph for the fish population shown below. How would you describe the growth rate? Is this population sustainable?

8. Examine the data in the Global Human Population graph provided below. Based on your work in this activity, how would you describe the global human population growth rate? Explain your reasoning.

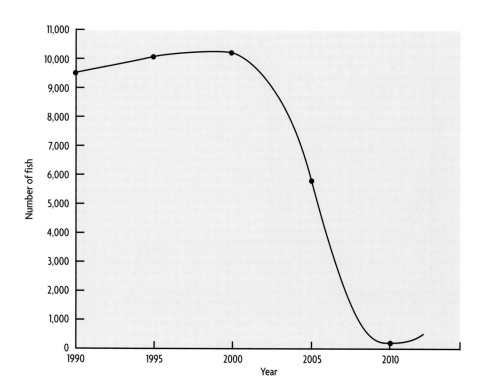

9. Some people claim that the human population has passed its carrying capacity. What kind of environmental, social, and economic indicators would you examine to support or argue against this claim?

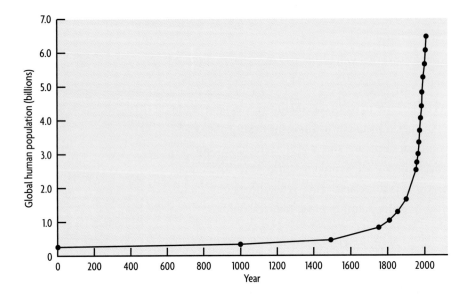

KEY VOCABULARY

carrying capacity   population

density-dependent factors   **population growth rate**

density-independent factors

15 Changes Due to Population Growth

"I **DON'T UNDERSTAND WHY** *overfishing is such a big deal,*" *you overhear someone say in the grocery store.* "*Why don't they just grow fish on fish farms for us to eat and leave the wild ones alone? That way the wild ones can reproduce and increase their population. Besides, I thought that fish had lots of offspring, what are we worried about?*"

As the human population continues to grow, and the need for food grows with it, more and more fisheries are being overfished. Some fisheries, such as the salmon fishery along the west coast of the United States, have been temporarily closed due to shrinking populations.

Many people suggest that the solution to overfishing is aquaculture. **Aquaculture** is the growing of fish and other aquatic species for human consumption. There are species of fish that can be sustainably farmed. For example, tilapia farms in the United States are often viewed as sustainable and very successful. Native to Africa, tilapia grow and reproduce well in captivity and are raised in enclosed inland ponds where their wastewater is treated. Since more and more wild fish populations are declining, aquaculture is becoming an important food source.

It does not, however, work for all species. Some fish need specific habitats that cannot be recreated in captivity, some do not breed in captivity, and some have other limitations. On top of that, species such as salmon that can be farmed often cause major problems for the local, natural ecosystems.

Challenge

► How can the environmental harm from salmon farming be minimized?

MATERIALS

FOR EACH GROUP OF FOUR STUDENTS
    number cube

FOR EACH STUDENT
    sheet of graph paper

Aquaculture Systems

Aquaculture can be located on land, in oceans, or in bays, depending on the species raised. The most familiar aquaculture systems consist of inland ponds that hold a particular fresh or saltwater species, such as trout, tilapia, shrimp, or catfish. Some of these ponds are enclosed systems in which the water is treated and recirculated to prevent contamination of the environment. This is costly and requires electricity.

Raceways are another type of system. They divert water from a river or other source and guide it through long channels that house the fish being raised. The water is then treated before it rejoins the original source. In the United States raceways are used to raise rainbow trout, striped bass, and other species. Among ecologists there is concern that the farmed fish might escape and either interbreed with the wild fish or compete with them for food.

In this activity you will examine the aquaculture system of open-net pens. These are large net pens suspended in coastal waters or lakes and are frequently used for tuna and salmon farming. The water from the pens exchanges freely with the water in the surrounding habitat. This causes pollution and can spread disease from the farmed fish to the wild populations. There is also the chance that the farmed fish will escape, as with the raceway systems. You will explore some of the benefits and trade-offs involved in a widespread debate over farmed salmon. ∎

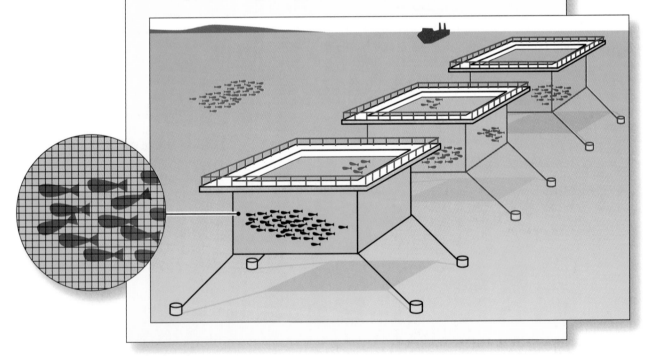

Net pens are used to farm salmon.

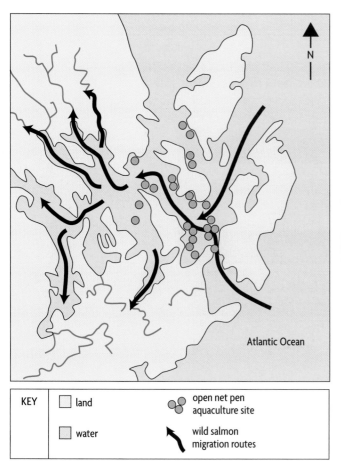

Most wild salmon hatch from their eggs in fresh water, and migrate down rivers or waterways to the ocean. Mature salmon migrate back to the same fresh water location to reproduce. The simplified map at left shows net pens located along wild salmon migration routes. Below, a wild salmon swims upstream during the fall.

Atlantic Ocean

KEY		
☐ land		open net pen aquaculture site
☐ water		wild salmon migration routes

Procedure

Your group will track two salmon populations, one wild and one farmed. The salmon farm is an open-net system set up in the coastal waters off of the East Coast of the United States, as shown in the illustration on the previous page. The wild salmon's migration routes, similar to those shown in the map of net pens and migration routes, bring them into close contact with the salmon farms.

1. Your group will collect data for 20 generations of salmon. In your science notebook set up a data table, similar to the one below, in which you enter your data on the salmon generations.

Comparing Wild and Farmed Salmon Populations

Generation	Wild population size	Wild population status	Farmed population size	Farmed population status
1	10,000		1,500	
2				
3				
4				
5				
6				

2. In Steps 3–6 you will follow the guidelines in the tables below to determine the status of your salmon population.

Wild Salmon Population

NUMBER OF FISH	≤5,000	5,001–7,000	7,001–9,000	9,001–12,000
Population status	critically overfished	marginally overfished	stable	at carrying capacity

Farmed Salmon Population

NUMBER OF FISH	≤5,000	5,001–7,000	7,001–9,000	9,001–12,000
Profit level	negative profit (loss)	no profit (break even)	moderate profit	substantial profit

3. Begin your simulation by rolling the number cube to determine what happens to the first generation of salmon. The number cube key below tells you what the number you rolled means. Add to or subtract from the salmon populations as directed, and record the results in your data table. If you roll a 5 or 6 and your population is not 1,400 or greater, keep rolling until you get a 1, 2, 3, or 4.

Number Cube Key: Environmental Impacts

NUMBER ROLLED	SITUATION	ENVIRONMENTAL IMPACT	WILD POPULATION EFFECT	FARMED POPULATION EFFECT
1	Farmed salmon escape.	Escapees interbreed and compete for resources with wild population.	Loss of 500 salmon due to lack of resources and reduced fitness because of interbreeding	No change in population size
2	Disease at salmon farm	Disease spreads to wild population.	Loss of 1,500 salmon from disease	Loss of 250 salmon from disease
3	Antibiotics given to farmed salmon to prevent disease.	Kills "good" bacteria that the ecosystem needs to function	Ecosystem disrupted; causes loss of 750 salmon.	Disease decreases; population increases by 250 salmon.
4	Decrease in density of salmon in pens	Milder environmental impact	Improved habitat causes increase of 500 salmon	Fewer salmon per pen, loss of 350 salmon
5	If farm has over 1,400 salmon, waste accumulates under pens.	Wastewater in local ecosystem causes habitat and food loss.	Reduction of available resources causes loss of 1,000 salmon.	Decrease in water quality causes loss of 500 salmon.
6	If farm has more than 1,400 salmon, new pen is built.	Takes up the space of wild salmon's habitat.	Decrease of resources causes loss of 500 salmon.	New pen houses more salmon; increase by 350 salmon

4. Record in your data table the status of each population, based on the information provided in Step 2.

5. Repeat Steps 3 and 4 until you have gone through 20 generations of salmon. If either population reaches 0 during the simulation, stop and move on to Step 6.

6. Construct a line graph that shows the population curves for the wild and farmed salmon populations.

Analysis

1. **a.** Define aquaculture.

   b. Describe at least two kinds of aquaculture systems.

2. Based on the graph you constructed in Procedure Step 6, explain the relationship between the population growth in the farmed salmon population and the wild population.

3. What are some of the possible environmental impacts of aquaculture? Which of these impacts are density-dependent factors and which are density-independent factors?

4. What are the benefits and trade-offs involved with aquaculture? Discuss at least two aquaculture systems.

5. Your model in this activity involved random events happening to the salmon populations. If you were to build and operate an open-net salmon farm, what are some steps you could take to minimize environmental harm and make the farm more sustainable?

KEY VOCABULARY	
aquaculture	population
density-dependent factors	population growth rate
density-independent factors	

Ecosystems Out of Balance

ORGANISMS WITHIN an ecosystem interact at all levels, depending on each other for their survival, either directly for food or shelter, or indirectly through the carbon cycle. As you saw in the previous activity, both native and introduced species have a significant effect on the ecosystem around them. The entire ecosystem is a complex network that can be drastically altered if the population of one (or more) species goes into a decline or a surge. In this activity you will take on the role of a fisheries biologist and determine how to make several fisheries more sustainable.

You are a fisheries biologist who has, in the past, advised the Pacific halibut (Hippoglossus stenolepis) *fishery, which is known for its successful sustainable practices. The Pacific halibut fishery is carefully monitored, and each year you and other fisheries biologists make a new set of recommendations on where and how many fish can be caught. The limits are adopted by the entire fishery. Several other fisheries have asked for your expert advice. These fisheries would like you to examine population data and other information for the species they fish and the species' ecosystems and, if they are not sustainable, to advise on how to make them more sustainable.*

A fisherman weighs the Pacific halibut he caught.

Challenge

▶ How does information about relationships among organisms help to determine the sustainability of a species and an ecosystem?

Pacific halibut are large flatfish that live on the ocean floor in coastal waters off the western United States and Canada.

MATERIALS

FOR EACH STUDENT

Student Sheet 16.1, "Cod-dominated Ecosystem"

Student Sheet 16.2, "Tiger-shark-dominated Ecosystem"

Student Sheet 16.3, "Orca-dominated Ecosystem"

Student Sheet 16.4, "Caspian-seal-dominated Ecosystem"

Procedure

Part A: Evaluating Fisheries' Sustainability

1. With your group, examine the food chain for the cod-dominated ecosystem, and the corresponding graph on Student Sheet 16.1, "Cod-dominated Ecosystem." This ecosystem is found in the North Atlantic Ocean.

2. Identify the role of each species in the food chain by determining what they eat and what they are eaten by.

3. With the key, label each line on the graph with the name of the organism.

4. Choose one time point on the graph, toward the beginning. Based on the information provided in the graph, explain in detail what is happening at this point with each species, relative to the other populations in the ecosystem. Write your description in your science notebook.

5. Choose a time point on the graph that is toward the end. Based on the information provided in the graph, explain in detail what is happening at this point with each species in the ecosystem. Include what this means about the food-chain relationships between the species. Write your description in your science notebook.

6. Summarize the population growth rates for each population for the full time period shown on the graph. Write your summary in your science notebook.

7. Discuss with your group what the graph shows overall. Note any patterns or anything that seems out of the ordinary, as compared to the Pacific-halibut-dominated ecosystem you reviewed with your teacher. Write your observations in your science notebook.

8. Repeat Steps 1–7 for the tiger-shark-dominated ecosystem. This ecosystem is found in the Atlantic Ocean off the southern coast of the United States.

9. Repeat Steps 1–7 for the orca-dominated ecosystem. This ecosystem is found off the northwestern Pacific coast of North America.

10. Repeat Steps 1–7 for the Caspian-seal-dominated ecosystem. This ecosystem is found in the Caspian Sea, the world's largest enclosed body of water, located between the southern border of Russia and the northern border of Iran.

Part B: Fishery Histories

11. Read the brief history of the cod fishery below.

ATLANTIC COD

The Atlantic cod (*Gadus morhua*) fishery is one of the oldest fisheries in the world. There are records of explorers from Europe hunting for new cod fishing grounds as far back as 1000 A.D. Atlantic cod are found throughout the North Atlantic in waters up to 400 meters deep. While the Atlantic cod has been fished for more than 1,000 years, the invention of steamships and on-ship refrigeration in the early 1900s brought huge changes to the fishery. Overfishing of the cod intensified to the point that, in 1992, Canada declared a two-year moratorium on cod fishing off its shores. Soon other nations began to apply strict rules limiting the size and number of cod that were fished in an attempt to bring the cod population back to sustainable levels that would maintain a healthy ecosystem and support the fishery.

cod

12. With your group, compare this information with your observations of the cod-dominated-ecosystem graph. How does this information support or inform your conclusions about what the graph shows? Write down any additional observations or thoughts about what might be happening in the cod-dominated ecosystem.

13. Repeat Steps 11 and 12 for the tiger shark fishery.

TIGER SHARK

The tiger shark *(Galeocerdo cuvier)* is one of the largest predatory sharks found in the world's oceans. Like many other shark species, the tiger shark is fished for its fins to make shark fin soup, a dish in Chinese cuisine that has become more popular around the world over the past few decades. The tiger shark is also fished for its liver, which is high in vitamin A. The shark is highly valued by sport fishers, particularly because it is known as a dangerous predator. Tiger sharks' gestation period is very long: 14–16 months between fertilization and birth. They give birth only once every three years, producing, on average, 40 pups. As shown in the food chain, tiger sharks feed on cow nose rays, which feed on bay scallops. The bay scallop population crashed in the early 1960s due to overfishing. Limits were set on scallop collection and the population started to recover in the 1970s.

tiger shark

14. Repeat Steps 11 and 12 for the perch fishery (part of the orca-dominated ecosystem).

PACIFIC OCEAN PERCH

Pacific ocean perch *(Sebastes alutus)* are caught primarily for human consumption. The population was heavily fished starting in the early 1960s. The fishery grew rapidly, but in 1990, the perch were declared overfished off the west coast of the United States. In 2003, a fishery management council put in place a plan that they hoped would allow the population to recover. Perch are slow growing, and only mature (are able to have offspring) after they are at least five years old. Some females do not mature until they are 15 years old.

perch

15. Repeat Steps 11 and 12 for the anchovy kilka fishery (part of the Caspian-seal-dominated ecosystem).

ANCHOVY KILKA

The anchovy kilka *(Clupeonella engrauliformis)* is one of the main commercially fished species in the Caspian Sea. Major fishing of the kilka began in the 1950s, and by the 1990s there were record catches as large as 400,000 tons annually. In 1999, an invasive comb jelly *(Mnemiopsis leidyi)* was found in the Caspian. It reproduced quickly, feeding on the same plankton the kilka relied on for food. Meanwhile, as the area around the sea became more developed, pollution in the sea began to take a toll, and by 2001, the kilka population plunged dramatically, resulting in catches of less than 60,000 tons annually.

kilka

Analysis

1. How does the size of the apex (top) predator population affect the other populations in the cod-dominated ecosystem? Is the effect similar or different in the orca-dominated ecosystem? Explain.

2. Choose one of the four ecosystems you examined in this activity, and draw a graph showing what you think the populations would look like if there were no fisheries present.

3. How is what is happening in the Caspian-seal-dominated ecosystem different from what is happening in the other ecosystems?

4. What impact might sustainable fisheries have on these four ecosystems?

5. Choose one of the four ecosystems, and in your role as a fisheries scientist, explain to the people who run the fishery what you think is happening in the ecosystem. Citing evidence from the graph and from the history of the fishery, write a summary that explains what is happening in the ecosystem. Include in the summary:

   a. your explanation of whether you think the fishery is sustainable

   b. what changes in the ecosystem indicate that the fishery is or is not sustainable

   c. how the overall biodiversity of the ecosystem has been affected

   d. what advice you would provide about making the fishery sustainable, based on the other fisheries in this activity

KEY VOCABULARY	
fishery	population growth rate
invasive species	sustainability
population	

Ecosystem Change and Resiliency

THROUGHOUT THIS UNIT, you have mainly learned about human activities that cause ecosystems to change and some that allow them to resist change. These include overfishing, the introduction of invasive species, and runoff of chemicals, and more responsible interventions, such as sustainable fishery management and aquaculture.

However, a single event, whether natural, such as a volcanic eruption or forest fire, or human error, such as a large oil spill, can also bring long-lasting changes to ecosystems.

Challenge

▶ What determines if an ecosystem can recover from a major event?

Both natural phenomena such as volcanic eruptions (above) and human-caused phenomena such as oil spills (left) cause change in the ecosystems where they occur.

MATERIALS

FOR EACH STUDENT

5 sticky notes

Procedure

1. Use the "Read, Think, and Take Note" strategy as you complete the following reading.

2. When you have completed the reading, share your "Read, Think, and Take Note" responses with your partner. If possible, answer any questions your partner had about the reading. Note any similarities in your responses. Choose one response to share with the class.

3. Share your response to the reading in a class discussion, as directed by your teacher.

Reading

Ecosystem Change and Resiliency

In today's world there are few, if any, ecosystems left untouched by people in some way. In some cases this has resulted in major changes, and in others there have been very minor changes. Humans have influenced ecosystems for thousands of years, but current technology and large population size have intensified human impact. Yet while scientists previously thought that ecosystems would basically stay the same in the absence of human intervention, decades of research have shown that ecosystems are constantly changing and shifting.

Many things cause disturbances in an ecosystem. Ecologists use the term **disturbance** to refer to an abrupt event in an ecosystem that suddenly and significantly changes the resources available, the number or type of organisms, or the kinds of species present in an ecosystem. Natural disturbances include volcanic eruptions and fires. Two examples of disturbances caused by humans are oil spills and clear-cutting of forests. The response of an ecosystem to a disturbance depends in part on how major the disturbance is and the extent of the damage done.

An area like this Hawaiian coastline where there has been a recent lava flow has no soil and few, if any, living organisms present.

This area has undergone primary succession after a volcanic eruption.

In responding to a disturbance, an ecosystem undergoes what is referred to as ecological succession. **Ecological succession** is the natural process in which a disturbed area is gradually taken over by a species or groups of species that were not there before. For example, if a volcano erupted and the molten lava smothered a large area of land, eventually that area would undergo succession. In Hawaii and other volcanic locations, barren expanses of hard lava rock have turned into thick forest ecosystems in fewer than 150 years.

Primary succession is ecological succession that starts in an area where there are essentially no living organisms. In the lava-covered area, the first life you would see would be small organisms, such as spiders, that can live without soil. Eventually, dust and leaves from surrounding areas would collect in the cracks and crevices of the lava, and some of the more hardy plants, introduced by wind-blown seeds or birds, would begin to grow there. As the decades passed, more of the surface would become covered in plants, as leaves and other debris decayed and formed soil. The level of biodiversity would rise as more soil developed.

When an ecosystem undergoes a disturbance and the soil remains, **secondary succession** develops instead of primary succession. This might occur after a wildfire, or in a now-unused field where generations of ranchers had grazed cattle. Often there are still plants that survived the disturbance. If there are no further disturbances, those areas tend to return to their previous states. In Yellowstone Park after the huge wildfires in 1988, some of the first plants to grow back were grasses, small flowering bushes, and a bush called fireweed (named for its ability to grow well after fires). By 2000, small pine trees were beginning to replace the trees that had burned down, and today there are sections of burn areas in Yellowstone where it is difficult to tell that such a large fire ever occurred.

An ecosystem's ability to return to a stable state after a disturbance is a measure of its **resilience**. If an ecosystem has a high level of resilience, it will be much more likely to recover from a major disturbance. The level of resilience depends on several important factors, one of which is the native biodiversity within and surrounding the disturbed area. Because different species occupy different habitats and perform different roles within an ecosystem, the more species that survive the event the more likely those habitats and roles will be quickly filled again after a major disturbance. Another critical element for ecosystem resilience is the presence of species in nearby areas that might repopulate the disturbed area. For example, if a coral reef has been severely damaged by a large storm, fish and other organisms in nearby areas might help to repopulate the reef. Major disturbances, however, also increase the chances that an area will be occupied by invasive species, because there is so much available habitat. The resistance of an ecosystem is one factor that can help prevent this. The **resistance** of an ecosystem results from the natural factors within an ecosystem that help it to withstand external pressures and maintain normal functions. For example, if an invasive species of fish were released in a lake where there were native turtles that preferred to prey on those fish, the resistance of that lake to the invasive fish is high.

As ecologists learn more about ecosystem disturbance, resilience, and resistance, they have found that while ecosystems are often able to recover from major disturbances, they also have a point after which they cannot. One concern is that evidence suggests that many of the world's fisheries are at or beyond this point. Fisheries biologists and ecologists are working with many of the world's commercial fisheries to try to determine what, if anything, can be done to prevent our ocean ecosystems from being fished past the point of resilience. As you will see in the next activity, there are several possible solutions that may help to repair commercial fisheries around the world.

After wildfires in 1988, areas of Yellowstone National Park underwent secondary succession.

Analysis

1. What is the difference between primary and secondary successions?

2. How does the native biodiversity of an ecosystem affect its resilience?

3. How is the resilience of an ecosystem different from its resistance to disturbance?

4. What factors would you investigate to help you decide whether an ecosystem is nearing the point where it is no longer resilient and, therefore, unable to recover from a disturbance? Explain why you chose those factors.

KEY VOCABULARY

disturbance	**resilience**
ecological succession	**resistance**
invasive species	**secondary succession**
primary succession	

18 Fishery Case Studies

YOU ARE A *fisheries biologist who has been asked to provide input on an upcoming decision on whether to reopen the tuna fishery in Avril Gulf (a fictitious fishery modeled after a combination of fisheries in the United States). The tuna near Avril Gulf spend most of their lives off the coast, or in the open ocean. The Avril Gulf tuna fishery was closed to fishing in 2000 after years of declining fish catches. The ecosystem reached such a state of depletion that federal and state officials decided to ban all commercial and sport fishing of this species.*

In this activity you will read about fishery management approaches that two fishery regions adopted when facing a fishery crisis. Your group will explore how the strategies might work with the Avril Gulf tuna fishery.

Challenge

▶ How can case studies guide what should be done with the Avril Gulf tuna fishery?

MATERIALS

FOR EACH STUDENT
3   sticky notes
    Student Sheet 18.1, "The Avril Gulf Tuna Fishery"

Procedure

1. Due to the decline in the Avril Gulf tuna fishery, the governments of the areas near Avril Gulf are considering one of two strategies:

    a. creating a marine reserve to protect the Avril Gulf tuna, or

    b. opening aquaculture farms to farm tuna near Avril Gulf's shore

2. Your teacher will assign you one of these two strategies. Read the case study about your assigned strategy undertaken in a fishing region similar to Avril Gulf. Apply the "Read, Think, and Take Note" technique to your reading.

3. As you read describe the following in your science notebook:

    - the challenge the fishery was facing

    - the plan used to address the challenge

    - the impact the strategy had on the ecosystem's food web

    - the trade-offs associated with the strategy

    - how the strategy affected the community:

      a. economically

      b. environmentally

      c. socially

4. With your group, decide how the fishery management approach in your case study might affect the sustainability of the Avril Gulf tuna population and the community near Avril Gulf. Record your predicted outcomes.

Analysis

1. List the types of indicator data that could be used to monitor the environmental, economic, and social impacts of one plan on the community near Avril Gulf.

2. How can case studies help suggest solutions for communities facing sustainability challenges?

KEY VOCABULARY	
aquaculture	marine reserve
ecosystem	

CASE STUDY 1

Creation of the Goat Island Marine Reserve

GOAT ISLAND BACKGROUND INFORMATION

Goat Island is a tiny, 0.1-km^2 island north of the town of Leigh, which is on the eastern coast of New Zealand (see map below).

The 5-km^2 marine ecosystem in the waters surrounding the island once supported large populations of snapper fish and spiny lobsters. This allowed thriving fishing communities to develop in nearby shoreline towns. With its clear water and abundant, diverse fish species, the ocean around Goat Island

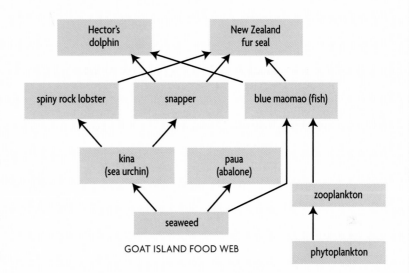

GOAT ISLAND FOOD WEB

also was popular for recreational scuba diving. Unfortunately, the snappers and lobsters were

fished at such a high rate that their populations crashed in the late 1960s. Without any predators, the sea urchin population soon grew out of control. They devastated the kelp forests, which eventually became barren and rocky underwater flats.

ESTABLISHMENT OF THE MARINE RESERVE

In 1975, the local communities convinced the New Zealand government to establish the first marine reserve in New Zealand in the waters surrounding Goat Island, as shown in the map at left. This meant that no more sport or commercial fishing was allowed in the protected waters. No plants or animals could be trapped, fished, or removed from the reserve.

MAP OF THE
GOAT ISLAND
MARINE PRESERVE

(Continued on next page)

141

(Continued from previous page)

When the marine reserve was established, fishing ceased and few boats roamed the Goat Island waters, allowing scientists the opportunity to study the ecosystems and changing populations of the reserve. In 1977, a marine education center opened to provide educational tours and guide diving expeditions in the waters of the reserve.

THE MARINE RESERVE BENEFITS THE WATERS OF GOAT ISLAND

The growth of the fish and lobster populations on the marine reserve was slow but steady. Within several years, fish and lobster populations grew at such a rate and density within the reserve that some spilled over into non-reserve waters. This "spillover effect" was a welcome surprise for sport and commercial fishermen who fished the waters beyond the boundaries of the marine reserve.

The vegetation on the marine floor gradually changed. Algae grew back in many of the rocky flats. The ecosystem became lush with mixed algae, including kelp—key producers in the marine ecosystem. As the algae returned, so did other organisms that depended on the algae for food and shelter.

QUESTIONS STILL REMAIN

While the marine reserve has provided valuable shelter to the endangered populations of fish and invertebrates of the Goat Island waters, questions remain about its long-term benefits. Since the creation of the marine education center, more roads and public facilities have been built near the mainland beach to accommodate growing numbers of visitors who snorkel in the waters. This has led to heavier road and beach traffic and erosion of the land. Tourism in the area has increased, providing jobs and raising awareness about the importance of protecting marine populations. But environmental protection agencies question how this increased use of the land might affect the long-term sustainability of the Goat Island Marine Reserve and the ecosystems it was built to protect. ■

Densities of Snapper (*Pagrus auratus*) Inside and Outside the Marine Reserve 2000–2003

SURVEY DATE	RESERVE SNAPPER DENSITY (NUMBER OF FISH PER M²)	NON-RESERVE SNAPPER DENSITY (NUMBER OF FISH PER M²)
Late 2000	4.23	0.05
Early 2001	7.79	0.75
Late 2001	6.17	0.87
Early 2002	10.33	0.79
Early 2003	21.92	0.79

Habitat Type on the Goat Island Marine Reserve

HABITAT TYPE	% OF RESERVE AREA, 1979	% OF RESERVE AREA, 1996
Shallow mixed algae	22	35
Large kelp forests	31	46
Rock flats	30	3
Other	17	16

CASE STUDY 2

Open-ocean Aquaculture in Hawaii

COMMERCIAL FARMING OF YELLOWTAIL

Since 1927, fish farmers have been growing yellowtail, a tasty fish and very popular sushi item. More than 75% of yellowtail that is sold worldwide comes from yellowtail farms, which are mainly in Japan, Australia, and Hawaii. The oldest farms are in Japan, and they provide a majority of the yellowtail to the world's markets.

Over the past several decades concerns over the sustainability of yellowtail farms have emerged. One of the biggest problems is that the yellowtail are farmed in nets kept in shallow, coastal areas, where the waste from the fish and leftover fish food pollutes the surrounding ecosystems. In Japan this has caused algal blooms. Also, at the Japanese farms the yellowtail are fed wild-caught sardines, which has caused a decline in the local sardine population. Another problem with the Japanese farms is that they catch wild, juvenile yellowtail and then raise them at the farms, which means the farms are depleting the wild population of yellowtail. Australian farms use a dried food, which causes less pollution, but still contains a high percentage of wild-caught fish.

KONA, HAWAII TO THE RESCUE

In 2005, as the consequences of the farming of yellowtail became more worrisome, an aquaculture farm in Kona, Hawaii, was built to be the world's first sustainable yellowtail fish farm. Open-ocean pens were anchored in ocean waters less than 1 km off the coast of the island of Hawaii, where deep water and fast currents could move clean water through the pens and help prevent pollution of the surrounding habitats.

The fish farmers chose to raise a species of yellowtail native to Hawaii, kahala *(Seriola rivoliana)*, to minimize the risk of escaped farmed fish introducing genes that would be new to the wild fish populations. The farm went through a rigorous permitting process, and even set some of its fishery management policies to be stricter than required by the state and federal governments. The yellowtail farmers set up a system where a few adult fish are caught in the wild and kept as brood stock in tanks at the land-based hatchery to

(Continued on next page)

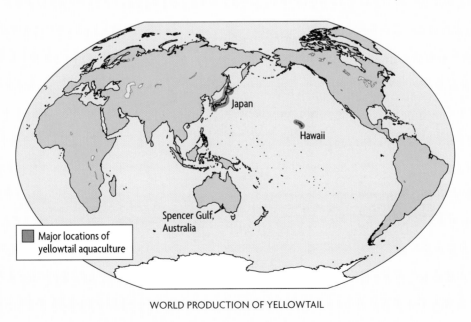

WORLD PRODUCTION OF YELLOWTAIL

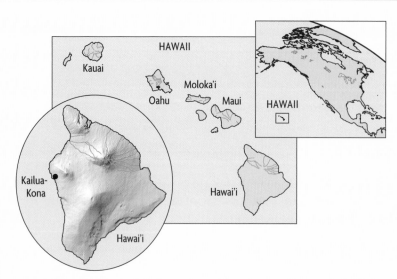

(Continued from previous page)

spawn offspring. The larval off-spring are then fed a special type of zooplankton, which is also raised at the hatchery. Once the young fish have been weaned onto a commercial feed and are large enough, they are moved to the open-ocean pens to grow until they are big enough to be harvested and sold.

THE FOOD CHALLENGE

The yellowtail is carnivorous, and the adults feed exclusively on other fish. Initially the Hawaiian farm used a dried food that was approximately 80% fishmeal and oil from wild-caught fish. This did not meet the criteria the farm had set for being sustainable. Something had to change.

Through consultation with scientists and environmentalists, the Hawaiian farmers worked with their feed company to develop a food that contained only 30% fishmeal and oil, all of which they obtained from the sustainable Peruvian anchovy fishery or from canneries or other businesses that process caught fish for human consumption. The remaining 70% of protein in the food comes from agricultural protein and grains.

GREAT ESCAPES

A big problem with open-net pens everywhere is that they attract predators. Seals and dolphins have been known to rip open aquaculture net pens, freeing fish to escape—some

right into the mammal's jaws. This has prompted farmers to install detection devices to prevent escapes. Despite these efforts, escapes still occur. This presents two main problems: first, escaped fish may carry parasites and viruses that infect wild populations, and second, escaped farmed fish compete with wild fish for resources.

For the new Hawaiian farm, however, escapes are not as threatening as elsewhere. Farmed fish often have more parasites than wild fish because they live in such close conditions. The Hawaiian farm carefully controls the diet of their fish, which leads to fewer parasites. In fact, when the farm studied the parasites in wild fish from nearby waters they found that their farmed fish had fewer parasites. Because this species of fish has been heavily overfished in nearby waters, the addition of escaped fish to the wild population does not lead to increased competition for resources. Furthermore, the fear of new genes being introduced to the wild population is not a concern. The farm's yellowtail are so closely related to the wild fish that any escapees are considered part of the wild population. ■

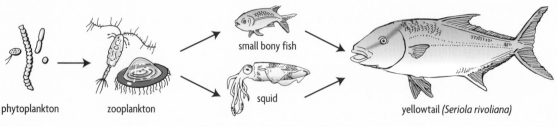

HAWAIIAN YELLOWTAIL FOOD WEB

phytoplankton   zooplankton   small bony fish   squid   yellowtail (*Seriola rivoliana*)

19 Making Sustainable Fishery Decisions

YOUR GROUP HAS *been given $500,000 by the Avril Gulf Wildlife Protection Agency (AGWPA) to monitor a fishery management strategy for Avril Gulf. You will develop a monitoring plan and follow the results of implementing both of the strategies you analyzed in Activity 18, "Fishery Case Studies," and determine the effects of the strategies on the sustainability of the Avril Gulf tuna fishery.*

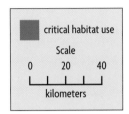

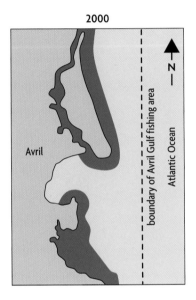

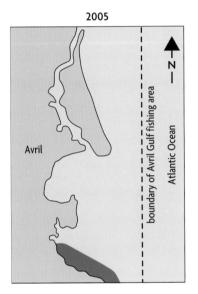

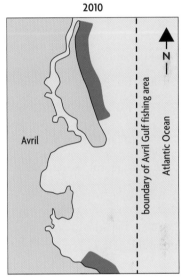

Challenge

▶ Which fishery management strategy is the best choice for the sustainability of the Avril Gulf tuna fishery?

MATERIALS

FOR EACH GROUP OF FOUR STUDENTS

  Set of 6 Fishery Indicator Cards

FOR EACH STUDENT

  Student Sheet 19.1, "Tracking Indicators"

  Student Sheet 19.2, "Comparing Aquaculture and Marine Reserves in Avril Gulf"

Procedure

1. Obtain a set of the Fishery Indicator Cards. With your group, lay out the cards on the table, and review the information they provide about the Avril Gulf tuna fishery.

2. Decide which pair of students in your group will investigate the aquaculture operation in Avril Gulf, and which pair will investigate the marine reserve.

3. With your partner, predict what each indicator might show if the strategy you chose in Step 2 were used in Avril Gulf. Record your thoughts in the "Predicted outcome" column on Student Sheet 19.1, "Tracking Indicators."

4. Develop a plan with your partner to monitor the fishery indicators. You have been allotted a budget of $500,000.

   Choose which of the six indicators on Student Sheet 19.1 you will monitor. The cost per indicator is

   • $125,000 for 5 years of monitoring, or

   • $250,000 for 10 years of monitoring

5. Record your plan in your science notebook.

6. Ask your teacher for the data collected as a part of your monitoring plan.

7. With your partner review the data.

8. On Student Sheet 19.1 record the "Actual outcome" for each indicator you monitored.

9. Share your results with the other pair in your group. Record evidence about the results of each strategy on Student Sheet 19.2, "Comparing Aquaculture and Marine Reserves in Avril Gulf."

10. With your group, discuss how each strategy affected the Avril Gulf fishery. Be sure to reference evidence from Student Sheet 19.2 in your discussion.

11. Obtain additional information on each strategy by comparing data with other groups in your class. Your teacher will explain how to do this.

12. Write a report to the Avril Gulf Wildlife Protection Agency (AGWPA) that recommends the continued use of either a marine reserve or aquaculture. In your report recommend one of the strategies, include a discussion of the trade-offs of your recommended strategy, and predict how well the strategy might reestablish the sustainability of the wild fish population. Be sure to include evidence from this activity, and Activity 18, "Fishery Case Studies," to support your recommendation.

Analysis

1. Which fishery strategy appears to be the most sustainable for the Avril Gulf tuna fishery? Explain why.

2. What other options might the communities near Avril Gulf consider implementing to meet the challenge of the declining fishery?

3. How do you think it would affect the ecosystem if the communities near Avril Gulf continued fishing spotted flying fish instead of Avril Gulf tuna?

4. What are two sustainability challenges your community is facing?

KEY VOCABULARY	
ecosystem	population
fishery management	sustainability

Unit Review: Ecology

Ecosystems

Ecosystems incorporate the interactions between communities of living organisms (biotic factors) and the involvement of the organisms with their nonliving environment (abiotic factors). Abiotic factors include light, temperature, precipitation, soil, rocks and minerals. Organisms, which live in habitats within ecosystems, play particular roles in their ecosystems. Some species are better suited to certain environmental conditions than others.

Natural and human-caused events often stress ecosystems in many ways. Ecosystem disturbances vary in degree, from minor disturbances to major events. When an ecosystem is able to recover from, or accommodate, stress it is demonstrating resiliency. Some events that disturb an ecosystem have only a short-term effect, while others cause long-lasting harm or change.

Ecosystem resilience is often related to the biodiversity within and around a disturbed area. Biodiversity refers to the variety of organisms in an ecosystem that fill multiple roles in the ecosystem. A heightened biodiversity does not necessarily increase the sustainability of an ecosystem, but constantly reducing biodiversity will make an ecosystem less sustainable.

An ecosystem responds to a disturbance through ecological succession, if the disturbance is not ongoing. Depending on the condition of the ecosystem once the disturbance ends, the ecosystem undergoes either primary or secondary succession.

Scientists group the ecosystems of the world into distinct types, or biomes. However, there is not perfect agreement on the number and types of biomes found on earth. Discussions of biomes in this unit and elsewhere in *Science and Global Issues* are based on the system that identifies biome groups as follows: tropical rain forest, desert, savanna, chaparral, temperate grassland, taiga, temperate deciduous forest, and tundra.

KEY VOCABULARY

abiotic	ecosystem
biodiversity	habitat
biome	organism
biotic	primary succession
community	resilience
disturbance	resistance
ecological succession	secondary succession
ecology	

Relationships within Ecosystems

Ecosystems rely on many organisms to make up the food webs that will maintain the flow of energy through the ecosystem and keep the ecosystem running. Producers are the organisms that form the basis of food webs, and, when consumed, provide energy for consumers. Often microscopic organisms, such as plankton, form the basis for large food webs. Within food webs there are different levels of consumers— primary, secondary and tertiary consumers—designated as such by what they consume. An energy pyramid picture shows how much energy is available for each level of organism. Changes in the population of a species within an ecosystem can affect other species within the ecosystem. Removal of an organism (or organisms) can cause a food web to collapse or have other unintended results because organisms frequently have close ecological relationships with each other, and these are known as symbiotic relationships. The four main categories of symbiotic relationships are: parasitism, commensalism, amensalism, and mutualism.

An adaptation is a trait (or traits) that helps an organism survive in a habitat. If the conditions in a habitat change sufficiently, or if the organism moves to an entirely different environment, the trait(s) may no longer be useful and the organism might not be as well adapted to the conditions.

Eutrophication is caused when a large increase in particular nutrients in aquatic environments causes an increase in phytoplankton. Dramatic increases in phytoplankton will increase the organic matter available for bacteria, thus increasing the amount of bacteria. Too much bacteria depletes surrounding waters of oxygen, causing other organisms in the ecosystem to migrate or die. The absence of organisms as a result of eutrophication creates areas referred to as dead zones.

KEY VOCABULARY

amensalism	mutualism
commensalism	parasitism
consumers	phytoplankton
dead zone	plankton
decomposers	producers
energy pyramid	symbiosis
eutrophication	zooplankton
food web	

Population Dynamics

Population growth rate is the change in a population over a given period of time. A positive growth rate indicates that the population is getting larger. A negative growth rate indicates that the population is getting smaller. Populations with a positive growth rate eventually reach a carrying capacity, at which point the ecosystem cannot support those populations. Continued negative growth rates eventually lead to population extinction.

Factors that affect population growth are birth rate, death rate, disease, predators, food availability, and human impact. The trend of a growth rate is likely to change if the factors influencing the growth rate change. Some conditions lead to exponential population growth for certain species.

KEY VOCABULARY

carrying capacity	limiting factor
density-dependent factors	population
density-independent	population growth rate

Invasive Species

Native species are those that are naturally found in an ecosystem. Because it is impossible for humans to know exactly which species are natural to an environment, it is generally considered that a species is native if it is thought to have existed in an environment for thousands of years. An introduced species is one that has been brought in to an environment in which it does not naturally occur. Such species are also referred to as nonnative, exotic, or nonindigenous. If a nonnative species causes harm to the environment, the economy, or human health, it is considered to be invasive.

No two species perform the same role in an environment. If a nonnative species displaces a native species from its role a decrease in biodiversity of the ecosystem might result, which may have an effect on other species in that ecosystem. In such a case, the nonnative species has had a negative effect on the environment, and that species is deemed invasive. Not all introduced species will succeed in a new environment. If an introduced species has traits that are well-suited to the new environment, it is more likely to become established. Changes in the population dynamics of an ecosystem are factors in the success of an invasive species becoming established within an ecosystem.

KEY VOCABULARY

invasive species	nonnative species

Photosynthesis and Respiration

Photosynthesis is a cellular process by which an organism captures light from the sun and uses it to store energy. In photosynthesis light energy, carbon dioxide, and water are taken in to produce glucose and oxygen. Only producers perform photosynthesis. Although sunlight is required for photosynthesis to occur, parts of photosynthesis can happen in the absence of light. The stages of photosynthesis that produce oxygen happen in the presence of sunlight. Photosynthesis happens in chloroplasts, which contain chlorophyll. Different variables, such as temperature and amount of light, affect the rate of photosynthesis and cellular respiration. Chemical indicators show chemical changes in a substance, such as the addition of oxygen or carbon dioxide. From changes in chemical indicators, therefore, it can be inferred that a cellular process, such as photosynthesis, is occurring.

Cellular respiration takes in oxygen and glucose and produces carbon dioxide, water and ATP. Most organisms perform cellular respiration, including plants and other producers. Cellular respiration happens in the mitochondria and the area just outside the mitochondria. Plants can perform cellular respiration independently of photosynthesis. Cellular respiration occurs at different rates under different conditions.

The substances produced and consumed in photosynthesis and cellular respiration are complementary. For example, aquatic environments depend on a balance of photosynthesis and cellular respiration to prevent dead zones.

The carbon cycle moves carbon between several major reservoirs. Reservoirs in the carbon cycle include rocks and soils, the ocean and other bodies of water, plants/producers, animals/consumers, the atmosphere, and fossil fuels. Although the amount of carbon in the different reservoirs fluctuates, the amount of carbon contained in the carbon cycle is a fixed amount. The carbon in different reservoirs is in different chemical forms, such as carbon dioxide and glucose. The carbon cycle is one of several biogeochemical cycles that move elements through different reservoirs and allow them to be used repeatedly by living organisms.

KEY VOCABULARY	
carbon cycle	chemical indicator
carbon reservoir	enzymes
cellular respiration	photosynthesis

Inquiry and the Nature of Science

Experimental design requires a clear, reproducible procedure and the choice of an experimental variable that will be manipulated independently of other variables. Many experiments include a control and an experimental setup.

Scientists develop models for representing actual phenomena and to compare theoretical situations to actual situations.

Historical case studies provide information that is helpful in decision-making.

KEY VOCABULARY	
evidence	variable
trade-off	

Fisheries Management

People around the world employ many types of aquaculture, some of which are detrimental to the surrounding ecosystem. Some species are better suited for aquaculture than others. The effects of aquaculture on the surrounding ecosystem can be mitigated in a variety of ways.

There are many types of ecosystem services, some of which provide direct benefits and some of which provide indirect benefits to people. Sustainable management of ecosystem services depends on continual input from scientists and other experts. One type of ecosystem service is fishing. Some fisheries have had a significant impact on the associated ecosystems. Over-fishing can be prevented with appropriate regulations and enforcement, and there are various approaches to fisheries management.

Limits, such as fishing limits, must be monitored to ensure they are set at appropriate levels. Analysis of indicators informs resource management decision-making. Indicators from a variety of fields should be examined, if possible.

KEY VOCABULARY

aquaculture	indicator
ecosystem services	marine reserve
fisheries	sustainability
fishery	Tragedy of the Commons

Cell Biology: World Health

ALL ORGANISMS ARE susceptible to disease. The effects of diseases vary from mild to devastating and affect sustainability at the environmental, economic, and social level. For example, foot-and-mouth and mad cow diseases have periodically wiped out huge herds of cattle, causing economic hardship for those whose livelihoods depend on the cattle. Influenza pandemics have killed millions of people, and recent epidemics of H1N1 and SARS viruses have threatened entire cities.

Diseases are caused by infectious microbes, such as bacteria and viruses, genetic factors, and other events that cause breakdowns in the structure or function of cells. Understanding the mechanisms of a disease is essential to people's ability to prevent, eradicate, and cure it and to maintain the sustainability of populations and communities.

In this unit you will examine several diseases and their social, environmental, and economic consequences. You will learn about the mechanism of these diseases at the cellular level. You will also investigate the structures and functions of normal cells and some of the processes that occur inside these cells. At the end of the unit, you will make recommendations for how best to allocate limited funding to address world health problems.

1 World Health and Sustainability

LIVING ORGANISMS ARE vulnerable to disease. The effects of large-scale epidemics on human societies can be devastating. In the 14th century about one-third of the population of Europe died of the Black Death—bubonic plague. From 1918 to 1919 one-fifth of the world's population caught influenza during a pandemic that quickly killed as many as 40 million people—most of them between the ages of 20 and 40. The plague and influenza are examples of communicable—or infectious—diseases. **Infectious diseases** are transmitted from one person to another. **Noninfectious diseases** (also called noncommunicable diseases) are not transmitted from one person to another, and are caused by such factors as the environment, genetics, and aging. Noninfectious diseases also affect people everywhere in the world. The World Health Organization estimated that in 2005 more than 14 million people died of infectious diseases, while 35 million people died of noninfectious diseases.

Diseases affect human populations in many ways, including socially, economically, and environmentally. When people are sick or die from a disease, their suffering or death might touch a community on a social level or heighten a society's demand that a cure be found. There are negative economic effects related to the cost of

The World Health Organization is monitoring the emerging infectious diseases shown here.

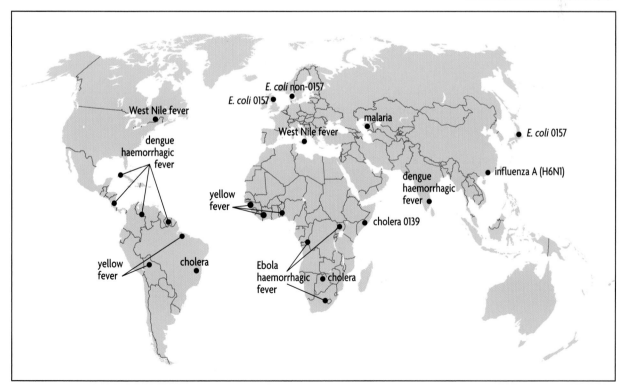

treatment and the loss of individuals' productivity, and a positive economic effect in terms of the numbers of people employed in the health-care industry. There is sometimes a link between the environment and disease, as is the case when polluted air or water or the presence of disease-carrying organisms makes people sick. With such social, economic, and environmental relationships disease is a major factor in the sustainability of populations and communities. **Sustainability** is the ability to meet a community's present needs without compromising the ability of future generations to meet their own needs.

In this unit, you will study life at the cellular level and see how research by cell biologists and medical professionals has advanced society's efforts to cure and prevent diseases. In this activity you will examine health indicators as you look at world health from a sustainability perspective.

Challenge

▶ What do health indicators show about world health and sustainability?

MATERIALS

FOR EACH GROUP OF FOUR STUDENTS
    World Health Data Set 1
    World Health Data Set 2
    World Health Data Set 3
    World Health Data Set 4

SOURCE: *The data in this activity come from two major public health organizations, the World Health Organization (WHO) and the U.S. Centers for Disease Control and Prevention (CDC).*

Procedure

1. With your team of four, decide which pair will examine World Health Data Set 1 and which will examine Data Set 2.

2. Work with your team to classify, and record in your science notebook, the indicators on the data sets into the following sustainability categories:

   • Social

   • Economic

   • Environmental

   Note: Some of the indicators may be placed in more than one category, or not in any of the three categories.

   Follow your teacher's directions for sharing your classifications with the class.

3. With your partner, examine the data, and from that information sort the countries into two, three, or four groups. Record your groupings and the reasons for the way you sorted them in your science notebook.

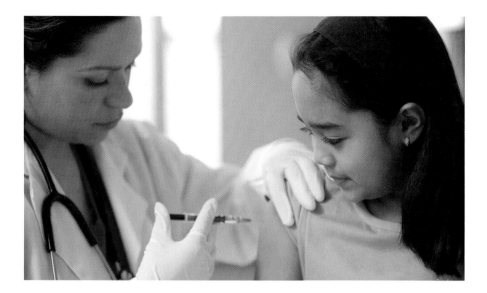

4. In your science notebook, record the following for your groupings:

   • Trends in the data

   • Claims you can make about the data

5. Share your groupings with the other pair in your team. Explain the reasoning for your groupings.

6. In your science notebook, record the following for the groupings of the countries based on Data Sets 1 and 2:

   • Similarities and differences between the groupings of Data Sets 1 and 2

   • Claims you can make about the data

   • Questions you have about the data

7. In your science notebook list the countries that are missing certain indicator data, and note which they are. For each missing indicator, write what you predict the missing measurement might be, based on the other data given. Explain your reasoning.

8. Repeat Steps 1–7 for Data Sets 3 and 4.

9. Discuss with your team the similarities and differences in the groupings for Data Sets 1and 2 and Data Sets 3 and 4. Record them in your science notebook.

Analysis

1. What similarities and differences did you notice in the groupings for World Health Data Sets 1 and 2 and Sets 3 and 4?

2. Which indicator(s) in the data sets did not seem to show a trend? Suggest reasons why, using the data as evidence. **Evidence** is information used to support or refute a claim.

3. How is the sustainability of a community tied to disease? Give examples of social, environmental, and economic factors in your answer.

KEY VOCABULARY

evidence	**noninfectious disease**
indicator	**sustainability**
infectious disease	

2 Cells and Disease

IN THE PREVIOUS activity, you learned about some of the factors that influence world health and disease. A **disease** is any breakdown in the structure or function of an organism. Scientists who study a particular disease gather information about how that disease affects the organism. They look at all levels of the organism, from molecules and cells to organs and the whole organism. Some scientists, like cell biologists, use microscopes to study the structure and function of cells in the full array of organisms, from humans to plants to insects to microbes. A **microbe** is a microscopic cellular organism or a virus, and some microbes cause infectious diseases. One way to detect and study many diseases is to compare blood from healthy and sick individuals under a microscope. In this activity you will examine samples of blood from healthy and diseased people.

Challenge

▶ How do observations of cells help doctors and scientists diagnose and study diseases?

MATERIALS

FOR EACH GROUP OF FOUR STUDENTS
    prepared slide, "Patient A Blood"
    prepared slide, "Patient B Blood"

FOR EACH PAIR OF STUDENTS
    microscope
    prepared slide, "Typical Human Blood"

FOR EACH STUDENT
  6 Student Sheet 2.1, "Disease Information"
  3 sticky notes

Focusing a Microscope

Be sure that your microscope is set on the lowest power before placing your slide onto the microscope stage. Place the slide on the microscope stage. Center the slide so that the sample is directly over the light opening, and adjust the microscope settings as necessary. If the microscope has stage clips, secure the slide in position so that it does not move.

Observe the sample. Focus first with the coarse-focus knob, and then adjust the fine-focus knob.

After switching to a higher power magnification, be careful to adjust the focus with the fine-focus knob only.

Return to low power before removing the slide from the microscope stage.

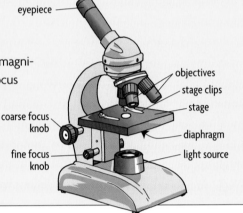

Procedure

Part A: Using the Light Microscope

1. Your teacher will demonstrate the different parts of a microscope, as shown in the figure above.

2. In your group of four, review the rules for handling a microscope. Demonstrate your knowledge of the parts of a microscope, according to your teacher's instructions.

3. Review the guidelines for focusing a microscope shown above.

Part B: Observing Blood

You are a doctor who has recently seen two patients who reported similar symptoms. From your examination of each patient you have gathered more information, which is shown below.

HISTORY FROM PATIENT A:

• Patient reports periods of feeling sick, but feels well most of the time.

• Patient recently returned from working in Africa with the Peace Corps.

• Patient reports frequent fevers, chest pains, and lung infections throughout youth and adulthood.

• After a two-hour hike a few months ago, she became so tired and out of breath that physical movement was difficult. She experienced joint and muscle pain in her arms and legs.

SYMPTOMS SEEN ON EXAMINATION TODAY:

• Vision problems and yellowing of eyes and skin.

• Abdominal area is tender to the touch.

HISTORY FROM PATIENT B:

• Patient reports becoming sick shortly after returning from a trip to Africa in the past month.

• Patient reports severe headaches and fatigue for the past few weeks.

• Patient reports a fever and muscle and joint pain in the past week.

SYMPTOMS SEEN ON EXAMINATION TODAY:

• Yellowing of the eyes.

• Abdominal area is tender to the touch.

4. Prepare a chart with four columns labeled as shown below.

Observations of Blood Samples

Slide	Shape of cells	Color of cells	Number of cells in field of view

With your partner, obtain a slide labeled "Typical Human Blood." This blood sample will serve as your reference. As you observe on medium or high power, record your observations in the chart.

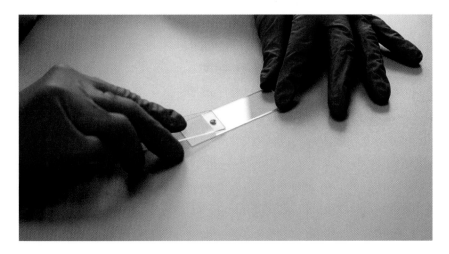

A lab technician prepares a blood sample for viewing under the microscope.

5. Based on the patient's report and the examination, the patient's symptoms suggest one of four possible diseases. Read the descriptions of those diseases below. For each disease, draw a sketch of what you predict you would observe in a blood sample under the microscope as compared to the typical human blood you just observed.

Possible Diseases

DISEASE	SYMPTOMS	DESCRIPTION
Polycythemia vera	weakness, disturbed vision, headache, dizziness, enlarged liver, abdominal pain due to an enlarged spleen	An abnormality in the bone marrow causes an overproduction of red blood cells, almost double in some cases. This increases blood volume and thickness, leading to life-threatening blood clots.
Sickle cell disease	joint and muscle pain, anemia, vision problems, abdominal pain, yellowish color of skin and eyes, and frequent infections	An inherited genetic mutation (error) changes the hemoglobin protein, causing the proteins to stack on one another within the red blood cells. This produces a sickle- or banana-shaped blood cell. Sometimes under the microscope the sickle cells appear flattened.
Spherocytosis	yellowish color of skin and eyes, abdominal pain from an enlarged spleen, pale skin, and weakness	A genetic disorder causes the red blood cells to become small, spherically shaped and fragile. These cells are destroyed by the spleen. It is often diagnosed in childhood.
Malaria	fever, headaches, extreme fatigue, mild yellowish color of skin and eyes, abdominal pain, and body aches	An infectious disease, malaria is caused by a single-celled parasite of the genus *Plasmodium* and is carried by mosquitoes. A *Plasmodium* appears as an irregular purple spot containing dark dots when a sample is stained and viewed under a microscope.

6. Decide with your group which pair will first observe Patient A's blood and which will first observe Patient B's.

7. Observe, and draw what you see on the slide sample at medium or high power.

8. Switch patients' slides with the other pair in your group. Repeat Step 7 for the other patient.

9. In your science notebook, write hypotheses for which disease is affecting each patient. Include the information from the slide samples you observed and the "Possible Diseases" table to support your hypotheses.

10. Follow your teacher's directions for reading the case study about malaria. As you read, follow the "Read, Think, and Take Note" strategy. To do this:

   • Stop at least three times during the reading to mark on a sticky note your thoughts or questions about the reading. Use the list of guidelines below to start your thinking.

   • After writing a thought or question on a sticky note, place it next to the passage in the reading that prompted your note.

   • Discuss with your partner the thoughts and questions you had while reading.

Read, Think, and Take Note: Guidelines

As you read, from time to time, write one of the following on a sticky note:

- Explain a thought or reaction to something you read.

- Note something in the reading that is confusing or unfamiliar.

- List a word that you do not know.

- Describe a connection to something you learned or read previously.

- Make a statement about the reading.

- Pose a question about the reading.

- Draw a diagram or picture of an idea or connection.

11. Complete the information for malaria on Student Sheet 2.1, "Disease Information" after you read the case study.

Analysis

1. Compare each patient's blood sample to a normal blood sample. What abnormalities do you observe?

2. Based on your observations, which patient has an infectious disease? Explain how you know.

3. Observe the diagrams below. Which patient would you diagnose with sickle cell disease? Explain, using evidence from this activity.

Patient 1

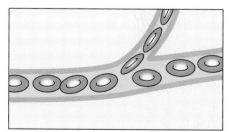

Patient 2

4. How do microscope observations of cells help doctors and scientists diagnose and study diseases? Give specific examples from this activity.

5. From what you learned about malaria in the case study

   a. A **trade-off** is an exchange of one thing in return for another, giving up something that is a benefit or advantage, in exchange for something that may be more desirable. What are the trade-offs of using insecticides to kill the mosquitoes?

   b. What are the benefits of using insecticides to kill mosquitoes that might be carrying *Plasmodium?*

6. Based on the malaria case study, how does resistance develop in a population of disease-causing microbes?

KEY VOCABULARY

cell	noninfectious disease
disease	protein
infectious disease	protist
malaria	sickle cell
microbe	**trade-off**
mutation	**vector**

CASE STUDY

Malaria

MORE THAN THREE billion people worldwide live in areas where malaria transmission is a risk. Most of the deaths from malaria are in children. In the 1950s and 1960s, world health experts began an effort to wipe out malaria. Although their techniques reduced malaria for a while, they ultimately failed. Today, malaria still exists, and is even spreading to parts of the world where it was thought to have been wiped out or was not a high risk.

Burden of Disease		
	NUMBER OF NEW CASES PER YEAR	**NUMBER OF DEATHS PER YEAR**
Worldwide	350–500 million	1 million
United States	1,500	0–10

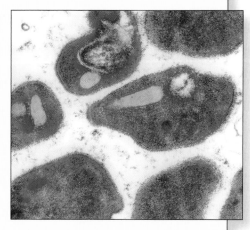

SYMPTOMS AND DISEASE MECHANISM

People once thought that malaria was caused by inhaling the fumes from stagnant water, such as that in swamps. In 1880, a French army doctor first observed parasites inside the red blood cells of malaria patients. It has since been found that the cause of malaria in humans is one of several species of the single-celled parasitic protist *Plasmodium.*

(Continued on next page)

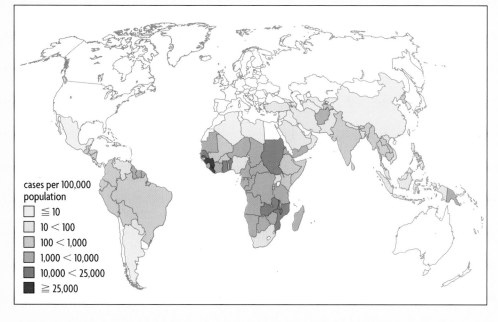

cases per 100,000 population

☐ ≦ 10
☐ 10 < 100
☐ 100 < 1,000
☐ 1,000 < 10,000
☐ 10,000 < 25,000
■ ≧ 25,000

Plasmodium *parasites in the blood (above)*

Locations where malaria occurs (left)

(Continued from previous page)

Shortly after the discovery of *Plasmodium*, scientists determined that female mosquitoes, which breed in standing water, are the vectors for malaria. A **vector** is an organism that does not cause the disease itself, but spreads disease-causing microbes from one host to another.

The symptoms of malaria can be mild to deadly and include fever, chills, fatigue, an enlarged liver, an enlarged spleen, anemia (reduced number of red blood cells), seizures, coma, and kidney failure.

The following traces the steps of malaria infections:

1. A mosquito becomes infected with *Plasmodium* when it bites and sucks the blood of a human infected with *Plasmodium*.

2. When the infected mosquito bites a person it injects *Plasmodium* in its saliva into that person.

3. The *Plasmodium* travels from the point of the mosquito bite through the bloodstream to the liver and infects liver cells. The *Plasmodium* then begins to reproduce inside the liver cells. Sometimes *Plasmodium* remains in a person's liver and causes no symptoms. Other times the liver cells burst, releasing *Plasmodium*.

4. The *Plasmodium* travels back into the bloodstream from the liver, where it invades red blood cells and then reproduces. The infection is active at this point, and the person experiences symptoms.

5. The red blood cells eventually rupture, which releases the parasites back into the bloodstream where they might be picked up by another mosquito.

MALARIA PREVENTION AND TREATMENT

In the 1950s and 1960s, world health officials hoped to eradicate malaria worldwide with the chemical DDT (dichlorodiphenyltrichloroethane). DDT is a powerful insecticide that kills many insects, including mosquitoes. From 1947 to 1951, in areas where malaria was present in the United States, DDT was applied inside millions of households and over miles of swamps, fields, and forests. Through these DDT applications, malaria protists were effectively wiped out in this country. However, less concentrated efforts in other malaria-ridden parts of the world, and widespread spraying of DDT to kill all sorts of other insects, created *Plasmodium*-carrying mosquito populations that are now resistant to DDT.

Resistance develops if a few mosquitoes in a population are genetically able to withstand

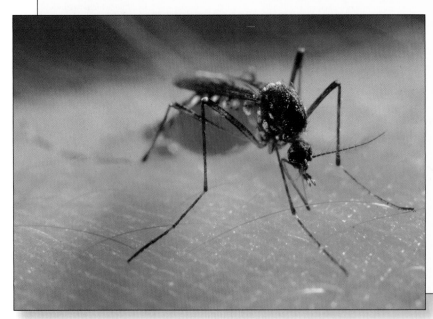

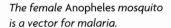
The female Anopheles *mosquito is a vector for malaria.*

the toxic effects of DDT. When more DDT is applied, more mosquitoes that are sensitive to DDT die. The resistant mosquitoes, however, survive and reproduce greater numbers of resistant mosquitoes until they are a significant proportion of the population, making DDT ineffective.

Scientists also learned that DDT harms other organisms in the environment and is a threat to wildlife, especially birds. One effect of DDT on birds is eggshell thinning, causing the shells to break too soon and the embryo inside to die. Some evidence also suggests that DDT might cause cancer or neurological problems in humans. Today, DDT is banned for agricultural use worldwide, but it still is used in some places to control *Plasmodium*-carrying mosquitoes and prevent them from biting people.

DDT or alternative insecticides are typically sprayed on the inner walls of homes and on protective nets that are draped over sleeping areas, discouraging mosquitoes from coming near.

Studies have shown that insecticide-treated nets are an effective and low-cost tool to control mosquitoes. A large study in Tanzania, where there is a high rate of malarial transmission, investigated the effect of insecticide-treated and untreated nets on infection in children aged one month to four years. The results, summarized below, show that both reduce the risk of death from malarial infection, but that there is greater success with the insecticide-treated nets.

Treatment of malaria infections centers on several drugs that kill the *Plasmodium* parasites that cause malaria. Some drugs attack the parasites when they are present in the blood, while others kill them when they are in the liver. Currently, physicians prescribe combinations of drugs that act together to kill *Plasmodium*.

CHALLENGES TO PREVENTION AND TREATMENT

There are two problems health officials must overcome to make mosquito-net programs more successful in preventing malaria. First, nets that are manufactured and sold pretreated with insecticide must be retreated within

(Continued on next page)

Effectiveness of Mosquito Nets	
PREVENTION METHOD	PERCENT REDUCTION IN RISK OF DEATH
Insecticide-treated nets	27
Untreated nets	19

(Continued from previous page)

6 to 12 months for them to remain fully effective. Also, the nets, even though relatively low in cost, are still too expensive for some people living in countries with few economic resources. They must rely on programs that donate or reduce the price of the nets and retreatment kits.

There are also major challenges emerging with the drugs that treat malaria. In some areas, two types of *Plasmodium* that cause malaria have become resistant to the medication available for treatment, which means it no longer kills the parasite. The resistance of *Plasmodium* to drugs arises in the same way that mosquitoes acquire resistance to DDT. Since *Plasmodium* is less likely to develop resistance to several drugs at once, a combination of drugs is often given to patients. This approach often succeeds—as long as patients take all of the required doses of the medicine. But multidrug treatment is costly, and health care workers must monitor patients to make sure they complete their courses of treatment. In addition, it is often difficult to get all the right medicines to isolated communities.

Another potential challenge is the movement of malaria to areas with temperatures that were once too cold for the mosquitoes and *Plasmodium*. If the climate of an area changes in a way that favors the breeding and survival of mosquitoes and *Plasmodium*, the risk for malaria in that area increases. Scientists are working with models to predict how climate change could affect the risk of malaria around the world. The model below shows malaria returning to parts of the United States. The effect of climate change on malaria distribution continues to be a point of discussion in the scientific community. ■

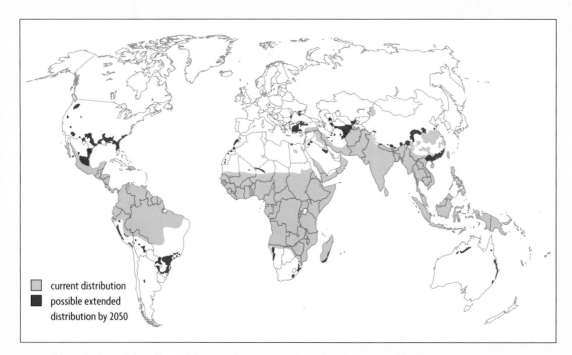

current distribution
possible extended distribution by 2050

A model prediction of the effect of climate change on malaria distribution worldwide

3 What Is a Cell?

ALL LIVING THINGS are made of one or more cells. The **cell** is the basic unit of life and is where many life processes occur. Organisms made up of a single cell are called **single-celled organisms.** Bacteria and protists are examples of single-celled organisms. Other organisms, such as humans, dogs, and plants, are made up of trillions of cells, and therefore, are **multicellular organisms.** In this activity you will observe microscope slides of cells from various single-celled and multicellular organisms.

Challenge

▶ What are the similarities and differences in cells from various living organisms?

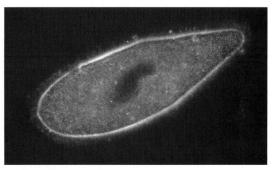

A Paramecium, *shown above, is a single-celled organism. Grass, dogs, and people, shown at left, are multicellular organisms.*

MATERIALS

FOR EACH GROUP OF FOUR STUDENTS

    prepared slide of human cheek cells

    prepared slide of animal sperm cells

    prepared slide of typical *Bacillus* bacteria

    prepared slide of typical *Coccus* bacteria

    piece of onion

    piece of *Elodea* plant

    mixed protist culture

    bottle of Lugol's solution

    cup of water

    dropper

    pair of forceps

FOR EACH PAIR OF STUDENTS

    microscope

    microscope slide

    microscope slide with a well

    coverslip

    paper towel

    colored pencils

FOR EACH STUDENT

    Student Sheet 2.1, "Disease Information" from Activity 2

  3 sticky notes

Procedure

1. In your science notebook, use a full page to draw a diagram of what you think a typical cell is like, including its various parts. On your diagram, write labels for as many parts of the cell as you can. If you know the function of the part, write a brief description of it next to the label.

2. Review the Microscope Drawing guidelines on the next page.

3. View the prepared slide of human cheek cells. Select two cells at high power and sketch them in your science notebook.

4. Repeat Step 3 for the prepared slide of animal sperm cells.

5. In your group of four, decide which pair will prepare a slide of onion and which will prepare a slide of *Elodea*.

Microscope Drawing Made Easy

Below is a picture taken through a microscope of the alga *Spirogyra*.
The diagram to the right shows what a biologist or biological illustrator
might draw and how he or she would label the drawing.

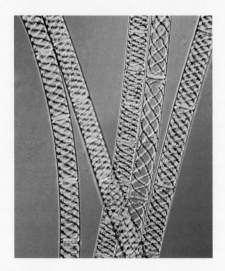

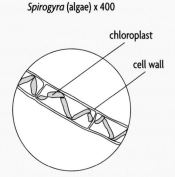

Spirogyra (algae) x 400

chloroplast

cell wall

SOME TIPS FOR BETTER DRAWINGS:

- Use a sharp pencil and have a good eraser available.

- Try to relax your eyes when looking through the eyepiece. You can cover
  one eye or learn to look with both eyes open. Try not to squint.

- Look through your microscope at the same time as you do your drawing.
  Look through the microscope more than you look at your paper.

- Don't draw every small thing on your slide. Just concentrate on one
  or two of the most common or interesting things.

- You can draw things larger than you actually see them. This helps
  you show all of the details you see.

- Keep written words outside the circle.

- Use a ruler to draw the lines for your labels. Keep lines parallel—
  do not cross one line over another.

- Remember to record the level of magnification next to your drawing.

6. With your partner, follow the instructions below to prepare your slide.

IF YOU ARE PREPARING ONION:

- Place one drop of water and one drop of Lugol's iodine solution on the slide.

- Use forceps or your fingernail to peel off a piece of the very thin inner layer of the onion.

- Place the piece of onion into the drops on the slide.

IF YOU ARE PREPARING *ELODEA*:

- Place 1–2 drops of water on the slide.

- Select one small, thin, light-green leaf.

- Place the leaf into the drops on the slide.

7. Carefully touch one edge of the coverslip to the water, at an angle. Slowly allow the coverslip to fall into place. This should prevent trapping of air bubbles under the coverslip.

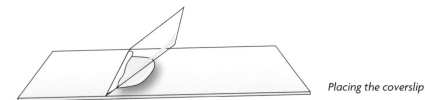

Placing the coverslip

8. Observe the plant cells that you just prepared. Draw what you see at high magnification. Be sure to label your drawing with the name of your plant. When you have finished, do the same for the plant cell slide that was prepared by the other pair in your group.

Plant cells

9. With your partner, place 1–2 drops of the mixed protist culture on a clean microscope slide with a well. Observe and draw at high magnification two different types of protists.

10. View the prepared slide of typical *Bacillus* bacteria, focusing on one or two cells at high magnification. Draw one or two of the bacteria cells. Be sure to label your drawings with the name of the sample.

11. Repeat Step 11 for the prepared slide of typical *Coccus* bacteria.

12. Clean up according to your teacher's instructions.

13. Go back to the drawing of a cell that you made in Step 1. Add or change any information on that drawing based on your work in this activity.

14. Follow your teacher's directions for reading the case study about tuberculosis (TB). As you read, follow the "Read, Think, and Take Note" strategy.

15. Complete the information for tuberculosis on Student Sheet 2.1, "Disease Information," after you read the case study.

Analysis

1. Compare the four different types of cells (animal, plant, protist, bacteria) you observed. What structures do they have in common?

2. When you compare the *Plasmodium* protist you observed in Activity 2 and the two protists you observed in this activity, what similarities and differences do you notice?

3. When you compare the two types of bacteria you observed, what similarities and differences do you notice?

4. In your science notebook, create a larger version of the Venn diagram shown below. Use what you have learned about cells to record the unique features of the cells of each group of organisms in the appropriate space. Record any common features between groups in the spaces created by overlaps.

5. Based on the Venn diagram you created, what features are common to all cells?

6. One focus of TB treatment is ensuring that people who are being treated are closely monitored by health care workers. Explain why this is important, citing evidence from the tuberculosis case study.

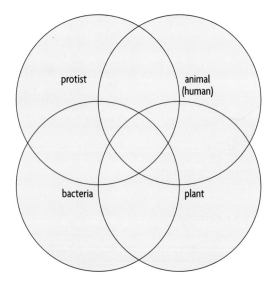

KEY VOCABULARY	
antibiotic	**multicellular organism**
bacteria	protist
cell	**single-celled organism**
latent	tuberculosis
macrophage	

CASE STUDY

Tuberculosis

TUBERCULOSIS IS A disease that has appeared in the human population for centuries. Evidence of TB infection has been found in the skulls of Egyptian mummies estimated to be at least 3,000 years old. TB is caused by the *Mycobacterium tuberculosis* bacterium and was common in Europe and North America in the 18th and 19th centuries. It declined in those regions as living conditions, nutrition, and treatment improved. Worldwide today, however, it is estimated that at least one-third of the human population is infected with TB bacteria.

Burden of Disease			
	TOTAL NUMBER INFECTED	**ESTIMATED NUMBER OF DEATHS PER YEAR**	**ESTIMATED NUMBER OF NEW CASES PER YEAR**
Worldwide	2 billion	1.7 million	9 million
United States	10–15 million	650	12,900

SYMPTOMS AND DISEASE MECHANISM

The physical symptoms of TB include appetite and weight loss, coughing, night sweats, fever, fatigue, and chills. TB usually infects tissue in the lungs, but can also infect other organs in the body, including the brain, kidneys, and spine. Since TB is an extremely infectious disease that can be passed through a cough, sneeze, or even talking with an infected person, people are at higher risk of infection if they live in densely packed urban areas or may be exposed to infected individuals in crowded, closed environments, such as hospitals, prisons, clinics, or airplanes.

(Continued on next page)

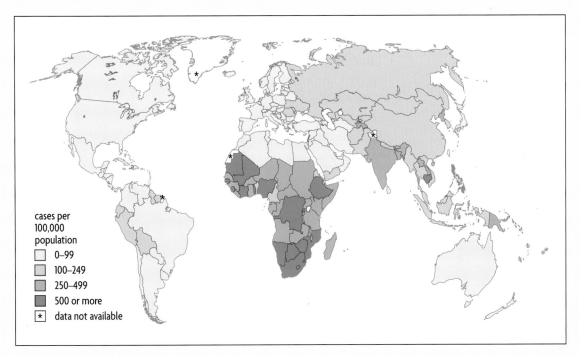

cases per 100,000 population
- 0–99
- 100–249
- 250–499
- 500 or more
- * data not available

Global distribution of tuberculosis cases

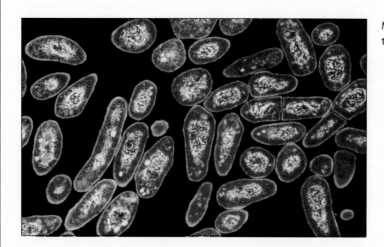

Mycobacterium
tuberculosis *bacteria*

(Continued from previous page)

TB infection is latent or active. In a latent infection, the person has a positive skin or blood test for TB, but a normal chest X-ray. The bacteria are alive inside the body, but they are inactive. A person with a latent infection does not feel sick, has no symptoms, and cannot transmit the TB bacteria to others. Sometimes the latent form becomes active, and symptoms develop. Only 5–10% of people who are infected with TB bacteria, however, ever become sick or infectious. Antibiotic treatments after a person has tested positive for TB reduce the risk of latent TB becoming active, if the person takes the drugs for many months.

The following traces the steps that lead to a tuberculosis infection:

1. An uninfected person inhales TB bacteria in droplets that were released into the air by an infected person, whether minutes or hours earlier.

2. The bacteria enter the lungs, and if they are not immediately killed by the body's immune system, they are ingested by macrophages, a type of white blood cell. The macrophages do not destroy the bacteria.

3. Most of the time, the bacteria are held in check by the immune system. In this case, the infection is referred to as a latent infection.

4. If the infection becomes active, the TB bacteria multiply and travel to the blood. Possible reasons for a latent infection to become active include a weakened immune system, often due to HIV/AIDS infection, malnutrition, cancer, or aging. The bacteria might spread to other organs, but they can only be transmitted out of the body and to other people by the infected person's exhaling them from the lungs.

TUBERCULOSIS PREVENTIONS AND TREATMENTS

While there is a vaccine available to prevent TB, its effectiveness is limited. Worse, the vaccine has caused HIV-positive children to develop a TB infection. Health experts think that being able to accurately detect active TB infections is more beneficial than vaccination to prevent infections.

In 1943, a man critically sick with TB was the first to be given an antibiotic to treat TB. Impressively, the bacteria quickly disappeared, and the man recovered. Now there are a number of antibiotics to treat TB, and they are usually prescribed in combinations of two to four different drugs. Two of the most commonly prescribed today are isoniazid and rifampin. Isoniazid interferes with a bacterium's ability to make a compound needed in its cell walls. Rifampin prevents the bacterial cells from making proteins.

CHALLENGES TO PREVENTION AND TREATMENT
ANTIBIOTIC RESISTANCE

Like *Plasmodium,* TB bacteria have become resistant to many antibiotics. As with malaria, people who do not have access to timely and effective medical care or who don't complete a full course of treatment contribute to the resistance problem. In 2007, the World Health Organization (WHO) was notified of more than 400,000 cases of multidrug-resistant tuberculosis. Multidrug resistance in TB means that the bacteria are

resistant specifically to the two main antibiotics, isoniazid and rifampin. Because WHO is not notified of all cases, experts think that there are many more cases. The cost of treating multi-drug-resistant TB infections can be 1,000 times more expensive than treating non-resistant TB infections.

HIV/AIDS AND TB CO-INFECTION

Another reason for the high numbers of TB infections is the relationship between TB and HIV/AIDS. These two diseases are so closely tied to one another that they are often referred to as a co-infection.

HIV weakens the immune system, which then allows latent TB to become active and infectious or makes the patient more vulnerable to TB droplets inhaled from the air. A person who is infected with HIV/AIDS

is 50 times more likely to develop active TB in a given year than is an HIV-negative person. Also, the disease progresses more rapidly and deaths are higher in people infected with both HIV and TB than those who are infected only with TB. The primary cause of death in people infected with TB and HIV is the TB. Yet the vast majority of people with HIV worldwide have not been screened for TB. ■

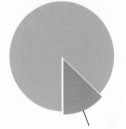

HIV/AIDS co-infections as a percentage of the 9 million new TB cases per year

HIV co-infections (13%)

4 What Do Cells Do?

UNDERSTANDING NORMAL CELL structures and their functions helps scientists understand what goes wrong to allow diseases, including the infectious diseases caused by microbes, to progress. Although there are many differences between cells of various organisms, such as plants, animals, and microbes, there are some key similarities in all cells.

One structure common to every cell is a cell membrane that separates it from the outside environment. Similarly, every cell has genetic material in the form of DNA, and a large number of proteins and other molecules that carry out the chemical reactions needed for a cell to live, grow, and reproduce. Some cells contain structures that are surrounded by a membrane, which creates a barrier between the inside of the structure and the rest of the cell. These membrane-bound structures are called **organelles.**

In this activity, you will learn about some common cell structures and their functions in the cell.

Challenge

▶ What are the functions of the structures in cells?

MATERIALS

FOR EACH PAIR OF STUDENTS
> computer with Internet access

FOR EACH STUDENT
> Student Sheet 4.1, "Structure and Function of Cells"

Procedure

Part A: Computer Simulation

1. Visit the *Science and Global Issues* page of the SEPUP website at *sepuplhs.org/sgi*. With your partner, go to "What Do Cells Do?" and follow the simulation.

Part B: Comparing Cells

2. Read the following information about bacterial cells. This will prepare you to compare the cells of bacteria with those of animals and plants, which you investigated in Part A.

Reading

Bacterial Cell Structure

A bacterial cell does not have a nucleus or other membrane-bound structures. The genetic information of bacterial cells is stored in a large circular chromosome in the cytoplasm. The cell membrane of a bacterial cell performs the functions of many of the organelles of other organisms' cells. For example, to generate energy, a bacterial cell uses specific enzymes located in its cell membrane. Some bacterial cells can also perform photosynthesis at the cell membrane. The ribosomes in bacteria differ from ribosomes in eukaryotes in size and molecular composition, but like the ribosomes in eukaryotes, they carry out protein synthesis. In bacteria, as in eukaryotes, the cytoplasm also contains numerous enzymes that speed up reactions, such as the ones involved in digestion. Bacteria have an outer cell wall that makes them rigid and gives them shape. The cytoskeleton of prokaryotic cells serves some of the same functions as the eukaryotic cytoskeleton, but is made of different proteins. To move around, some bacteria use long tail-like structures called flagella, or short hair-like fibers called cilia. Although these flagella and cilia may appear similar to those of eukaryotes, they are made of different proteins and produce motion by a different mechanism than that of eukaryotic cilia and flagella.

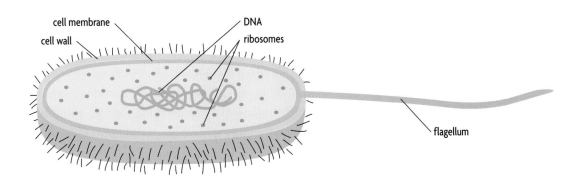

Antibiotics

There are a number of antibiotics that can treat bacterial infections. The chart below shows how some antibiotics kill bacterial cells or keep them from reproducing.

Four Classes of Antibiotics	
ANTIBIOTIC CLASS	**MODE OF ACTION IN BACTERIAL CELL**
ß-lactams	Interfere with cell wall structure
Tetracyclines	Interfere with protein synthesis
Quinolones	Interfere with the copying of bacterial DNA
Sulphonamides	Interfere with the production of an enzyme needed to copy the bacterial DNA

3. Use your understanding from the simulation and the reading above to make changes and additions to the Venn diagram you created in the simulation

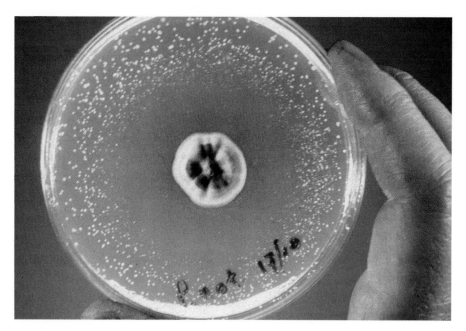

Penicillium *mold produces an antibiotic that has saved many lives.*

Analysis

1. Label each of the following cell types as eukaryotic or prokaryotic:

   • Animal

   • Plant

   • Bacteria

2. **a.** Describe the structures an animal cell must have for it to produce a protein.

   b. Explain how these structures work together to produce a protein.

KEY VOCABULARY	
bacteria	Golgi apparatus
cell membrane	lysosome
cell wall	nucleus
cilium, cilia	**organelle**
cytoplasm	prokaryotic cell
cytoskeleton	ribosome
endoplasmic reticulum (ER)	vacuole
eukaryotic cell	vesicle
flagellum, flagella	

5 What Do Specialized Cells Do?

IN THE PREVIOUS activity you examined some basic structures and organelles in cells. Many types of cells also have specialized structures that allow the cells to perform specific functions. For example, a muscle cell is specialized for movement, while a red blood cell is specialized for carrying oxygen throughout the body. In this activity you will examine the functions of some specialized cells.

Challenge

▶ What are the specialized structures and functions of cells?

MATERIALS

FOR EACH PAIR OF STUDENTS
    computer with Internet access

FOR EACH STUDENT
    Student Sheet 5.1, "Specialized Cells"

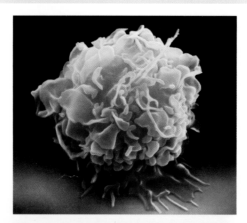

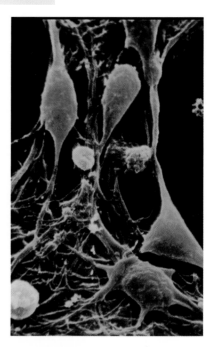

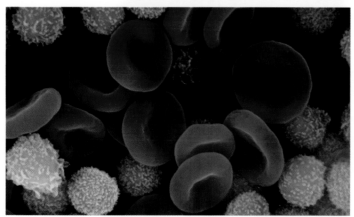

Some examples of specialized cells

Procedure

1. Visit the *Science and Global Issues* page of the SEPUP website at *sepuplhs.org/sgi*. With your partner, go to "What Do Specialized Cells Do?" and follow the simulation.

Analysis

1. Pick two of the specialized cells that you observed in the computer simulation. For each cell:

   a. pick one specialized organelle or structure and explain its function.

   b. explain what would happen to the cell if the specialized organelle or structure were damaged or missing.

   c. explain what would happen to the organism if the specialized organelle or structure were damaged or missing.

KEY VOCABULARY	
cell	organelle
microbe	

6 Cell Structure and Function

BIOLOGISTS STUDY LIFE at many levels, from the whole biosphere to the molecules that make up the cells of organisms, as shown in the diagram below. **Cell biology** is the study of the compositions and functions of cells; cell structures and organelles; and cell molecules.

Challenge

▶ What are the fundamental structures and functions of cells?

MATERIALS

FOR EACH STUDENT
   sticky notes

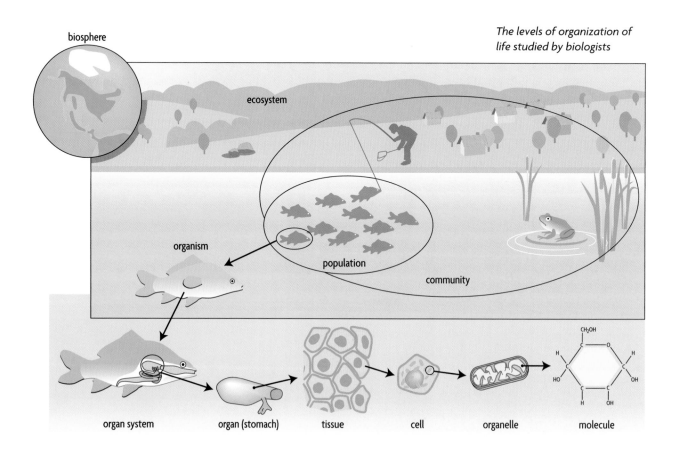

The levels of organization of life studied by biologists

biosphere

ecosystem

organism

population

community

organ system   organ (stomach)   tissue   cell   organelle   molecule

Procedure

1. Follow the "Read, Think, and Take Note" strategy as you complete the Reading.

Reading

The Cell Principle

Englishman Robert Hooke was an influential scientist in the 17th century, who, while looking at thin slices of cork under a microscope, became the first scientist to observe and record cells. What he saw in the cork looked like a series of boxes that reminded him of the rooms, or cells, of a monastery. His observations led him to call these structures cells.

It was not until 1839, however, that German botanist Matthias Schleiden, from studies with a more powerful microscope, declared that entire plant organisms were made up of cells. This was a momentous discovery at the time, but within a year Schleiden's colleague, Theodor Schwann, a professor of animal studies, proposed that animals were also made up of cells. In 1855, physician Rudolf Virchow theorized that new cells could only come from existing cells.

The ideas of Schleiden, Schwann, and Virchow led to the development of the cell principle, which has been confirmed by many scientists. The **cell principle** states that

- all living organisms are made of cells.
- cells are the basic units of structure and function in living organisms.
- new cells are made from existing cells.

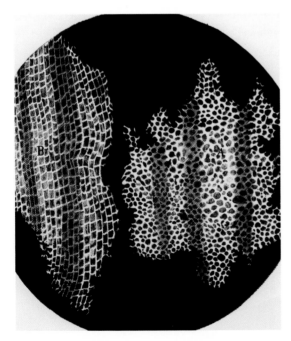

Robert Hooke's drawing of cork cells, 1659

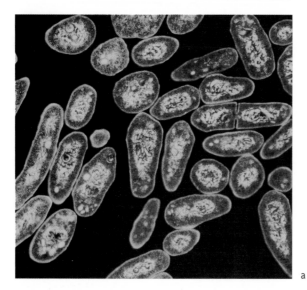
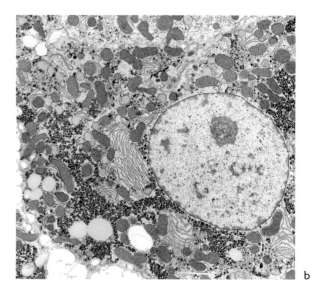

a

b

These prokaryotic cells (a) lack a nucleus. The single chromosome is located in the cytoplasm. In the enlarged human liver cell (b), the chromosomes are inside the nucleus.

All Cells Contain Genetic Information

All living cells contain hereditary information in the form of a molecule called deoxyribonucleic acid (DNA). From the information that is stored in DNA the cell makes the proteins and other molecules it needs to carry out all of its chemical processes and, for multicellular organisms, function within the larger organism.

Based on the location of the DNA in the cell, scientists classify living cells into two major categories—eukaryotes and prokaryotes. **Eukaryotes** are organisms with cells that contain a **nucleus,** a large organelle surrounded by a double membrane, where the DNA is stored. Of the organisms you have observed, animals, plants, and protists are eukaryotes. In most of the cells of multicellular eukaryotes, the nucleus contains the genetic instructions for the entire organism. **Protists** are single-celled microbes that have a nucleus. Examples of protists are the paramecium and amoeba, most algae, and some fungi. **Prokaryotes** are organisms with cells that do not have a nucleus, and their DNA is located in the cytoplasm. The **bacteria** you observed in Activity 3, "What Is a Cell?" were single-celled prokaryotes. Prokaryotes also lack many other cell structures found in eukaryotes.

All Cells Have a Cell Membrane and Cytoplasm

Every living cell has a **cell membrane** that serves as a barrier between the cell and its environment. The cell membrane lets some substances into and out of the cell, while preventing the movement of other substances. Within the boundary of the cell membrane of all cells, but outside the nucleus in eukaryotes, is a semi-fluid substance called the **cytoplasm.** All of the cell's internal structures and organelles are suspended in the cytoplasm. As you will see

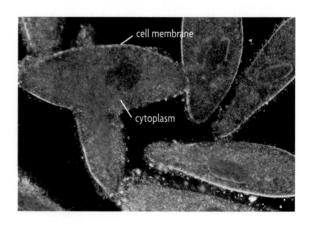

cell membrane

cytoplasm

through the rest of this unit, many of the cell functions and reactions of metabolism occur in the nucleus and cytoplasm. **Metabolism** is the term for all of the chemical processes that maintain life and that occur within living cells.

All Cells Must Maintain Internal Balance

The external conditions in the environment surrounding cells can vary. To survive, however, cells must maintain constant internal conditions, such as water content and temperature—just as a whole organism, such as a human, must do. The process by which cells maintain constant internal conditions is called **homeostasis,** and it depends greatly on the membrane's regulation of what substances go into and out of the cell.

The Cytoskeleton

Inside the cytoplasm is a system called the **cytoskeleton.** As you might guess from its name, the cytoskeleton provides structure and organization to the cytoplasm and maintains the shape of the cell. But the cytoskeleton has other important functions. It plays a role in the transport of materials within cells, in the division of cells, and in the movements of cells when they crawl, swim, or contract. The cytoskeleton is made of three types of long, thin structures built of proteins. These are the actin microfilaments, intermediate filaments, and microtubules. These tubules and filaments are both able to assemble and disassemble in the cell when and where they are needed. Motor proteins cause microfilaments and microtubules to slide past each other as well, producing shortening or lengthening movements.

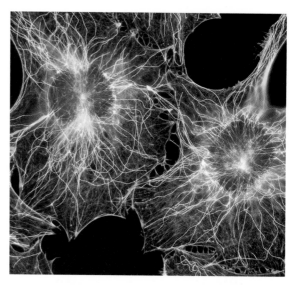

These cytoskeletons radiate from near the nuclei.

Cells in Multicellular Organisms Specialize

Multicellular organisms have anywhere from a few to many types of cells. In humans there are more than 220 types of cells, each with a specialized function and its own arrangement of cellular structures needed for the body to survive and reproduce.

Muscle cells, for example, are specialized to contract, whether as part of the skeletal muscles that interact with and move bones or the muscles surrounding digestive organs that contract to move food through your digestive system. These cells contain a highly developed system of microfilaments, which function to shorten the muscle cells when the muscle contracts. Muscle cells also contain many mitochondria, which supply the large amounts of energy needed for contraction.

Red blood cells, too, are specialized cells, but, unlike other human cells, they do not have nuclei, mitochondria, or other cell structures. Instead, red blood cells are packed with hemoglobin, a protein that carries oxygen.

A third example of specialized cells is the intestinal epithelial cells of the small intestine, which have microscopic structures called microvilli that function to increase the surface area of the cell. The increased surface area increases the rate of nutrient absorption.

Analysis

1. What are the similarities between all cells?

2. What is the major characteristic that classifies a cell as a prokaryote or eukaryote?

3. How did technology, namely the microscope, advance scientists' understanding of cells and microbes?

4. Some substances are damaging to cell membranes. What effects on the function of the membrane might the cell experience if the cell membrane is damaged?

KEY VOCABULARY

bacteria	eukaryote, eukaryotic
cell	homeostasis
cell biology	metabolism
cell membrane, membrane	nucleus
cell principle	prokaryote, prokaryotic
cytoplasm	protein
cytoskeleton	protist
deoxyribonucleic acid, DNA	

7 A Model Membrane

DESPITE THEIR VARIETY, all cells have certain structures in common that perform essential functions. One such structure is the cell membrane. The cell membrane is the outermost membrane and the barrier between the cell and its external environment.

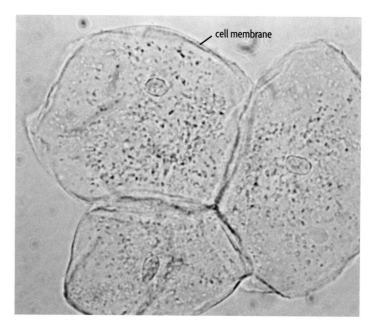

Human cheek cells

The cell membrane supports and protects the cell. If you compare a cell to a house, the membrane of a cell functions like the outside walls, roof, and doors of the house. It separates the cell from its environment, and helps maintain the homeostasis that lets the structures and molecules in the cell function. This includes regulating amounts of vital substances in the cell, such as salts and glucose, by controlling their movements into and out of the cell. Other key roles of the cell membrane are keeping out dangerous substances and organisms, such as disease-causing microbes, and sending and receiving signals from other cells.

Both infectious and noninfectious diseases may involve the cell membrane. When the membrane is unable to keep out disease-causing microbes, infection results. HIV and *Plasmodium* are examples of microbes that must first interact with and enter cells in order to infect humans. Noninfectious diseases can disrupt normal membrane function. Some forms of the genetic disease muscular dystrophy, for example, prevent damaged muscle cell membranes from healing by interfering with their normal ability to reseal small tears.

In this investigation you will explore a model that displays some of the features of a cell membrane.

Challenge

▶ What structures and characteristics help the cell membrane perform its functions?

MATERIALS

FOR EACH GROUP OF FOUR STUDENTS

    tray

    500 mL of bubble solution

8 straws

    ball of cotton string

    plastic tube

    spool of cotton thread

    toothpick

    paper clip

    scissors

    supply of paper towels

FOR EACH STUDENT

    Student Sheet 2.1, "Disease Information" from Activity 2

3 sticky notes

Procedure

1. To make the model, begin by filling the tray with a shallow layer of bubble solution.

2. Each person in your group should unwrap a clean straw, and use a piece of masking tape to label the straw with your initials. Keep track of your own straw throughout the activity.

3. Allow each of you, one by one, to make a single large bubble by gently blowing into the bubble solution. In your science notebook record your observations of the solution film—the membrane—that forms the bubble. If your bubble pops before you can finish your observations, make a fresh bubble. Let everyone in your group practice making a bubble. Take turns making the additional bubbles when they are needed in the rest of the Procedure.

4. Make a fresh bubble. Try dropping a toothpick through the film. In your science notebook record your observations. Remove the toothpick, and dry it with a paper towel.

5. Make a fresh bubble. Then insert the plastic tube into the bubble. In your science notebook, record your observations.

6. Now coat the plastic tube completely with the bubble solution in the tray. Make a fresh bubble. Insert the coated tube through the bubble. Record your observations. While the tube is inserted in the membrane, drop a toothpick through the plastic tube. In your science notebook, record your observations.

7. Move the plastic tube slowly and carefully from side to side, while it is in the bubble. Insert a second solution-coated object, such as a straw, into the bubble film, and move it around the bubble membrane also. In your science notebook, record your observations.

8. Carefully remove the tube and straw from the bubble. In your science notebook, record your observations.

9. Thread the cotton string through four of the straws to make a square about three-fourths the size of the tray. Knot the ends together. Then tie handles onto two opposite sides of the square, as shown below.

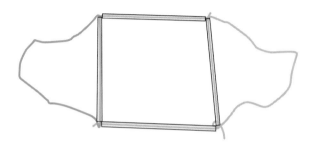

10. Submerge the square in the solution. Then, slowly pull it up, first from an angle, and then vertically as shown in the diagram below at left, until you have removed the square with the film from the tray. Then grasp both string handles and adjust the square to a horizontal position as shown below at right. Gently move it up and down, and observe the film. (If it pops, form a new one). In your science notebook, record your observations of the film.

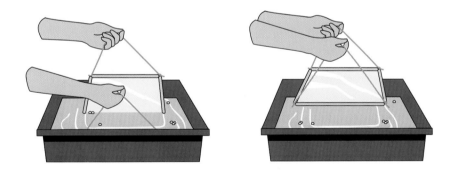

11. Cut a piece of cotton thread 6–7 cm in length. Knot it to form a small circle.

Cell Membrane Structure

The cell membrane is made mainly of proteins and phospholipids. The phospholipids form two layers—a bilayer—that gives the membrane both flexibility and strength. You saw this property with the detergent bubbles, which are also made of a type of lipid. The phospholipids in each layer of the cell membrane move from side to side in the cell membrane, trading places with each other and making the membrane a fluid structure.

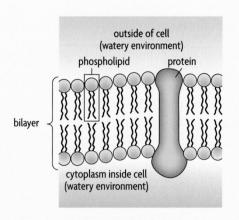

12. Float the circle of thread on the film made with the straws, and form an opening in the film by popping the inside of the circle with the end of a partially unfolded paper clip. In your science notebook, record your observations.

    Note: Be patient and gentle during Steps 12 and 13. If your film breaks, place the square of straws back in the bubble solution to form another film.

13. Use the straight end of the paper clip to gently remove the circle of thread from the film. In your science notebook, record your observations.

14. Now that you have worked with a simple model of the cell membrane, read the box above about the actual structure of the cell membrane.

15. Follow your teacher's directions for reading the case study about diabetes. As you read, follow the "Read, Think, and Take Note" strategy.

16. Complete the information for diabetes on Student Sheet 2.1, "Disease Information" after you read the case study.

Analysis

1. Based on your observations of the bubble film in Procedure Steps 3 and 7, what do you think scientists mean when they say that the cell membrane is fluid?

2. **a.** What did you have to do to make objects pass through the bubble membrane without breaking the bubble?

   b. A cell membrane is mostly made of phospholipids. Which would be more likely to be able to move across a cell membrane: a structure made of proteins, or a structure made of proteins coated with phospholipids? Explain, based on the model.

   c. The cell membrane can be described as a selective barrier. What does that mean?

3. A small break in a cell membrane sometimes closes back up. What properties of the model that you just explored showed how the membrane can reseal itself?

4. In addition to the phospholipid bilayer, cell membranes also include specialized proteins. These proteins are embedded in the membrane and, like the phospholipids, are able to move side to side in the membrane. Some of these proteins function as transporters, allowing other molecules into the cell. Explain how you modeled transport proteins in the Procedure.

5. From what you learned about diabetes in Case Study 3, explain the effect a destroyed transport protein has on the membrane and the cell.

6. Based on the diabetes case study, what conclusions can you make about the relationships between body weight, a country's income level, and diabetes?

KEY VOCABULARY

cell membrane	membrane
diabetes	transport protein

CASE STUDY

Diabetes

THE WORLD HEALTH ORGANIZATION (WHO) states that the world is experiencing a global diabetes epidemic. Between 1985 and 1995, the number of people with diabetes rose to 135 million from 30 million. The number of young people with diabetes is increasing especially rapidly.

The WHO projects that the number of people worldwide with diabetes will almost double by 2030.

SYMPTOMS AND DISEASE MECHANISM

Diabetes mellitus is a noninfectious disease that affects people of all ages and from all countries. The early symptoms of diabetes include excessive urination, thirst, hunger, weight loss, changes in vision, fatigue, and possibly coma. Blood glucose tests can detect diabetes in very early stages, before symptoms appear. Diabetes-related

Burden of Disease			
	TOTAL NUMBER WITH DISORDER	NUMBER OF DEATHS PER YEAR	NUMBER OF NEW CASES PER YEAR
Worldwide	180 million	2.9 million	6.5 million
United States	17 million	233,619	1.6 million

complications that may develop over a number of years include blindness, kidney failure, coronary heart disease, stroke, and serious infections that may lead to amputation of toes, feet, or legs. Any of these can result in disability.

Diabetes disrupts the body's ability to process sugars and is caused by a breakdown in the normal function of certain cells. There are two common types of diabetes, both of which involve high levels of glucose in the blood. The first, Type I diabetes, occurs when the body's immune system destroys the cells in the pancreas that produce insulin, the hormone that regulates the

level of glucose in the blood. Type II diabetes occurs when the body either does not produce enough insulin or specific cells are not responding to insulin. For example, the membranes of liver cells have protein receptors that recognize insulin and activate the glucose transport protein that moves glucose into the cell. If this process does not work, the liver cells do not take up glucose from the blood. Glucose builds up in the blood, and the cells cannot get the energy they need from the glucose.

Both Type I and Type II diabetes disturb the normal balance of glucose within and outside the cell. This in turn leads to other

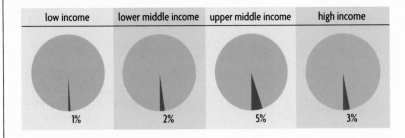

Percentage of people with diabetes in countries at four average income levels

problems of metabolism that disrupt homeostasis and cause the complications that may lead to disability or death.

People with Type I diabetes must give themselves regular insulin injections and carefully monitor their blood sugar levels and intake of carbohydrates. Some people with Type II diabetes require insulin shots, while others take only an oral medication and follow a healthy diet.

The more carefully people maintain their blood glucose levels within the normal range, the lower the risk of serious health consequences from either type of diabetes.

DIABETES PREVENTION AND TREATMENT

Approximately 90% of the people around the world with diabetes have Type II diabetes. Excess body weight and lack of physical activity increase the risk of developing Type II diabetes. Previously, Type II diabetes was observed mostly in adults, but today it is becoming common in children as well. Actions people can take to help prevent or control Type II diabetes include:

- maintaining a healthy body weight.
- exercising with moderate intensity on most days of the week.
- avoiding tobacco use.

Regular blood tests will detect elevated levels of blood sugar that predict Type II diabetes. This gives at-risk individuals an opportunity to take the actions described above, and reduce their chances of developing diabetes and the serious complications that may follow and reduce life expectancy. World health experts estimate that lifestyle changes by people at high risk could reduce Type II diabetes by 35 to 58%.

The causes of the immune reactions that lead to Type I diabetes are unknown, although there is evidence that genetic and environmental factors may increase the risk of developing Type I diabetes. There are currently no preventive measures.

CHALLENGES TO PREVENTION AND TREATMENT

Diabetes has serious social and economic impacts on afflicted individuals, their families, and the health care system. These include effects on people's ability to work and the costs of treatment. Body weight is an important indicator for the risk of Type II diabetes. Although losing weight and exercising reduce the risk of Type II diabetes—and sometimes reverse its course— making lifestyle changes is difficult. This is a key challenge to preventing Type II diabetes. ■

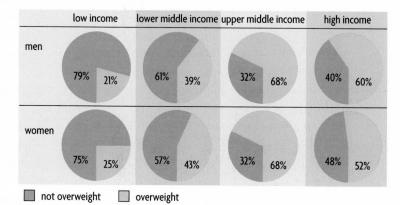

Overweight and nonoverweight men and women in countries at four average income levels.

8 The Cell Membrane and Diffusion

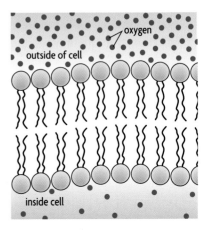

A KEY FUNCTION OF the cell membrane is regulating what substances enter or leave the cell. In many cases, substances move into or out of the cell through the process of diffusion. In **diffusion,** a substance moves from a solution with a high concentration of the substance to a solution with a low concentration of the substance. This is shown in the diagram at right.

In this activity, you will test a variety of substances to see if they will diffuse through a model cell membrane made of plastic, rather than the detergent film you used in Activity 7, "A Model Membrane."'

Challenge

▶ What factors determine whether a substance moves across a model of the cell membrane?

MATERIALS

FOR THE CLASS

    supply of 20% sucrose solution

    supply of 40% sucrose solution

FOR EACH GROUP OF FOUR STUDENTS

  4 pieces of dialysis tubing (to model the cell membrane)

  3 9-oz clear plastic cups

    180-mL bottle of distilled water

    60-mL bottle of liquid glucose solution

    60-mL dropper bottle of glucose indicator

    30-mL bottle of Lugol's iodine solution

    60-mL bottle of liquid starch solution

    250-mL beaker

    50-mL graduated cylinder

  2 small test tubes

    funnel

    dropper

    timer

    permanent marking pen

    colored pencils

    ruler

FOR EACH STUDENT

    Student Sheet 2.1, "Disease Information" from Activity 2

  3 sticky notes

Procedure

Part A: Investigating Water and Sucrose Solutions

1. Have someone in your group use the marking pen to label one cup "40% sucrose," one cup "20% sucrose," and one cup "0% sucrose." Fill each cup half-full with the appropriate sucrose solution.

2. Obtain three pieces of dialysis tubing, which represent cell membranes, and prepare them for use:

   a. Wet them by dipping them into a beaker of tap water.

   b. Squeeze one end of each membrane between your thumb and forefinger to make an opening.

   c. Use a clean dropper or faucet to run water through each membrane.

3. Fill each dialysis tube with 20% sucrose solution by following these directions:

   a. Tie a very tight knot in one end of the dialysis tube. Use the beaker and funnel to add enough 20% sucrose solution to the tube to fill approximately 3–4 cm of the tube, as shown at left below.

   b. Tie a knot in the top end of the tube, leaving a little space in the tube above the level of the liquid, as shown at right below. This "bag" is now a model of a cell enclosed by its cell membrane.

a

b

Fill (a) and close (b) the tube.

4. Rinse the tied tubes in running water and dry them carefully on a paper towel. Set the filled tubes on a clean paper towel. Do not place them in a cup.

5. Rinse and dry the beaker.

6. In your science notebook, create a data table to record your results.

7. Place one tube in each of the cups of sucrose solution (40%, 20%, and 0%) at the same time. The solutions in the cups represent the environment outside each cell.

8. Allow the tubes to remain in the cups for 20 minutes. Every 5 minutes, observe the tubes, and record any changes in the model membrane or its contents.

   Note: Lift the tubes out of the cups to make observations and then place them back in the solutions.

Part B: Membranes and the Movement of Molecules

9. Add the following to two small test tubes:

   test tube 1: 2–3 drops water

   test tube 2: 2–3 drops starch

10. Add 1 drop of Lugol's solution to test tubes 1 and 2 to be sure the indicator solutions are working properly. In your science notebook, record your observations.

11. Your teacher will demonstrate the glucose indicator. In your science notebook, record your observations from the demonstration.

12. Based on the information in the table below, which molecules do you think will pass through the model membrane? In your science notebook

    a. record your hypothesis of which will pass through.

    b. explain your reasons for your hypothesis.

Molecular Formulas for Three Molecules	
MOLECULE	MOLECULAR FORMULA
Glucose	$C_6H_{12}O_6$
Iodine	I_2
Starch	polysaccharide made of thousands of glucose molecules linked together

13. Investigate your hypothesis.

   a. Fill the 50-mL graduated cylinder with 35 mL of water.

   b. Test a few drops of the water in your test tube to be sure it doesn't contain any glucose or starch. Then clean your tray.

   c. Wet a piece of dialysis tubing by dipping it into the beaker of water. Squeeze one end of the membrane between your thumb and forefinger to make an opening. Use a clean dropper or faucet to run water through the tube.

   d. Tie a tight knot in the bottom of the tube.

   e. Add about 5 mL of glucose and 5 mL of starch to the tube.

   f. Tie the tube shut, just above the level of the solution.

   g. **Rinse the outside of the tube thoroughly under running water. This is important: there must not be any glucose or starch on the outside of the tube!**

   h. Slowly place the filled membrane tube into the graduated cylinder so that it is surrounded by water, as shown at right.

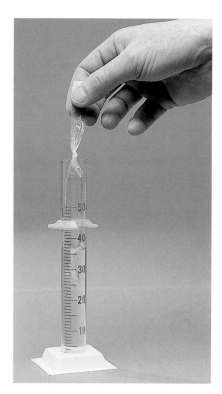

Placing the tube into the cylinder

14. In your science notebook, create a data table to record your observations.

15. After 5–10 minutes, remove a dropper full of liquid from the graduated cylinder.

   a. Test a few drops of the solution from the graduated cylinder with Lugol's solution in a small test tube.

   b. Test 5 mL of the solution from the graduated cylinder with 10 drops of glucose test solution in a small test tube.

   c. In your science notebook, record your results and what they tell you about the movement of glucose and starch across the membrane.

16. Add 3 drops of Lugol's solution to the liquid in the cylinder.

17. Observe for 5–10 minutes. Record your observations and what they tell you about the movement of iodine across the membrane.

18. Follow your teacher's directions for reading the case study about HIV/AIDS. As you read, follow the "Read, Think, and Take Note" strategy.

19. Complete the information for HIV/AIDS on Student Sheet 2.1, "Disease Information" after you read the case study.

Analysis

1. In Part A, what changes did you observe in the model cell when the external environment surrounding the model cell contained each of the following:

    a. a less concentrated solution than the cell's contents. Explain.

    b. a more concentrated solution than the cell's contents. Explain.

    c. equally as concentrated as the cell's contents. Explain.

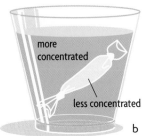

2. In Part B, which substances passed through the model membrane? Explain why. Support your explanation with evidence from the laboratory.

3. In Part B, did the results support your hypothesis? Explain.

4. Some substances, including glucose, cannot directly cross the lipid bilayer of a cell membrane. What structures do you think are in the membrane to allow for the transport of substances that cannot cross on their own?

    Hint: Think back to the bubble film model.

5. The diffusion of water across a membrane to equalize the concentrations of solutions on either side of the membrane is called osmosis. Explain:

    a which part of the model illustrated osmosis.

    b. what conditions are necessary for osmosis to take place.

6. Based on the HIV/AIDS case study, what are the advantages and trade-offs of working to develop an HIV/AIDS vaccine, as opposed to focusing on education?

KEY VOCABULARY	
cell membrane, membrane	hypothesis
control	osmosis
diffuse, diffusion	phospholipid (lipid) bilayer
HIV/AIDS	

CASE STUDY

HIV/AIDS

BEFORE 1981, HIV/AIDS was unknown to the medical community. Today 30 million people across the world are infected with HIV/AIDS.

The distribution of cases worldwide is shown in the map below. Of the 2.7 million new cases, 370,000 are in children age 14 and younger. More than 90% of these newly infected children are babies born to mothers who are HIV positive.

SYMPTOMS AND DISEASE MECHANISM

In the summer of 1981, doctors in the United States observed an unusual number of cases of a rare skin cancer and a rare pneumonia. All of the patients had one other disease characteristic in common: reduced immunity to certain diseases. It soon became clear that some populations, such as intravenous drug users and hemophiliacs, were more likely to be affected than the general U.S. population, indicating that at least one way it was acquired was from blood. The disease was named acquired immunodeficiency syndrome (AIDS).

Within three years after its discovery, scientists showed that an infectious blood-borne virus was the cause of AIDS. They named this virus human immunodeficiency virus (HIV) because it reduces the function of the immune system. At first, doctors and scientists hoped that the discovery of the virus would soon lead to effective vaccines for HIV/AIDS prevention. HIV, however, proved to be a rapidly mutating virus, and over a fairly short period of time, new variations of the virus emerged. Because the virus changes so rapidly, the

(Continued on next page)

Burden of Disease

	TOTAL NUMBER INFECTED	NUMBER OF DEATHS PER YEAR	NUMBER OF NEW CASES PER YEAR
Worldwide	30 million	2 million	2.7 million
United States	1.1 million	14,110	44,000

Global distribution of HIV/AIDS cases

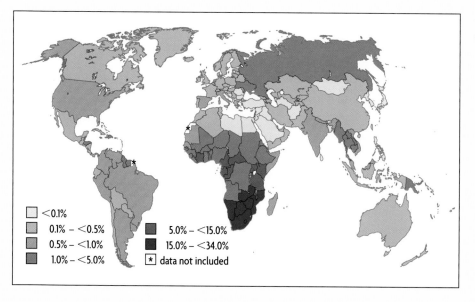

- ☐ <0.1%
- 0.1% – <0.5%
- 0.5% – <1.0%
- 1.0% – <5.0%
- 5.0% – <15.0%
- 15.0% – <34.0%
- ☒ data not included

(Continued from previous page)

development of vaccines and treatments has been a much greater challenge than anticipated.

HIV is an infectious disease that destroys a specific type of white blood cell in the immune system. The virus membrane attaches to and fuses with the cell membrane of these white blood cells. The virus appears in blood, semen, vaginal fluids, and breast milk of infected individuals and is transmitted in one of four ways:

- transfusion of infected blood.
- sexual contact with an infected person.
- needle or syringe contaminated with the blood of an infected person.
- an infected mother to her child during pregnancy, birth, or breast-feeding.

While some people show symptoms shortly after infection with HIV, many do not develop symptoms for 10 years or more. Early symptoms include fatigue, fever, diarrhea, weight loss, and swollen lymph glands. The diagnosis of HIV infection is upgraded to AIDS when the patient develops at least one serious illness, such as pneumonia, TB, or hepatitis C, and that patient's number of specific white blood cells (lymphocytes) falls below a certain level. Because the immune system also protects against cancer,

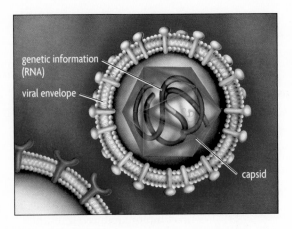

A model of an HIV virus approaching the cell membrane of a white blood cell

genetic information (RNA)

viral envelope

capsid

HIV/AIDS increases the risk of some cancers.

HIV/AIDS PREVENTION AND TREATMENT

There are a number of preventions and treatments for HIV/AIDS infection. An early intervention was rigorous screening of blood donors to prevent transmission of the disease from a blood transfusion. One primary area of prevention today focuses on educating teenagers and adults about risky sexual activities. For example, HIV/AIDS education that promotes using condoms or abstaining from sexual activity is an effective prevention measure. Programs that focus on drug users and convince them not to share needles have also been effective in prevention. A major medical advance was the creation of a drug that prevents mother-to-child transmission of the virus during pregnancy and labor.

Treatment of HIV/AIDS involves a combination of

several drugs, which do not cure HIV/AIDS, but greatly improve the length and quality of life. In the 1990s, combinations of drugs, which cost about $15,000 per patient per year, became available in developed countries. Then generic drugs were developed, which drove down the price of the drugs. This, along with support from organizations, made the combination drugs accessible to people in developing countries at $295 per year. Today, generic drugs are available in developing countries for $88 per year.

HIV/AIDS RESEARCH

For years, a major focus of HIV/AIDS research has been on a vaccine to prevent transmission of the virus. As yet, however, there is still no effective vaccine, in part because the virus evolves so rapidly. Most vaccines, such as the ones against polio and seasonal flu, cause a person's immune system to produce proteins called antibodies. Antibodies disable or kill a disease-causing microbe, such as a virus. With this type of vaccine, the antibodies stop the infection before the person gets sick. The antibodies produced by vaccination against one variation of AIDS, however, will not protect against other variations. And once a person is infected, HIV "hides" inside cells of the immune system, where antibodies cannot reach the virus. Research for an effective HIV/AIDS vaccine continues to be the focus for scientists who study HIV/AIDS.

CHALLENGES TO HIV/AIDS PREVENTION AND TREATMENT

Despite significant progress in prevention and treatment, the global level of success in controlling HIV/AIDS infections worldwide has not been as high as hoped. In some places providing educational programs and other preventive measures are not effective in reaching and changing the behavior of enough people to make much of a difference. Data from 64 countries show that young people, a key audience for AIDS information, do not have accurate and complete knowledge about HIV/AIDS. This means they are less likely to take measures to prevent infection. To this date only about half of those countries have set goals for education and other prevention strategies. Additionally, many people already infected are not able to get the drugs they need because they cost too much or are not available. ■

9 Cell Membrane Structure and Function

UNDERSTANDING THE CELL membrane is the key to understanding many diseases, and is of great value in developing treatments. Some diseases disable the ability of the cell membrane to reseal after it has been penetrated, and some destroy the function of the cell's transport channels. The immune system recognizes foreign cells through receptors on the membrane of both the foreign and immune cells. Many disease-causing pathogens, such as the HIV/AIDS virus and the polio virus, infect humans by recognizing and binding to the cell membrane, and then entering the cell. Preventing and treating such diseases as HIV/AIDS can improve the quality and length of people's lives and improve their social and economic well-being.

Challenge

▶ How do the structures of the cell membrane help it function?

Procedure

1. When reading, answer the Stopping to Think Questions in your mind.

Reading

Molecular Building Blocks of Cells and the Cell Membrane

Four types of large molecules, called **macromolecules,** are essential building blocks for all of the structures in a cell. These macromolecules are carbohydrates, lipids, proteins, and nucleic acids. Each type of macromolecule is made of one or more chains of simpler compounds, or subunits. The table below shows the kinds of subunits that make up each type of macromolecule.

Macromolecule Subunits	
MACROMOLECULE	SUBUNITS
Carbohydrates	sugars
Lipids	fatty acids
Proteins	amino acids
Nucleic acids	nucleotides

A phospholipid molecule

The cell membrane is made mostly of lipids and proteins. The lipids give the membrane its strength, yet allow it to remain flexible and fluid. The bubble film in Activity 7, "A Model Membrane," modeled the lipid layer that is the basis for the structure of the cell membrane. Most of the lipids in the cell membranes of animals, plants, protists, and bacteria are members of a special class of lipids, called phospholipids. A **phospholipid** is a lipid with a phosphate head attached to two long lipid tails.

The structure of the membrane results from the properties of the phospholipids. The heads of phospholipid molecules are attracted to water, so they face the watery environment inside and outside the cell. The tails line up and point toward the middle of the membrane. This results in a double-layered structure called a phospholipid (lipid) bilayer, as shown at right.

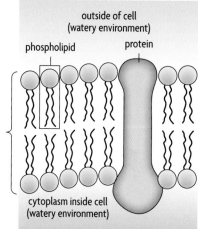

The phospholipid bilayer of the cell membrane with an embedded protein

Proteins are embedded in the membrane's phospholipid bilayer, also shown at right. Some of these proteins are linked to carbohydrate chains. Membrane proteins are able to move sideways through the membrane, just as you were able to move tubes through the bubble membrane. The complex arrangement of proteins in the membrane reminded scientists of the tiles in a mosaic. This led scientists to refer to the structure of the cell membrane as a **fluid mosaic model,** shown below.

There are many proteins in the membrane of a typical cell. One kind of protein acts as channels or pumps, controlling what enters and leaves the cell. You modeled these channels when you inserted straws and tubes through the bubble membrane. You also modeled the glucose channel with the dialysis membrane.

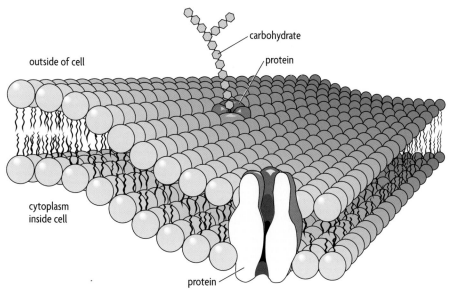

The fluid mosaic model for the cell membrane

Other membrane molecules made up of proteins or proteins linked to carbohydrates act as signaling or receptor proteins. These molecules are involved in cell-to-cell communication. An example of a receptor is the membrane protein that binds to insulin hormone. The body needs insulin to regulate blood glucose levels. When blood glucose levels are high, insulin attaches to receptors in the membranes of liver and muscle cells. This stimulates the cells to take up glucose from the blood and store it as glycogen or fat.

STOPPING TO THINK 1

What are the molecular building blocks that make up the cell membrane?

How are these molecules arranged in the cell membrane?

What are the functions of these molecules in the membrane?

The Cell Membrane Controls What Enters and Leaves the Cell

DIFFUSION AND OSMOSIS

The cell membrane is **semipermeable,** or **selectively permeable,** which means not all substances can cross it. This property helps the cell maintain homeostasis—stable internal conditions—by controlling what enters and leaves. You modeled this property of the membrane with the dialysis tubing in the last activity: small molecules, like water and glucose, could cross the dialysis membrane, while large molecules, like sucrose and starch, could not. Size is one factor that determines whether a molecule can cross the cell membrane. Other factors determining whether certain molecules can cross a cell membrane are the molecules' shape and electrical charge.

For the cell to function properly, it must allow desirable substances, such as nutrients, to enter, and allow wastes to leave. Many of these substances enter and leave the cell by diffusing from an area of high concentration to an area of low concentration. When a substance moves naturally from high to low concentration, the cell does not have to expend energy. For example, oxygen diffuses from a high concentration outside the cell across the membrane into the cell. As the oxygen is used up and the concentration in the cell drops, more oxygen enters the cell. Similarly, as carbon dioxide builds up inside the cells of the body it diffuses from high concentration across the cell membrane to lower concentration outside of the cell.

Water also diffuses naturally in both directions across the cell membrane. The overall direction of movement of water depends on the concentration of dissolved substances inside and outside the cell. Diffusion will continue until the two solutions have an equal concentration of the dissolved substance. When a cell is placed in a solution with a higher concentration of dissolved substances, water will move out of the cell, and the cell will shrink, as shown in the diagram at right. When a cell is placed in a solution with a lower concentration of dissolved substances, water will enter the cell and the cell will swell. This diffusion of liquid water across a semipermeable membrane is called **osmosis.**

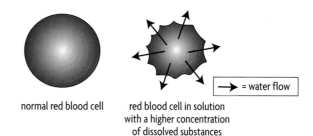

normal red blood cell

red blood cell in solution with a higher concentration of dissolved substances

→ = water flow

PASSIVE TRANSPORT

Not all substances used or produced by the cell can freely diffuse through its membrane, especially substances that are electrically charged or are very large in size. Proteins in the cell membrane must transport the substances in or out. When a membrane protein moves a substance from higher to lower concentration through a protein channel, the process is called **facilitated diffusion,** or **passive transport,** because it does not require energy. An example of facilitated diffusion is the movement of glucose from high concentrations outside the cell into the cell through a glucose transport protein.

ACTIVE TRANSPORT

In some cases, proteins transport substances into or out of a cell against the normal direction of diffusion. The molecules of the substance are moving from low to high concentration. This process is called **active transport** (shown below), and it requires the cell to expend energy. An example of active transport is the pumping of substances like calcium and sodium out of the cell.

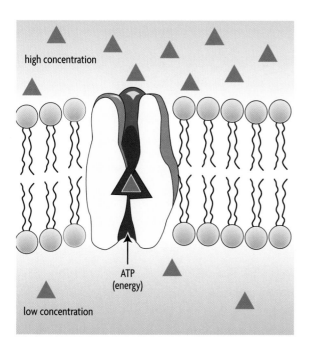

high concentration

ATP
(energy)

low concentration

The active transport of a substance from low to high concentration requires energy.

TRANSPORT BY VESICLES

Sometimes materials are transported across the cell membrane by vesicles, which are small compartments surrounded by a membrane. To transport materials into the cell, the membrane forms a pocket that then pinches into the cell, forming a vesicle. This formation and movement of vesicles into the cell is called **endocytosis.** To transport materials out of the cell, a vesicle in the cytoplasm fuses with the cell membrane, and re-forms a smooth outer membrane, releasing its contents to the outside. This process of releasing material in vesicles to the outside of the cell is called **exocytosis.** Both of these processes are shown below. The fluid nature of the membrane is key to its ability to form and release vesicles. The movement of the vesicles within the cell involves the cytoskeleton and requires energy.

Endocytosis

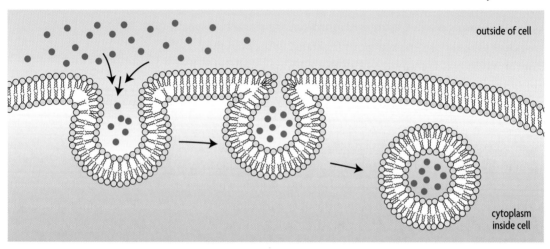

Exocytosis

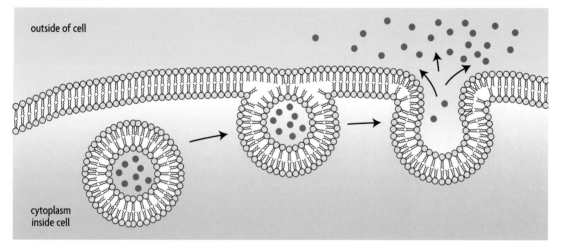

STOPPING TO THINK 2

What types of movement happen across the cell membrane?

Which type of movement(s) across the cell membrane need(s) energy? Why?

Viruses and the Cell Membrane

The causes of many human infectious diseases are viruses that enter our cells. HIV/AIDS is a well-known example. Like all viruses, HIV/AIDS is not made of cells, and is not capable of producing offspring on its own. Instead, a virus must invade a cell in order to reproduce. Viruses can infect cells in plants and animals, and can even infect bacteria. A virus is mainly composed of its genetic material and a few proteins, surrounded by a protein coat, and sometimes a lipid membrane. To make copies of itself, the virus invades a cell and uses the cell's structures. Because of this, the invaded cell is called a host cell. Most viruses don't infect every type of cell in the body. Instead, each virus infects one or a few types of cells. HIV/AIDS, for example, only infects cells of the immune system. When the virus comes into contact with an immune system cell, it must first cross the cell membrane. If the virus does not cross that first barrier, it does not infect the cell, cannot produce more viruses, and will eventually be destroyed.

STOPPING TO THINK 3

What makes a virus different from a bacterial or animal cell?

Why do viruses need host cells?

Viruses can infect many sorts of organisms, including animals, plants, and bacteria. They attach to a cell by interacting with the lipids, proteins, or carbohydrates of the cell membrane. Some viruses, such as those that infect bacteria, invade a cell by making a hole in the membrane and injecting themselves into the cell through the hole. Other viruses, like HIV, have an external membrane similar to the cell's membrane. The virus membrane fuses with the cell membrane, allowing the virus to enter the cell. Still other viruses, such as flu viruses, get a "free ride" into the cell through the cell's endocytosis mechanism. In endocytosis the part of the cell membrane in contact with the virus surrounds the virus and pinches into the cell, in a process similar to the one shown on the previous page. Once the virus is inside the cell it will use others of the cell's structures to make more viruses. These new viruses then exit the cell in one of two ways: 1) by pinching off, or budding, from the host cell without destroying the host cell, as is the case with HIV/AIDS; or 2) by breaking the host cell open, killing it in the process, as is the case with polio virus.

Analysis

1. What functions and properties of the cell membrane depend on each of the following?

   a. Phospholipids

   b. Proteins

   c. Carbohydrates

2. Explain why it is important for the cell membrane to be fluid.

3 **a.** What are the functions of the cell membrane?

   b. Explain which parts of the cell membrane allow it to perform these functions.

4. What determines whether or not a substance can cross the cell membrane?

5. Explain how the cell membrane helps the cell maintain homeostasis—a stable internal environment. Name specific structures of the cell membrane and describe their functions in your explanation.

6. Imagine a single-celled organism living in a pond. What would happen to the organism if runoff from irrigation caused the pond to become significantly salty? Use evidence to support your explanation.

KEY VOCABULARY

active transport	**macromolecule**
cell membrane, membrane	**osmosis**
diffusion	**passive transport**
endocytosis	**phospholipid**
exocytosis	phospholipid (lipid) bilayer
facilitated diffusion	protein
fluid mosaic model	**semi-permeable, selectively permeable**
lipid	vesicle
lipid bilayer	virus

10 Functions of Proteins in Cells

THERE ARE THOUSANDS of proteins at work in most cells. A **protein** is a macromolecule made up of one or more chains of amino acids folded together into a complex three-dimensional structure. Each protein performs a certain function, such as speeding up a chemical reaction, transporting a specific molecule into or out of the cell, or fighting disease. The information for producing all of the proteins a cell needs is stored in the cell's DNA. In eukaryotes the DNA is located in the nucleus, and in prokaryotes it is in the cytoplasm.

The genetic material of viruses is enclosed by a protein coat, or capsid. Viruses must have such proteins to be able to infect human cells, and they stimulate a body's immune-system response. In this activity you will research proteins to learn more about their functions in both human cells and viruses.

Challenge

▶ What are the functions of proteins in cells and viruses?

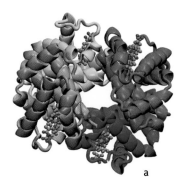

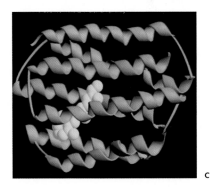

a   b   c

Models of three proteins: hemoglobin (a), insulin (b) , and rhodopsin (c)

Classes of Proteins

CLASS OF PROTEIN	FUNCTION	EXAMPLES
Enzymes	Catalyze (speed up) chemical reactions Thousands are present in most types of cells.	pepsin, DNA polymerase
Transport proteins	Carry small molecules and ions	hemoglobin, glucose transporter (GLUT 4)
Motor proteins	Enable movement in cells and tissues	myosin, dynein
Signaling proteins	Carry signals between cells	insulin, glucagon
Receptor proteins	Mediate a cell's response to a stimulus Many receptors interact with signaling proteins.	insulin receptor, rhodopsin
Immune system and disease proteins	Bind to and inactivate foreign substances and microbes, participate in infection and immune response	antibodies in the immune system, influenza virus, hemagglutinin protein
Storage proteins	Store such materials as amino acids and iron for later use	albumin, ferritin
Structural proteins	Provide protection and support	actin, keratin

Procedure

1. Your teacher will assign your group one of the eight classes of proteins to research and present to the rest of the class.

2. With your group, decide which example protein in your assigned class of proteins each pair will research. Examples are shown in the table above.

3. Work with your partner to research the following for your assigned protein:

   • Its function and location in specific cell types, cell structures, or viruses.

   • Other proteins or structures it interacts with, if relevant.

   • The effect on the cell or virus when this protein is damaged or missing.

4. With your group of four, create a presentation for your classmates about your assigned protein class. Your presentation must include the following:

   • A title that includes the name of the class of protein you were assigned and the general function that was provided in the chart, "Classes of Proteins."

   • All of the information each pair researched in Step 3.

Analysis

1. Why are proteins called "the workhorses" of the cell? Give at least three examples.

2. What are the similarities between all proteins?

3. What would happen to an organism if each of the following types of proteins is damaged or missing? Explain your answers.

   a. Antibody

   b. Myosin

   c. Glucagon

   d. Pepsin

KEY VOCABULARY	
enzyme	receptor protein
motor protein	signaling protein
protein	transport protein

11 Investigating Enzyme Function

WHEN HIV INFECTS a cell, enzymes aid in the virus's reproduction. On the other hand, when the body's immune system is activated, immune cells engulf the pathogen and use enzymes to digest it. Enzymes are required for the majority of reactions and activities that take place within cells. An **enzyme** is a type of protein that speeds up, or **catalyzes,** a specific chemical reaction. Each enzyme has a region called a binding site, which has a unique shape that matches the shape of the reactant it interacts with. Any factor that changes the binding site can reduce or prevent the action of the enzyme.

In this activity you will design, conduct, and report on an investigation to determine whether pH and temperature affect the function of the enzyme lactase. Lactase is a digestive enzyme found in the small intestine of humans. When people consume lactose, which is a sugar found in milk, lactase breaks down the lactose into two simple sugars, glucose and galactose. Both simple sugars are readily absorbed by your body.

$$\text{lactose} + \text{water} \xrightarrow{\text{lactase}} \text{glucose} + \text{galactose}$$

Some people's bodies no longer produce lactase, and so they can no longer break down the lactose in milk or foods that contain milk. Instead, bacteria that live naturally in the small intestine consume the lactose. A product of the digestion of lactose by bacteria is carbon dioxide gas, which can cause abdominal pain. When diarrhea also occurs, doctors may suspect that these are symptoms of lactose deficiency in a condition called lactose intolerance.

This milk has reduced lactose, allowing people who cannot break down lactose to drink it without unpleasant consequences.

Challenge

▶ How do pH and temperature affect the function of the enzyme lactase?

MATERIALS

FOR EACH GROUP OF FOUR STUDENTS

    30-mL dropper bottle lactase solution

    100 mL lactose solution

    100 mL glucose solution

    125 mL yeast suspension

    30-mL dropper bottle pH buffer 4

    30-mL dropper bottle pH buffer 6

    30-mL dropper bottle pH buffer 8

    30-mL dropper bottle pH buffer 10

    hot plate

    beaker of water

FOR EACH PAIR OF STUDENTS

  2 beakers

  2 10-mL graduated cylinders

 10 small test tubes

  9 small balloons

    large pipette

    test tube rack

    thermometer

    permanent marking pen

    water

FOR EACH STUDENT

    safety goggles

Safety

Wear safety goggles at all times during this laboratory. Keep your hands away from the hot plate, and wear insulated gloves or use potholders to move the beaker as you finish. Know the safety procedures in case of a fire. Do not allow solutions to touch your skin or clothing. Clean up spills immediately. If accidental contact occurs, inform your teacher, and rinse exposed areas.

Procedure

1. With your group of four, decide which pair will investigate pH and which pair will investigate temperature.

2. With your partner, design in your science notebooks an experiment to test how your assigned variable affects the enzyme lactase. While designing your investigation, think about the following questions:

   • What is the purpose of the investigation?

   • What will you observe, and how will you measure it?

   • What controls will you need?

   • What materials will you need for your investigation?
   Note: You may not need all of the materials on the Materials list.

   • How will you record your observations?

3. Your teacher will provide a list of guidelines you must follow to complete the investigation. Ask your teacher to answer any questions you have and to approve your procedure before starting your investigation. If necessary, change your procedure.

4. In your science notebook, write or draw a hypothesis about what you think will happen in each of the test tubes you will observe.

5. Conduct the investigation you designed, and record your results in your science notebook.

6. Share your results with the other pair in your group. In your science notebook, record the results of the other pair.

Analysis

1. What is the relationship between lactose and lactase?

2. What evidence from your experiment indicated whether lactase was functioning?

3. What were the controls in the experiment? What information did they provide?

4. **a.** Does temperature affect the function of lactase? If yes, what is the effect? Explain, using evidence from the investigation.

   b. Does pH affect the functioning of lactase? If yes, what is the effect? Explain, using evidence from the investigation.

5. Did the results support your hypothesis? Explain.

6. Most human cells function at a temperature of 37°C and a pH of around 7. From what you learned in this activity explain why it is important for humans to maintain temperature and pH homeostasis.

7. In areas with limited resources, the population may not have access to clean, treated water. Untreated water may contain pathogens, such as the bacteria that cause the disease cholera. In those places people must boil or treat the water they plan to drink or cook with. Apply evidence from this laboratory to explain why boiling destroys biological contaminants in drinking water.

KEY VOCABULARY	
binding site	lactose
catalyze	pH
enzyme	protein
lactase	

12 Photosynthesis and Cellular Respiration

EVERY LIVING CELL needs a source of energy. Without energy, metabolism—all of the chemical reactions that occur within cells—will not occur. In this activity, you will learn how the complex chemical reactions of photosynthesis and cellular respiration help meet the energy needs of living things. You will examine the organelles, molecules, and chemical reactions involved in these two processes. You will also learn how a microbe or chemical that disrupts one or more of the steps of photosynthesis or cellular respiration causes disease.

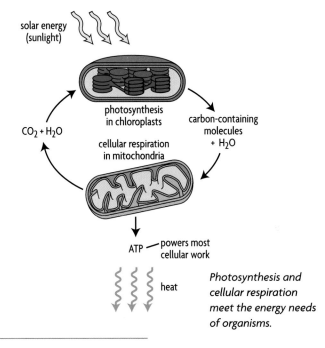

Photosynthesis and cellular respiration meet the energy needs of organisms.

Challenge

▶ How do photosynthesis and cellular respiration meet the energy needs of all organisms?

MATERIALS

FOR EACH STUDENT
Student Sheet 12.1, "Anticipation Guide: Photosynthesis and Cellular Respiration"

Procedure

1. Fill in only the Before column of Student Sheet 12.1, "Anticipation Guide: Photosynthesis and Cellular Respiration."

2. Visit the *Science and Global Issues* page of the SEPUP website at *sepuplhs.org/sgi*. With your partner, go to "Photosynthesis and Cellular Respiration" and follow the simulation.

3. Complete the Reading.

4. Fill in the After column on Student Sheet 12.1, "Anticipation Guide: Photosynthesis and Cellular Respiration."

Reading

Energy for Life

EVERY CELL NEEDS A SOURCE OF ENERGY

As you learned in the "Ecology: Living on Earth" unit of *Science and Global Issues,* all cells need energy if they are to function. **Cellular respiration** is the process by which cells break down complex molecules, such as sugars, to release energy. Some of the energy is released as heat while the rest is stored temporarily in other molecules, such as adenosine triphosphate (ATP). ATP is used when the cell needs energy. For example, whenever your muscles contract, ATP supplies the energy. As you also learned in the "Ecology" unit, **photosynthesis** is the process by which the cells of producers capture the sun's energy and store it in sugars. All producers and consumers ultimately depend on these sugars for their energy needs.

The following equations summarize the two processes.

Cellular respiration: sugars + oxygen → carbon dioxide + water + energy

Photosynthesis: carbon dioxide + water + light energy → sugars + oxygen

As you can see from the equations, the components of cellular respiration and photosynthesis are nearly identical. In fact, cellular respiration is often described as the opposite of photosynthesis. The two processes, however, are far more complex than the equations indicate.

PHOTOSYNTHESIS

Photosynthesis only occurs in certain pigment-containing cells of producers. This differs from cellular respiration, which occurs in all types of cells in all organisms. A **pigment** is a molecule that absorbs light energy. All producers contain pigments, which are essential for photosynthesis. The most common pigment in producers is chlorophyll. Chlorophyll is what makes the stems and leaves of producers green. In most producers the chlorophyll is contained in chloroplasts.

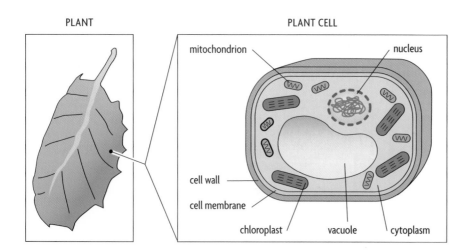

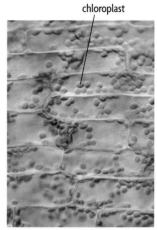

Light micrograph of **Elodea** *cells*

Chloroplasts are relatively large organelles surrounded by two membranes. Chloroplasts absorb energy from sunlight, as shown in the diagram below. Inside the chloroplast is a fluid-filled space called the **stroma** and stacks of connected membrane sacs called **thylakoids.** The thylakoid membranes contain the chlorophyll, and the stacked structure greatly increases the membrane surface area that can absorb light.

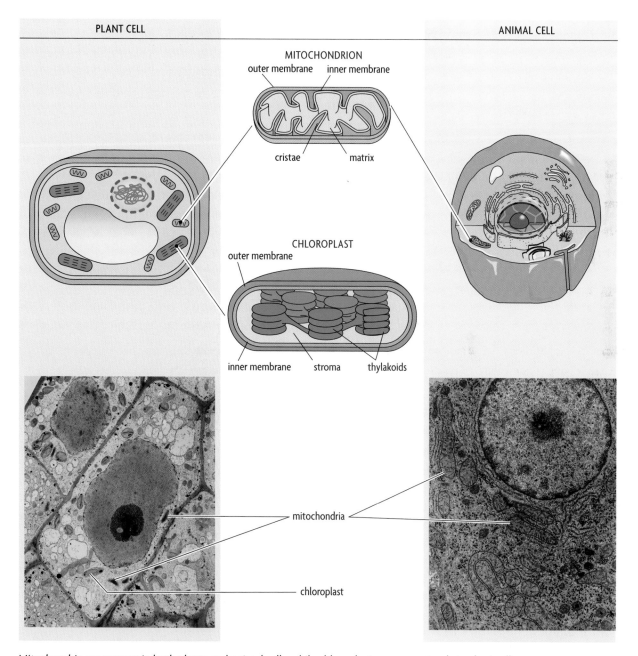

Mitochondria are present in both plants and animal cells, while chloroplasts are present only in plant cells.

THE REACTIONS OF PHOTOSYNTHESIS

The reactions occurring in photosynthesis are grouped into two stages, light-dependent and light-independent reactions. The **light-dependent reactions** rely on chlorophyll and other pigments in the thylakoid membranes to harness the energy of light. In a complex series of reactions, water breaks down into oxygen, hydrogen ions (protons), and electrons. Each reaction requires a unique enzyme. The oxygen is released to the atmosphere, some of the energy from the reactions goes into making ATP from ADP, and the protons and electrons combine with the carrier molecule, $NADP^+$, to form NADPH.

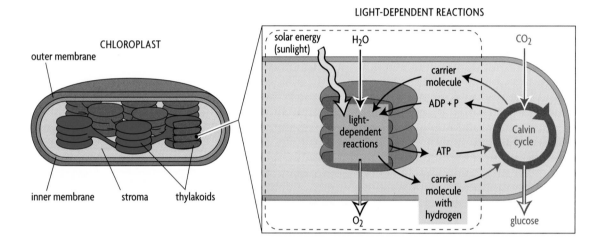

The NADPH and ATP are important to the light-independent **Calvin cycle,** which is a series of enzyme-catalyzed reactions that take place in the stroma of the chloroplast. During these reactions carbon dioxide combines with the hydrogen ions and electrons produced from water during the light-dependent reactions. This results in the production of the high-energy sugar glucose. The glucose is used in cellular respiration or is converted to another form, such as starch, and stored for later use. Starch is a type of carbohydrate. A starch macromolecule is made of many glucose molecules linked together.

The reactions in the Calvin cycle occur in the presence or absence of light and are referred to as **light-independent reactions.** During the Calvin cycle ATP and NADPH are converted back into ADP and NADP+. These will be used again in the light-dependent reactions in the thylakoid membranes.

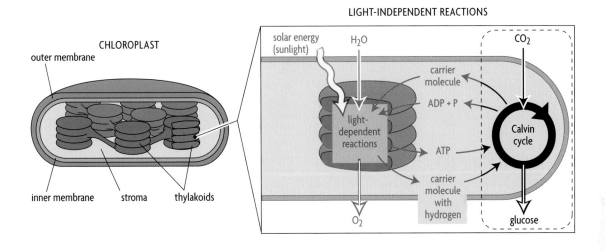

The reactions of the Calvin cycle continue as long as carbon dioxide, ATP, NADPH, and enzymes are present. Certain plant diseases, such as the plum pox virus that attacks several kinds of fruit trees, inhibit enzymes involved in the Calvin cycle. This prevents the plant from making the sugar it needs to support cellular respiration. Trees infected with plum pox may eventually stop producing fruit. Organisms that feed off the fruit may need to find another food source, and communities that rely on fruit sales may suffer economically.

CELLULAR RESPIRATION

Each reaction in cellular respiration also requires a unique enzyme, and, as in photosynthesis, diseases or poisons may reduce the activity of these enzymes. This can have serious consequences for an organism, since cellular respiration is the process by which energy is released for cells to use. It is important not to confuse cellular respiration with breathing, which is often called respiration. Breathing gets oxygen into your lungs, but the oxygen has no purpose until it enters your cells and plays its part in cellular respiration.

In prokaryotes, such as bacteria, the reactions of cellular respiration that require oxygen occur on the cell membrane. In eukaryotes, these reactions take place in the cells' mitochondria. **Mitochondria** are organelles that have two membranes, an outer membrane and an inner membrane that is folded within the outer, which play central roles in the reactions of cellular respiration. The outer membrane contains specialized proteins that make the membrane very permeable to ions and small molecules. The inner membrane is less permeable, but it contains transport proteins to allow for the passage of some molecules. The inner membrane also contains enzymes needed for cellular respiration. The inner membrane is folded to form many **cristae,** finger-like projections that provide a large surface area for the reactions of cellular respiration. Inside a mitochondrion is a space called the **matrix.**

THE REACTIONS OF CELLULAR RESPIRATION

Cellular respiration begins with the process of glycolysis. **Glycolysis** means "the breaking of sugar." This first step takes place in the cytoplasm. In glycolysis, the energy from ATP breaks a glucose molecule, releasing hydrogen ions and creating two smaller molecules of pyruvic acid. The carrier molecule, NAD$^+$, combines with these hydrogen ions and with electrons to form NADH. Glycolysis also produces new ATP molecules, resulting in a net gain of 2 ATP molecules for each molecule of glucose that is broken down.

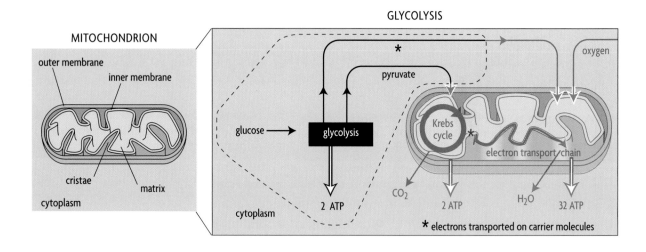

If oxygen is present, the pyruvic acid molecules produced during glycolysis are then further broken down, releasing large amounts of energy in a process called **aerobic respiration.** In eukaryotic cells, the pyruvic acid molecules first enter the mitochondrion where they are stripped of a carbon atom and are also temporarily combined with the enzyme helper, coenzyme A. This combination, called acetyl CoA, becomes part of the next stage of cellular respiration, the **Krebs cycle.** The Krebs cycle takes place in the matrix of the mitochondrion.

AEROBIC RESPIRATION

MITOCHONDRION

outer membrane

inner membrane

cristae

matrix

cytoplasm

glucose → glycolysis

cytoplasm

pyruvate

*

oxygen

Krebs cycle

electron transport chain

CO_2

2 ATP

2 ATP

H_2O

32 ATP

* electrons transported on carrier molecules

In the Krebs cycle the acetyl CoA breaks down and releases coenzyme A and pyruvic acid. The carbon atoms of the pyruvic acid end up in carbon dioxide, which is released as waste. Two molecules of ATP are produced and the carrier molecules NAD^+ and FAD^+ pick up electrons and hydrogen ions to form NADH and FADH, respectively. These are transferred by the carriers to the cristae of the mitochondria's inner membranes to take part in the final stage of cellular respiration, the **electron transport chain.**

During this stage, electrons and hydrogen ions are released when NADH and FADH, are converted back to NAD^+ and FAD^+. In a series of enzyme-catalyzed reactions, electrons combine with hydrogen ions and oxygen to make water, which then leaves the mitochondrion. The movement of electrons through the electron transport chain releases energy, which converts 32 more molecules of ADP into ATP. Aerobic respiration, therefore, produces a total of 36 ATP molecules for each glucose molecule.

Since the reactions of the electron transport chain need oxygen, they will stop if oxygen is not available, which prevents the Krebs cycle from operating.

Some organisms do not need oxygen for cellular respiration and instead use a process called **anaerobic respiration.** This process also occurs for short periods of time in muscle cells when insufficient oxygen is present to conduct aerobic respiration. Anaerobic respiration, also known as fermentation, takes place in the cytoplasm of a cell. There are two types of fermentation: lactate fermentation and alcoholic fermentation.

In lactate fermentation the pyruvic acid that is produced by glycolysis is changed into a form of lactic acid. This is the type of anaerobic respiration that occurs in muscle cells. However, anaerobic respiration does not sustain muscle cells for very long: as lactic acid builds up, fatigue and muscle cramps result. This same process in bacteria causes food to spoil, and with certain bacteria such fermentation allows us to make cheese and yogurt.

In alcoholic fermentation, shown in the figure below, pyruvic acid reacts with water to form acetaldehyde and release carbon dioxide. (When yeast is added to bread dough, alcoholic fermentation releases carbon dioxide, which helps the bread to rise.) In the presence of electrons and hydrogen ions that have been transported by NADH the acetaldehyde is then converted into ethanol. This is the same process that occurs, for example, when energy companies convert corn into the biofuel ethanol and when people make wine from grapes.

During fermentation there is a net gain of only two molecules of ATP. When compared to the net gain of 32 ATP molecules produced during the Krebs cycle and the electron transport chain stage, it is clear that aerobic respiration provides much more energy to cells than does anaerobic respiration.

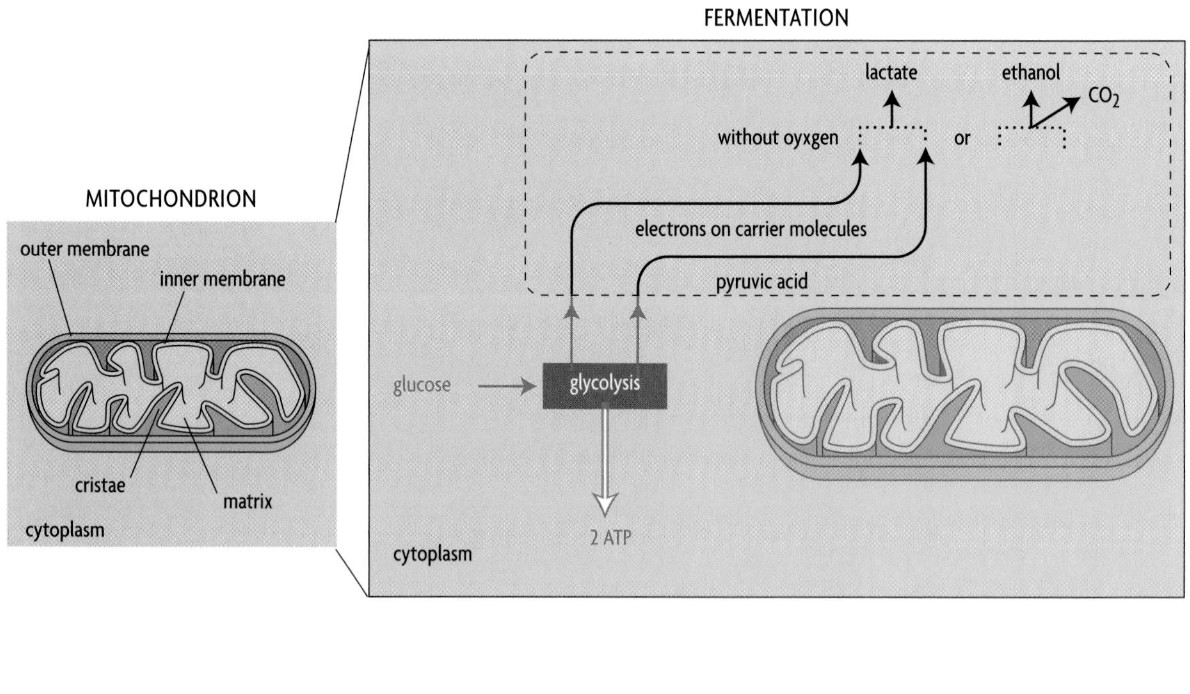

Some diseases and toxins disrupt cellular respiration in plants and animals. For example, powdery mildew fungus and cyanide both inhibit the electron transport chain. Powdery mildew causes premature death of infected plants, and cyanide is highly toxic to organisms that respire aerobically. Some genetic disorders involve mutations in certain enzymes of cellular respiration. In lactate dehydrogenase deficiency, for example, the enzyme that converts pyruvic acid to lactic acid is affected, which causes fatigue, and muscle damage if the afflicted person exercises intensely. Diabetes can also disrupt respiration. If insulin levels become too low, cells don't get enough glucose to meet their cellular respiration needs, and the body switches to fat as an energy source. As fat is broken down to be used for cellular respiration, a by-product of the process builds up and makes the blood acidic. This condition can lead to coma and death.

Analysis

1. Describe the roles of enzymes in photosynthesis and respiration.

2. **a.** What is chlorophyll?

   b. What is chlorophyll's role in photosynthesis?

3. Describe how a plant cell is specialized for photosynthesis at:

   a. the level of organelles and other cellular structures.

   b. the molecular level.

4. Compare aerobic and anaerobic respiration. What are the similarities? What are the differences?

5. In a chart like the one below, write the differences between photosynthesis and cellular respiration.

Photosynthesis and Cellular Respiration Comparison

	Photosynthesis	Cellular respiration
In what cells and cell structures does it happen?		
Reactants		
Products		
How does it contribute to the organism's energy needs?		

6. What are some of the similarities of photosynthesis and cellular respiration?

7. If you mixed carbon dioxide and water in a test tube, and placed the test tube in the sunlight, would photosynthesis take place? Explain.

8. How might reduced enzyme function lead to disease? Give at least two specific examples.

KEY VOCABULARY

adenosine triphosphate (ATP)	**light-dependent reactions**
aerobic respiration	**light-independent reactions**
anaerobic respiration	**matrix**
Calvin cycle	**mitochondria, mitochondrion**
cellular respiration	organelle
chloroplast	**photosynthesis**
cristae	**pigment**
electron transport chain	**stroma**
glycolysis	**thylakoids**
Krebs cycle	

13 The Cell Cycle

CELL DIVISION IS the basis of reproduction for all organisms, and also for the development and growth of multicellular organisms. The complete sequence of phases from the end of one cell division to the end of the next is called the **cell cycle.** The cell cycle is divided into a sequence of four phases, shown in the diagram below. One of these four phases, called **mitosis,** is the stage at which the cell divides to produce two new—or offspring—cells.

A group of cell-cycle control proteins regulates the phases of the cell cycle to ensure that all events needed for normal cell division take place before division begins. Cell-cycle regulation also ensures that specific cell types divide at the right time and place. For example, in the human body red blood cells must be replaced about every 120 days. If the stem cells that differentiate into red blood cells become under- or over-active, either too few or too many red blood cells are produced. Regulation of the cell cycle also ensures that a cell completes the growth and synthesis phases so that it will divide properly. When cell growth and division proceed abnormally, cancer might result.

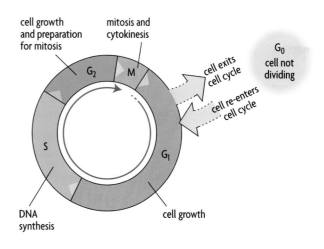

Challenge

▶ What happens during each phase of the cell cycle, and how are the phases regulated?

MATERIALS

FOR EACH GROUP OF FOUR STUDENTS

    Cell Cycle game board

4 cups, each containing a different color of modeling clay (red, green, yellow, and blue)

2 number cubes

    set of four Cell Cycle game keys (blood, liver, nerve, and skin)

FOR EACH STUDENT

    Student Sheet 13.1, "Cell Cycle Record Sheet"

    Student Sheet 2.1, "Disease Information" from Activity 2

    empty plastic cup

    sticky notes

Procedure

1. You will play the Cell Cycle game in your group of four. Each of you takes one of the four Cell Cycle game keys—blood, liver, nerve, or skin.

2. Based on your game key, you will play the game as a blood, liver, nerve, or skin cell. Record your cell type on Student Sheet 13.1, "Cell Cycle Record Sheet."

3. Distribute the cups of clay according to the key below, with each person taking the color for his or her assigned cell type.

Cell Cycle Game Key	
CELL TYPE	**CLAY COLOR**
Blood	red
Liver	blue
Nerve	green
Skin	yellow

4. Prepare a clay model of your cell. It should be about the size of a marble.

5. Place your model cell on the game board at the beginning of the game, near the start of the G_1 phase. Each player's cell has just completed the mitosis phase (M) of the cell cycle, and is ready to begin another cycle.

6. Begin round one of the game, with the blood cell person going first, and the rest of the group proceeding clockwise around your group. When it is your turn, roll both number cubes.

7. Look at your Cell Cycle game key to find out what the number you rolled means, and follow that instruction.

8. On Student Sheet 13.1, "Cell Cycle Record Sheet," record what happened to your cell in this round of the game.

9. Tell your group members what happened to your cell.

10. Continue to play the game for at least 20 rounds of rolling the number cubes. Each round, roll the number cubes unless you were told by your Cell Cycle game key to skip the turn. Each time you roll, follow Steps 7, 8, and 9 to find out what happens to your cell, record the outcome, and share it with your group.

11. Following your teacher's instructions, join a group of other students who had the same type of cell as yours. Discuss with these students, and record in your science notebook, what kinds of things happened to this cell type.

12. Rejoin your original group.

13. Work with your group to prepare a chart that summarizes what you learned about each of the four types of cells.

14. Follow your teacher's directions for reading the case study about cancer. As you read, use the "Read, Think, and Take Note" strategy.

15. Fill in the information for cancer on Student Sheet 2.1, "Disease Information," after you read the case study.

Analysis

1. Of the cell types you investigated, which divide:

   a. frequently?

   b. occasionally, as needed?

   c. never, or almost never?

   d. more frequently than normal and without control?

2. What kinds of factors regulate a cell's progress through the cell cycle?

3. Beginning with G_1, list the four phases of the cell cycle in order, and describe what happens in each phase.

4. Why is it important for each of the following to be regulated?

   a. Entry into the cell cycle

   b. Progress from one phase of the cell cycle to the next

5. A cell in the liver divides. Its offspring and all of their offspring continue to divide as fast as they grow and synthesize DNA. Is this likely to be a problem? Why or why not?

6. Many of the drugs given to people to fight their cancers damage the cellular structures involved in mitosis. Explain:

   a. why these drugs kill a higher percentage of cancer cells than normal cells.

   b. whether you would expect the drugs to have more of an effect on normal white blood cells or on normal neurons.

7. Explain the main reasons why the outcomes at age 35 for the two women with cervical cancer vary in the following scenario:

Outcomes for Two Cervical Cancer Patients		
AGE	**WOMAN 1**	**WOMAN 2**
16	No access to screening for abnormal cervical tissues with a Pap smear test or HPV test No access to vaccine for HPV	Begins regular screening for abnormal cervical tissues with a Pap smear test, and education from the doctor about the risks of cervical cancer Receives HPV vaccine that prevents infection by some types of HPV
30	Abnormal vaginal bleeding begins, indicating the likelihood of early stage cervical cancer. No access to adequate health care to detect and remove any abnormal cervical tissue	Pap smear reveals some precancerous cervical tissue from a type of HPV for which there is no vaccine. Precancerous tissue is removed with a simple surgical procedure to prevent progression to cancer.
35	A progression to advanced cervical cancer begins.	Leading a healthy life
36 and older	Advanced stages of cervical cancer No access to adequate health care, even to ease the pain associated with advanced stages of the cancer	Continues to get regular screening

8. Based on the cancer case study, how is cancer related to the social, economic, and environmental aspects of sustainability?

KEY VOCABULARY	
cancer	cytokinesis
cell cycle	daughter cell
chromosome	**mitosis**
cyclin	replication

CASE STUDY

Cancer

ONE IN EIGHT deaths worldwide is caused by cancer—more deaths than caused by AIDS, tuberculosis, and malaria combined. Scientists have made great progress in understanding, treating, and curing many types of cancer, but much about cancer is still unknown.

Cancer affects people living in all areas of the world, at all income levels. It usually develops over several years and has various causes, some environmental and some internal.

SYMPTOMS AND DISEASE MECHANISM

The term cancer refers to more than 100 diseases that result when cells lose the normal controls that regulate their growth and division in the cell cycle. These cells continuously divide even when no new cells are

Burden of Disease		
	NUMBER OF NEW CASES PER YEAR	NUMBER OF DEATHS PER YEAR
Worldwide	12 million	7 million
United States	1.7 million	570,000

needed. In most types of cancer, as an original cancer cell divides through multiple cell cycles, a mass of cells develops to form a tumor. However, some types of cancer, such as leukemia, rarely produce tumors. Leukemia results when abnormal white blood cells are produced too rapidly or do not die within the normal lifetime of white blood cells. These cells crowd the blood and prevent normal blood cells from performing their functions.

Mutations, or errors, in some genes can cause cancer. Some of these genes normally stimulate cell division, while others

normally stop cell division. Mutations in these genes can lead to unregulated cell growth and division that result in tumors.

Cervical cancer is an example of a cancer that is linked to an infection from a virus, in this case human papillomavirus (HPV). Women worldwide are at risk of being infected by this sexually transmitted virus. There are more than 100 types of HPV, about 30 types infect the genital regions of men and women, and a few have been shown to cause cervical cancer in women.

(Continued on next page)

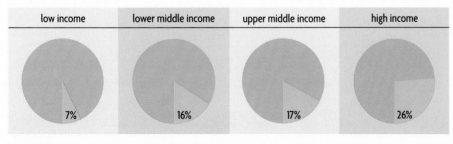

low income	lower middle income	upper middle income	high income
7%	16%	17%	26%

Projected deaths from cancer as a percentage of all deaths for all ages at four income levels, 2005 (left)

Normal skin (below left) and cancerous skin (below right)

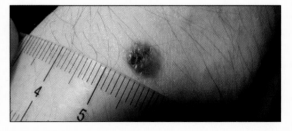

(Continued from previous page)

Cancer sometimes develops when environmental factors or viruses interact with certain genes to cause mutations. Environmental factors that lead to cancer include exposure to such chemicals as tobacco smoke, air pollutants, and asbestos. The chemicals produced when tobacco burns put people who smoke, and who are regularly exposed to tobacco smoke, at a higher risk of developing lung cancer than nonsmokers. In fact, approximately 10%–15% of smokers develop lung cancer, and smokers are 10–20 times more likely to get lung cancer than nonsmokers. Other environmental factors, including various kinds of radiation, also cause cancer.

CANCER PREVENTIONS AND TREATMENT

The World Health Organization reports that approximately 30% of cancer cases could be prevented by addressing such risk factors as:

- tobacco use
- being overweight or obese
- lack of physical activity
- lack of fruits and vegetables in the diet
- alcohol abuse
- sexually transmitted HPV infection
- urban air pollution
- indoor smoke from household use of solid fuels, such as wood

There are a number of programs and a few vaccines that help people reduce or eliminate their risk factors for cancer. The table below shows examples.

The main ways that cancers are treated are surgery, chemo-therapy, radiation therapy, or a combination of those. Surgeries to treat cancer include removing the tumor and surrounding tissues, removing the tumor and the organ it is in, and sometimes removing lymph nodes where the cancer may have spread. Surgeons also might remove just part of a tumor to relieve pain or open any blockages the tumor is causing. Chemotherapy involves taking certain drugs that kill cells, including cancer cells. Chemotherapy might follow surgery or be used alone or in combination with radiation therapy,

Some Preventive Measures for Cancer	
PREVENTIVE MEASURE	**EXAMPLES**
Vaccines	Vaccination for the hepatitis B virus that can cause liver cancer
	Vaccination for HPV, which causes cervical cancer
Tobacco and alcohol-abuse programs	Increase taxes on tobacco and alcohol
	Educate the public about health risks
	Ban smoking in public and commercial areas
Health education in schools and the workplace	Promotion of healthy diet and exercise
Screening	HPV test and pap smear for cervical cancer
	Colonoscopy or other screening for colon and rectal cancer

A diet high in fat and calories and low in fruits and vegetables, as shown at far left, increases a person's risk of developing some cancers, as compared to the diet shown at near left.

depending on the cancer. Radiation therapy directs X-rays or other high-energy particles to the area of the tumor to damage the genetic material inside the cancer cells and kill them. Normal cells in the radiated area are sometimes damaged but are usually replaced by division of the normal cells that remain.

CHALLENGES TO PREVENTION AND TREATMENT

Challenges vary depending on the type of cancer. It is often difficult for people to avoid or control environmental risk factors for cancer simply because some of these factors are found in the environment. For example, several industrial chemicals have been associated with increased lung cancer risk, including asbestos, arsenic, nickel, chromium, zinc, and radon. People might be exposed to these chemicals in their work environment or home. Research suggests that up to 15% of lung cancer cases in men and 5% in women are due to occupational hazards. Also, many people cannot avoid exposure to air pollution if they live in urban areas where pollution levels are high. And for many people, making a behavioral change, such as quitting smoking, is very hard to do.

While screening may detect cancer early, it can only be effective if there is a treatment strategy for that cancer. Also, for many cancers, cost-effective early diagnostic tests have not yet been developed. The drawbacks of chemotherapy and radiation therapy are that they kill many normal cells, not just cancer cells. Fatigue, nausea, diarrhea, loss of appetite, and hair loss are just some of the side effects that might be mild or severe, depending on the drugs and course of radiation.

Although cancer might strike anyone, poor people in low-income developing countries have a lower chance of surviving the disease than those in higher-income countries. The preventions and treatments available for cancer are often too expensive in the lower-income countries, and there may be few, if any, accessible hospitals or health care professionals capable of providing the care needed. ■

14 | Stem Cell Differentiation

THE HUMAN BODY is made of many kinds of specialized cells. Red blood cells, white blood cells, muscle cells, nerve cells, and skin cells are just some examples. Each specialized cell performs a function in the body. You have learned about several conditions that result when cells don't function normally. Diabetes damages the cells in the pancreas that make insulin. Sickle cell disease is a genetic condition that alters the functioning of the hemoglobin protein in red blood cells. And many kinds of cells may become cancerous when they lose their normal cell cycle controls.

Every cell in your body is the offspring of another cell and has the same genetic material as the fertilized egg from which it developed. It is amazing that the many different types of cells all arise from a single fertilized egg cell. Yet that is what happens during embryo development. Initially, all the cells in the embryo are alike. But as they divide, they become more specialized and produce their own characteristic proteins. Cells that have the ability to produce a variety of types of specialized cells are called **stem cells.** The process by which stem cells produce specialized cells is called **differentiation.** As differentiation progresses, segments of the genetic material are either activated or suppressed.

You have probably heard about stem cell research in the news. This is an important area of cutting-edge research. Once we understand exactly how a human develops from a single cell to a multicellular organism we might learn how certain conditions, such as some birth defects, and diseases, such as cancer, develop. Researchers around the world are trying to figure out how stem cells might be used to replace diseased or damaged tissues in any number of diseases.

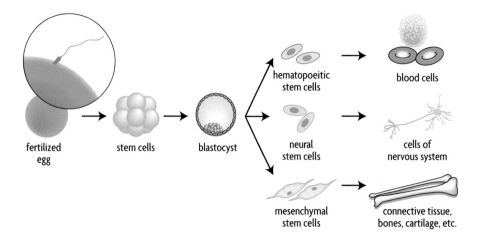

The development of specialized cells from stem cells.

In this activity, you will learn about the differentiation of human stem cells. In the next activity you will have a chance to apply what you learn about stem cells to stem cells' potential for curing diseases.

Challenge

▶ How do stem cells produce specialized cells?

MATERIALS

FOR EACH PAIR OF STUDENTS

     cup containing 9 chips (3 blue, 3 green, 3 orange)

 3 colored pencils

FOR EACH STUDENT

     Student Sheet 14.1, "Stem Cell Differentiation"

Procedure

1. The colors of the chips in the cup represent the specific protein or chemical factor that directs the differentiation of an embryonic stem cell. You and your partner will share the cup of chips, but you will each draw your own chips and follow your own cell on Student Sheet 14.1, "Stem Cell Differentiation." With your partner, decide who will begin. Take turns drawing one chip from the cup. When drawing a chip, look away to make sure your selection is random. Use the key below to find out how your stem cell differentiates. Put the chip back in the cup before your partner draws a chip. Select a colored pencil. On Student Sheet 14.1, draw a line from the embryonic stem cell to the type of stem cell it produced.

Note: Differentiation cannot be reversed from this point forward.

Differentiation Key 1	
DIFFERENTIATION PROTEIN (CHIP COLOR)	**STEM CELL TYPE PRODUCED**
Blue	Endoderm—the innermost layer of cells in an embryo
	These cells develop into the linings of the digestive tract and most of the respiratory system.
Green	Mesoderm—the middle layer of cells in an embryo
	These cells develop into muscles and most of the circulatory, reproductive, and excretory organ systems.
Orange	Ectoderm—the outermost layer of cells in an embryo
	These cells develop into sense organs, nerves, and the outer layer of skin.

2. Have the second person draw one chip and repeat Step 1.

3. Take turns drawing a second chip from the cup to represent the next step in the pathway of differentiation from the same stem cell. Use the key below to find out how your differentiated cell differentiates further. Sometimes, a protein will have no effect on a certain stem cell. If the factor has no effect, take a chip of another color. Put all of the chips back in the cup before your partner draws again.

Differentiation Key 2			
DIFFERENTIATION FACTOR (CHIP COLOR)	**ENDODERM**	**MESODERM**	**ECTODERM**
Blue	no effect	hematopoietic (blood-forming) stem cell	skin precursor cell
Green	pancreas precursor cell	no effect	no effect
Orange	intestinal epithelial stem cell	muscle stem cell	neural stem cell

On your Student Sheet 14.1, "Stem Cell Differentiation," using the colored pencil you used before, draw a line to show the next step in your cell's differentiation.

4. Take turns drawing a third chip. Using the colored pencil you used before, draw a line from your cell from Step 3 to the next type of cell on Student Sheet 14.1, based on the color key below. If the factor has no effect, draw another chip. Put all of the chips back in the cup before your partner draws chips.

Differentiation Key 3						
	PANCREAS PRECURSOR CELL	**INTESTINAL STEM CELL**	**MUSCLE STEM CELL**	**HEMATOPOIETIC (BLOOD-FORMING) STEM CELL**	**SKIN PRECURSOR CELL**	**NEURAL STEM CELL**
Blue	no effect	no effect	heart muscle cell (differentiation complete)	macrophage (differentiation complete)	hair follicle cells (differentiation complete)	motor neuron (differentiation complete)
Green	alpha (α) cell producing glucagon (differentiation complete)	intestinal epithelial cell (differentiation complete)	no effect	no effect	no effect	no effect
Orange	beta (β) cell producing insulin (differentiation complete)	no effect	smooth muscle cell (differentiation complete)	red blood cell (differentiation complete)	cheek lining cell (differentiation complete)	photoreceptor (differentiation complete)

5. Show the path of differentiation of your embryonic stem cells to your group. Discuss the various paths of differentiation that occurred for each person in the group.

6. Repeat Steps 1–4 to model a second course of differentiation. On Student Sheet 14.1, "Stem Cell Differentiation," trace the path of differentiation with a pencil of another color.

7. If you have time, repeat Steps 1–4 to model another differentiation process. Use a pencil of a third color.

Analysis

1. What is the difference between a stem cell and a differentiated cell, such as a red blood cell?

2. Use the information on Student Sheet 14.1, "Stem Cell Differentiation," to describe the pathway for each of the following as it differentiates:

   a. A smooth muscle cell

   b. A pancreatic beta (ß) cell

3. The two types of cells in Question 2 have the same genetic information. What process ensures that all cells get a complete set of the same genetic information?

4. Your friend has just learned that she will be starting erythropoietin treatment for anemia (lowered hemoglobin) that has developed as a result of kidney disease. She is worried because she does not know much about the treatment. The doctor gave her the following information:

   • Erythropoietin is a hormone that is naturally produced in the liver and kidney.

   • Erythropoietin stimulates the differentiation of red blood cells in the bone marrow.

   • Erythropoietin treatment increases red blood cell production in patients with anemia due to kidney disease, and in patients who have had chemo-therapy and radiation treatment for cancer.

   Using what you have learned about cell biology and stem cells, explain to your friend how erythropoietin works.

KEY VOCABULARY

---

differentiation   **stem cells**

15 Stem Cell Research

BECAUSE OF THEIR ability to differentiate into multiple cell types, stem cells hold the potential to treat a variety of human diseases. In fact, several stem cell-based treatments are already in widespread use, including bone marrow transplantation and umbilical-cord-blood stem cell therapy. One area of stem cell research, however, has generated a major social controversy. This is research performed with human embryonic stem cells.

In this activity, you will explore current scientific knowledge and social issues related to stem cell research.

Challenge

▶ What are the current scientific understandings and social debates about stem cell research?

MATERIALS

FOR EACH STUDENT
Student Sheet 15.1, "KWL: Stem Cells"

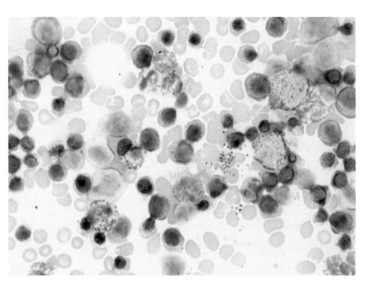

Bone marrow cells from a healthy donor, such as the stained cells shown here, can be transplanted into a patient with a disease such as leukemia.

Procedure

1. In your group, discuss each of the questions below. Record on Student Sheet 15.1, "KWL: Stem Cells," what you Know and Want to know about each of the questions.

   - What is a stem cell?

   - What kinds of human stem cells are there?

   - Why might stem cells be useful in treating certain diseases?

   - What is the debate about stem cell research and stem cell therapy?

2. Read the information below about stem cells, and then complete the Learned column of your KWL.

Reading

Several Types of Stem Cells

In the previous activity, you learned that stem cells often differentiate through multiple cell cycles to produce a variety of types of specialized cells. A human fertilized egg, or zygote, can produce cells that differentiate into every kind of specialized human cell. This means the zygote is **totipotent,** totally capable. When the zygote first begins dividing, its cells form a hollow ball, called a blastocyst. The inner cells of this blastocyst will form most types of human cells, and are called **pluripotent embryonic stem cells.**

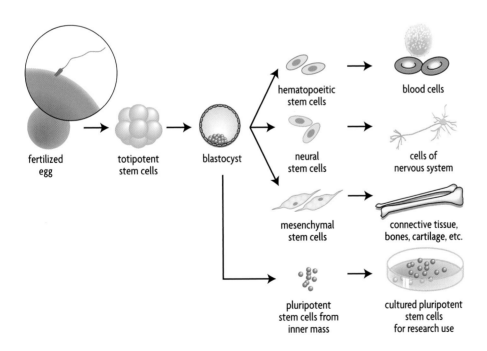

Unlike embryonic stem cells, the stem cells in a human adult—or a child or infant—can differentiate into only a limited number of kinds of cells and are usually found within the tissues that they will renew. Stem cells found in our bone marrow, for example, can form many types of blood cells, but not muscle or nervous tissue cells. These **multipotent stem cells** have a multiple, but limited, potential.

Stem Cell Therapy Today

A frequently used stem cell therapy, bone marrow transplantation, involves injecting blood stem cells from a healthy donor into the bone marrow of a recipient with a blood disease, such as leukemia. Leukemias are a group of cancers that cause an overproduction of white blood cells. The recipient is first treated with radiation and chemotherapy to kill all of the unhealthy bone marrow and blood cells before receiving blood-forming cells from the donor. These cells may be obtained from the donor's bone marrow or circulating blood. There are a number of risks to this procedure, including an immune system attack on the donor cells.

Umbilical cord stem cells are also used to treat leukemia. Like an adult's stem cells, they are multipotent, but they are less likely than fully developed stem cells to cause an immune response in the recipient.

The Potential of Stem Cells for the Future

Many diseases are caused by a problem with one particular cell type. These are the diseases that are current or potential targets for stem cell therapy. One possible target for adult stem cell therapy is diabetes. In Type-I diabetes, the afflicted person's immune system attacks cells in the pancreas that produce insulin, the protein hormone necessary for metabolizing sugars. One approach to treating this disease is to kill the person's immune cells with radiation or chemotherapy, and then provide adult stem cells that will restore a healthy immune system. A group of scientists has reported promising results from trying this treatment on a small number of diabetes patients. This treatment is highly experimental, and even if the results hold up over time, there are risks involved.

Embryonic stem cells can become any type of specialized cells. They are also easier to obtain than some types of adult stem cells, most of which are not easily located and isolated. For these reasons, embryonic stem cells might allow more rapid development of effective treatments.

One area of potential is treating neurological diseases, such as Parkinson's disease. In Parkinson's, the nerve cells in the brain that make the chemical dopamine stop functioning, and the person loses the ability to move properly and might eventually develop mental impairments. If these cells could be replaced in some way, it might relieve the symptoms or cure the disease. Because stable adult nerve cell lines are difficult to produce, using pluripotent embryonic stem cells might allow researchers to find cures more quickly.

The Stem Cell Debate

Working with stem cells from developed humans is not generally a controversial area of scientific research, but it is more complicated than starting with an embryonic stem cell that might be steered in any direction to re-create specialized cells. In contrast, embryonic stem cell research involves getting an early-stage embryo from a fertility clinic and isolating individual cells. This destroys the embryo. Although the cells of those embryos have not yet begun to differentiate into the specialized cells that will turn into a functioning human being, some people object to destroying any embryo because of its potential to develop into a human being. Another method being researched for creating embryonic stem cells is to take a human egg, remove its nucleus, and insert an adult cell nucleus from the person to be treated. This produces an embryonic stem cell with the same genetic makeup as the recipient, lowering the chance of an immune reaction to the stem cells. However, the same ethical considerations apply.

Analysis

1. What kinds of questions can scientists answer about stem cells?

2. What kinds of questions about stem cell research involve ethical considerations?

3. Why do you think scientists are not pursuing stem cell research and treatments to reduce deaths from infectious diseases?

KEY VOCABULARY	
multipotent stem cells	**totipotent**
pluripotent embryonic stem cells	stem cell

16 HIV/AIDS Infection and Cell Organelles

ALTHOUGH MANY OF their characteristics are similar to those of cells, viruses are not cells. They contain genetic material and a few proteins, but they do not conduct cellular functions. For example, a virus can neither metabolize nutrients needed to grow and to develop essential structures, nor can it reproduce on its own. To reproduce, a virus must infect a living host cell. Viruses are specific to their hosts. Some infect one kind of animal, while others infect plants or even bacteria. Once it is inside the host cell, the virus takes over the cell's structures, enzymes, and organelles that will enable it to reproduce.

Challenge

▶ How does HIV take over a cell's structures and organelles during infection and use them to reproduce?

MATERIALS

FOR EACH PAIR OF STUDENTS
    set of 13 Cell Structures and Organelles Cards
    colored pencils

FOR EACH STUDENT
    Student Sheet 16.1, "Scientific Diagram of HIV Infection"
    Student Sheet 2.1, "Disease Information," from Activity 2
    sticky notes

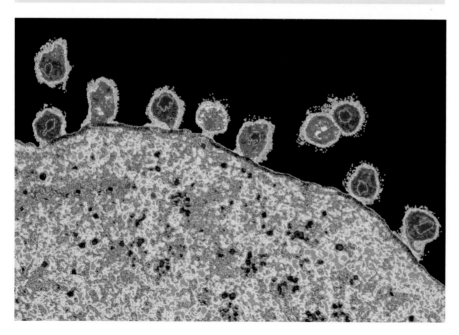

An electron microscope image of HIV virus budding from a human cell membrane

Procedure

1. With your partner, spread out the Cell Structures and Organelles cards on the table. Sort out the cell structures and organelles that you think the HIV virus would directly need in order to reproduce many copies of itself. Set the other Cell Structures and Organelles cards aside.

2. Discuss with your partner the path that you think the HIV virus would take within the cell as it takes over the cell. Lay out the cards in the order you decide on.

3. Pick a colored pencil, and on your Student Sheet 16.1, "Scientific Diagram of HIV Infection," do the following:

   a. Trace the path of the virus infection through the various structures or organelles you decided on in Step 2.

   b. Next to each structure or organelle in the path, write an explanation of why you think that structure or organelle is involved.

4. Visit the *Science and Global Issues* page of the SEPUP website at *sepuplhs.org/sgi*. With your partner, follow the simulation of the life cycle of the HIV virus.

5. Watch the narrated version of the simulation. As you watch and listen, with a different colored pencil add to or change the path you traced, where appropriate, on Student Sheet 16.1, "Scientific Diagram of HIV Infection."

6. For more detail, view the step-through version of the simulation and read the descriptions of each stage of the process. At each step you can click "Play" to watch the animation of only that stage.

7. Follow your teacher's directions for reading the case study about rotavirus. As you read, use the "Read, Think, and Take Note" strategy.

8. Complete the information for rotavirus on Student Sheet 2.1, "Disease Information" after you read the case study.

Analysis

1. Explain why HIV must infect a host cell.

2. Explain how the HIV virus uses specific structures to enter the cell.

3. **a.** List the structures and organelles inside the cell that an HIV virus needs if it is to reproduce.

   b. Describe how HIV uses each structure and organelle during the infection process.

4. In Activity 10, "Functions of Proteins in Cells," you learned about eight classes of proteins.

   a. Which classes of proteins were shown in the HIV infection animation?

   b. What function did each of those classes of proteins perform in the virus infection cycle?

5. How did your ideas about the steps of the HIV infection inside a cell change before and after viewing the simulation?

6. If you were a researcher of HIV/AIDS, explain which part of the infection process you would be most be interested in if you were trying to find a way to:

   a. prevent HIV from entering cells.

   b. prevent HIV from reproducing.

7. HIV infects cells of the immune system, while rotavirus infects cells of the intestine. What structures do you think are responsible for the ability of each virus to only infect specific types of cells?

8. What evidence from the rotavirus case study explains why more than 85% of rotavirus deaths occur in Southeast Asia and Africa?

KEY VOCABULARY	
DNA	protein
enzyme	rotavirus
organelle	

CASE STUDY

Rotavirus

GLOBALLY, ONLY A few infectious diseases cause the majority of deaths for children younger than five years old. Rotavirus, with the severe diarrhea it causes, is one of them.

Rotavirus causes approximately 40% of all cases of severe diarrhea in infants worldwide. More than 85% of rotavirus deaths occur in Asia and Africa.

SYMPTOMS AND DISEASE MECHANISM

The symptoms of rotavirus infection include severe

Burden of Disease		
	TOTAL NUMBER WITH DISORDER	NUMBER OF DEATHS PER YEAR
Worldwide	more than 100 million	500,000
United States	55,000–70,000 hospitalizations	20–60

vomiting, fever, abdominal pain, and watery diarrhea over several days. These symptoms are usually milder in adults, who normally recover. Rotavirus is an RNA virus that infects cells that line the small intestine, the ones that absorb nutrients and water.

When the virus infects and kills these cells, unabsorbed nutrients and water leave the body rapidly in diarrhea and vomit, making the patient weak and dehydrated. Rotavirus is transmitted

(Continued on next page)

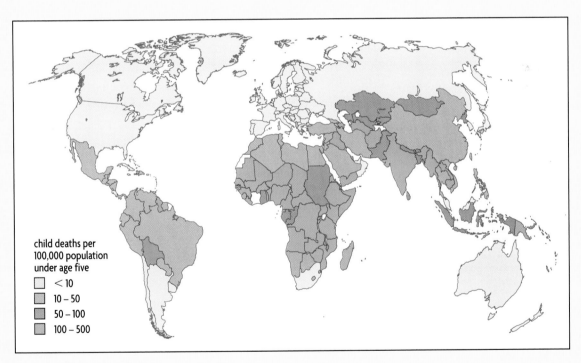

child deaths per 100,000 population under age five
- ☐ < 10
- ☐ 10 – 50
- ☐ 50 – 100
- ☐ 100 – 500

Rotavirus deaths of children younger than five

(Continued from previous page)

in contaminated water or food, airborne droplets, and contact with contaminated surfaces. Therefore, safe water, sanitation, and refrigeration of food are important for controlling rotavirus transmission.

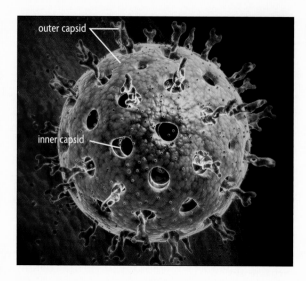

outer capsid

inner capsid

Model of a rotavirus

ROTAVIRUS PREVENTION AND TREATMENT

Exclusive breastfeeding is a strategy for preventing diarrheal infections, including rotavirus, in infants up to six months old. Exclusive breastfeeding means the baby ingests no food or drink besides its mother's breast milk. The baby is allowed vitamins, minerals, or medicines, but no water. Breast milk contains nutrients, antibodies, and other elements that boost the immune system, and breastfeeding eliminates the need for infants to eat food or take in drink that may be contaminated.

In 2007, a vaccine became available to prevent rotavirus infection, and widespread distribution of the vaccine could be a major

boost for prevention of the disease. Public health care workers estimate that in Asia vaccinations for rotavirus would prevent approximately 110,000 deaths, 1.4 million hospitalizations, and 7.7 million visits to the doctor.

Currently, there is no drug treatment for rotavirus infection. Only oral or intravenous rehydration with electrolytes is prescribed. This maintains homeostasis of water and salts in the blood.

CHALLENGES TO PREVENTION AND TREATMENT

For HIV-positive mothers, breastfeeding is not a good option for preventing rotavirus in their infants because breast milk can transmit HIV. In these cases it is safer to feed babies a breast milk replacement, such as infant formula. But with formula, the baby does not get the antibodies to protect against diseases that breast milk would carry from mother to child.

Currently there are two major roadblocks to global use of a

Distribution of Improved Sanitation (% of population)[1]

AFRICA	THE AMERICAS	EASTERN MEDITERRANEAN	EUROPE	SOUTHEAST ASIA	WESTERN PACIFIC
33	87	60	93	37	69

1. Data from WHO organization of world regions.

rotavirus vaccine. First, more vaccine is going to countries where rotavirus is much less of a problem than to those with the greatest need for the vaccine. This is partly a matter of the relatively high cost of the vaccine, which is about $20 or more per child. Second, the rotavirus vaccines, like many vaccines, must be kept refrigerated to prevent their spoiling—a difficult task in remote tropical and subtropical areas of the world that do not have a reliable supply of electricity. ■

☐ In routine immunization schedule in 2007 (11 countries)

■ Immunization support approved (3 countries)

Distribution of rotavirus vaccine

17 Disease Interventions

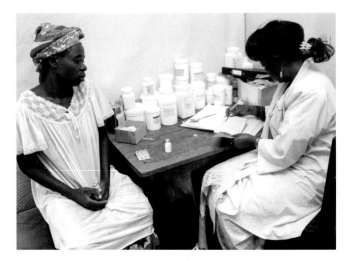

THROUGHOUT THIS Cell Biology unit, you have learned about the devastating impact of diseases worldwide, and about some of the ways to prevent or treat the diseases you have studied. Understanding human cells, microbes, and disease mechanisms helps people make informed decisions about where and how to focus efforts in combating the diseases.

In this activity, you will compare various interventions for diseases, and the trade-offs of these interventions. A **disease intervention** is a method used to prevent, treat, or eradicate a disease. For example, improving sanitation or vaccinating children prevents rotavirus infection. If a child is infected, giving the child fluids to keep him or her hydrated until recovery is another kind of disease intervention.

Challenge

▶ What are the benefits, drawbacks, and trade-offs of some disease interventions?

MATERIALS

FOR EACH GROUP OF STUDENTS
 sheet of chart paper
 markers

FOR EACH STUDENT
 Student Sheet 2.1, "Disease Information," from Activity 2
 version of Student Sheet 17.1 a–f, "Disease Intervention Information"

Procedure

1. Your teacher will assign your group one of the six diseases you studied in this unit—malaria, tuberculosis, diabetes, HIV/AIDS, cancer, and rotavirus. With your group, review the information that you each collected for your assigned disease and noted on your copies of Student Sheet 2.1, "Disease Information."

2. With your group, develop and draw in your science notebook a sketch that shows the infection mechanism of your assigned disease. The sketch should depict what occurs at the cellular level when a person has the disease. If the disease is infectious, also show how it spreads from one person to another.

3. Look over Student Sheet 17.1, "Disease Intervention Information." This sheet contains information on several types of interventions for your assigned disease. With your group, discuss the benefits and drawbacks of each of the interventions.

4. With your group, make a poster about your assigned disease that shows

   - the disease cycle you sketched in Step 2.

   - where in the disease cycle each prevention or treatment intervenes.

   - for each intervention, the cost per person, target age, and infrastructure needed.

   - labels for each intervention as "treatment" or "prevention."

   - a list of the social, environmental, and economic effects of the disease.

5. Your teacher will provide instructions for sharing your poster with the class.

Analysis

1. What is the difference between prevention and treatment of a disease?

2. Suppose you have enough money from a private foundation to implement one intervention for your assigned disease. Decide which intervention you would choose, and explain why. Be sure to identify the trade-offs of your decision.

KEY VOCABULARY

disease   trade-offs

disease intervention

---

18 World Health Proposal

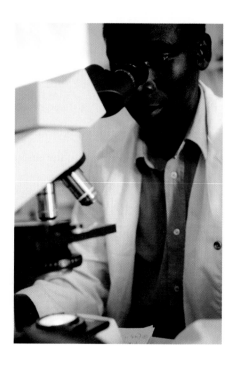

DETERMINING THE BEST ways to prevent and treat diseases that affect the global community is not an easy task. As you have learned in this unit, social, economic, and environmental consequences of diseases vary by country, and by region. Such variations create complications when deciding how to allocate funding for disease interventions. For example, if funding were so limited that there was a choice between dedicating it all to cancer research or directing it to several less costly interventions that would prevent thousands of children from dying of malaria or rotavirus, what is the best decision?

Currently a private foundation, whose mission is to fund projects that address problems related to world health, is about to review project proposals. Proposals must relate to prevention or treatment of one of the six global diseases you have studied—malaria, tuberculosis, diabetes, HIV/AIDS, cancer, and rotavirus. Your group will develop a proposal for funding, and then the class will decide how to allocate funding after considering all of the proposals.

Challenge

▶ How should funding be allocated to address sustainability problems related to world health?

MATERIALS

FOR EACH GROUP OF STUDENTS
    disease intervention poster from Activity 17

FOR EACH STUDENT
    Student Sheet 2.1, "Disease Information," from Activity 2
    Student Sheet 18.1, "World Health Proposals"

Procedure

1. With your group, review Student Sheet 2.1, "Disease Information," and the poster you created for your assigned disease in Activity 17, "Disease Interventions."

2. From the information you have already accumulated on your assigned disease, write a proposal to obtain funding from the foundation. Be sure to include the following information in your proposal:

   • The number of people affected by this disease and the age groups most affected, if appropriate

   • The number of deaths worldwide

   • Which parts of the world are experiencing more of the burden of the disease

   • Which intervention you chose to implement. Include evidence to support your choice of intervention.

3. Follow your teacher's instructions for presenting your proposal to the class. As you listen to the proposals, take careful notes on Student Sheet 18.1, "World Health Proposals."

4. The foundation has limited funding and, therefore, cannot fund every proposal. As a class, discuss all of the proposals and come to agreement on how to rank the proposals in terms of priority for funding.

Analysis

1. In Procedure Step 4 what reasoning most convinced the class to determine whether one proposal should be ranked as a higher priority than another?

2. Describe how you think the limited funds from the foundation should best be distributed among the proposals. For example, should all of the proposals receive equal funding, should all of the proposals receive some funding but with some getting more than others, or should one or two receive all of the funding? Explain the evidence and reasoning for your decision, and discuss the trade-offs of your decision.

3. Which do you consider to be a greater world health problem—infectious diseases or noninfectious diseases? Explain your reasoning.

4. How does an understanding of cells and microbes help scientists address world health issues?

VOCABULARY	
disease	sustainability
disease intervention	trade-off

Unit Review: Cell Biology

Cells and Disease

Diseases often hinder a community's or country's progress toward sustainable development. Without a healthy population and environmental, social, and economic conditions that allow children to experience a normal lifespan, a community may not be able to sustain itself. Disease interventions are actions taken to prevent or treat diseases, and they vary in effectiveness, cost, and ease of implementation.

Diseases are classified as infectious or noninfectious. Infectious diseases are transmitted from person to person either directly or by another organism, called a vector. Noninfectious diseases are instead caused by such factors as aging, the environment, behavior, genetics, or a combination of these. Less-developed countries tend to have a greater proportion of deaths from infectious diseases than do more-developed countries. Some human diseases are caused by abnormalities that develop within the body's cells, while others are caused by microbes. Some diseases, including sickle cell disease and malaria, are diagnosed by viewing blood samples from the affected individual through a light microscope.

KEY VOCABULARY

antibiotic	malaria
cancer	microbe
diabetes	mutation
disease	noninfectious disease
disease intervention	protist
HIV/AIDS	rotavirus
indicator	sickle cell
infectious disease	sustainability
intervention	trade-off
latent	tuberculosis
macrophage	vector

Cell Structure and Function

Every organism is made of one or more cells. All cells maintain homeostasis, a range of internal conditions that allows the cell to live and function. The structure and organization of cells and internal cell parts are essential for the cell to transform and release energy needed for cellular functions. The molecules in a cell form a variety of specialized structures, or organelles, to perform such cell functions as energy production, transport of molecules, waste disposal, synthesis of new molecules, and storage of genetic material. Bacterial cells have neither a nucleus nor other membrane-bound organelles. Multicellular organisms have specialized cells with an arrangement of structures that accomplish a specialized function.

A cell has a membrane that surrounds it and separates it from the outside environment. The cell membrane is a fluid mosaic of molecules, made mainly of phospholipids and proteins, which gives the cell flexibility and strength and controls what enters and leaves the cell. In addition to a cell membrane, plant cells have a cell wall that provides support and additional protection.

A cell also has a cytoplasm that contains a mixture of thousands of molecules. Within the cytoplasm of a eukaryotic cell is a cytoskeleton that provides support and structure for the cell. The cytoplasm of all cells (and the nucleus of eukaryotes) is the site of the reactions of metabolism. Nearly all cells contain genetic information. In eukaryotes, the genetic information is stored in the nucleus.

KEY VOCABULARY

bacteria	Golgi apparatus
cell	homeostasis
cell biology	lysosome
cell membrane	membrane
cell principle	metabolism
cell wall	multicellular organism
cilium, cilia	nucleus
cytoplasm	phospholipid
cytoskeleton	prokaryote, prokaryotic
deoxyribonucleic acid (DNA)	prokaryotic cell
endoplasmic reticulum	ribosome
eukaryote, eukaryotic	single-celled organism
eukaryotic cell	vacuole
flagellum, flagella	

Cell Transport

The cell membrane is selectively permeable, meaning that only certain substances are able to cross it to move into or out of the cell. Diffusion is the movement of a substance from an area of higher concentration to an area of lower concentration. The diffusion of a liquid, such as water, across a membrane is called osmosis. Some substances diffuse freely across cell membranes, while others must enter through protein channels in a process called facilitated diffusion. Some substances are transported into the cell by transport proteins against, or up, a concentration gradient. This process requires the cell to expend energy and is called active transport.

KEY VOCABULARY	
active transport	osmosis
diffuse, diffusion	passive transport
endocytosis	phospholipid (lipid) bilayer
exocytosis	selectively permeable
facilitated diffusion	semipermeable
fluid mosaic model	transport protein
lipid	vesicle
macromolecule	

Proteins

To support life cells need thousands of proteins, each with a specialized function. Cellular organelles, structures, and enzymes make the proteins cells require. The genetic information stored in DNA directs the synthesis of those proteins. Proteins are often classified according to their functions. Enzymes, for example, are a large group of proteins that act as biological catalysts to speed up the chemical reactions in cells. Enzymes' structures and functions are affected by such factors as temperature and pH.

Receptor proteins and enzymes are also a virus's key to entering a cell, reproducing itself, and spreading infection. The HIV virus, as well as other viruses, is not a cell and cannot reproduce on its own. When HIV infects a cell, it uses the host's cell organelles and proteins to make more HIV viruses.

Photosynthesis and Cellular Respiration

The energy for life comes primarily from the sun. The structure and organization of cells and internal cell parts transform and release the energy an organism needs for cellular functions. Some plant cells contain chloroplasts, the sites of photosynthesis. In photosynthesis, plants capture energy by absorbing light and using it to form chemical bonds between the atoms of carbon-containing molecules. The chemical bonds of food molecules store energy. Energy is released when the bonds of food molecules are rearranged in the reactions of cellular respiration to form new compounds. Cells temporarily store the energy released by cellular respiration in adenosine triphosphate (ATP) molecules.

Cell Growth, Division, and Differentiation

Cell functions are regulated to control and coordinate cell growth and division. The cell cycle is the complete sequence of phases from the end of one cell division to the end of the next. Some types of cells, including blood and skin cells, divide more often than other types, such as liver and nerve cells. When normal cell regulation is disrupted, serious consequences, such as cancer, may result.

Stem cells produce a variety of specialized cells. The process by which stem cells produce specialized descendent cells is called differentiation. An embryonic stem cell has the potential to produce any type of specialized cell, while stem cells from developed organisms can produce a limited set of specialized cell types.

KEY VOCABULARY	
cancer	mitosis
cell cycle	multipotent
chromosome	pluripotent embryonic stem cell
cyclin	replication
cytokinesis	stem cells
daughter cell	totipotent
differentiation	

Inquiry and the Nature of Science

In an experiment a control provides a standard of comparison for judging experimental effects.

Scientists develop models for representing actual phenomena and to compare theoretical situations to actual situations.

KEY VOCABULARY	
control	hypothesis

Genetics: Feeding the World

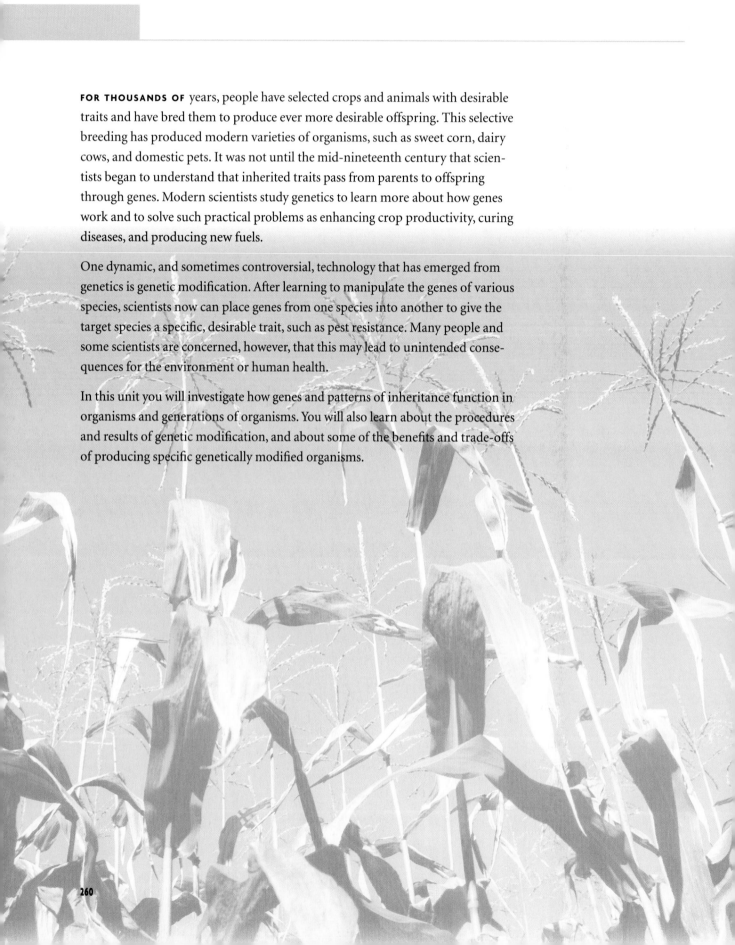

FOR THOUSANDS OF years, people have selected crops and animals with desirable traits and have bred them to produce ever more desirable offspring. This selective breeding has produced modern varieties of organisms, such as sweet corn, dairy cows, and domestic pets. It was not until the mid-nineteenth century that scientists began to understand that inherited traits pass from parents to offspring through genes. Modern scientists study genetics to learn more about how genes work and to solve such practical problems as enhancing crop productivity, curing diseases, and producing new fuels.

One dynamic, and sometimes controversial, technology that has emerged from genetics is genetic modification. After learning to manipulate the genes of various species, scientists now can place genes from one species into another to give the target species a specific, desirable trait, such as pest resistance. Many people and some scientists are concerned, however, that this may lead to unintended consequences for the environment or human health.

In this unit you will investigate how genes and patterns of inheritance function in organisms and generations of organisms. You will also learn about the procedures and results of genetic modification, and about some of the benefits and trade-offs of producing specific genetically modified organisms.

1 A Genetically Modified Solution?

THE **UNITED NATIONS** World Food Program has clearly stated, "Hunger and malnutrition are in fact the number one risk to health worldwide—greater than AIDS, malaria, and tuberculosis combined."

More than 1 billion people in the world today don't get enough nutritious food to lead healthy lives. As shown in the figure at right, this means that more than one in seven people are hungry or malnourished. Widespread sustainable farming practices and broader distribution of food would help meet nutritional needs and promote economic and social well-being of huge numbers of the world's hungry people.

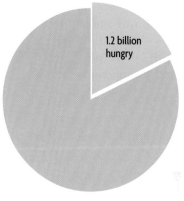

Hunger is one of the world's greatest sustainability challenges today.

Beginning in 1945, a private program in the United States started developing fast-growing, high-yield rice and wheat seeds and new fertilizers to help other countries grow enough food for their people. Results in Mexico, India, and Pakistan were so successful that in the 1960s the new farming practices became known as the Green Revolution. Those methods, however, included heavy use of fertilizers and pesticides, which caused water pollution and other environmental problems. Today, there is a call for new ways to improve crop yields while not harming the environment. Some people think that genetically modified (GM) crops provide a good solution.

To create **genetically modified organisms** (often called GMOs) scientists directly manipulate the genes of an organism, often by inserting or deleting one or more genes. The inserted gene is usually from another species. The purpose of this manipulation is to give the target organism and its offspring a new trait that improves it in some way. The improvement might, for example, give the organism higher vitamin content. The process is called **genetic engineering.**

Corn crop yield increased dramatically during the Green Revolution.

In the late 1990s, a few countries, including the United States and Brazil, began allowing farmers to grow genetically modified crops. Many other countries, however, were uncertain about the impacts the GMOs might have on human health, the environment, and unmodified crops, and have tightly restricted their import or growth. For example, GMOs have been highly restricted in Japan and several European Union countries. Today, as populations everywhere are growing and needing more food, some governments are considering changing their policies on the growing and importing of genetically modified organisms.

You are advising a country where many people suffer hunger. Corn is an important crop in that country for feeding both people and the animals they rely on for other foods. You have been called to meet with the country's Government Office of Agriculture, which has set up a committee to discuss allowing farmers to raise genetically modified crops. Today, you will examine evidence presented by a scientific panel that evaluated the benefits and risks of growing a genetically modified corn, called Bt corn.

a

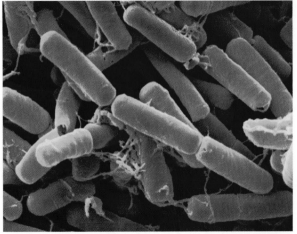

b

This corn (a) has been modified with a gene from these bacteria (b) to produce an insecticide.

Challenge

▶ Should your country allow farmers to grow genetically modified corn?

MATERIALS

FOR EACH GROUP OF FOUR STUDENTS
    sheet of chart paper
2 markers of different colors

FOR EACH STUDENT
    Student Sheet 1.1, "Genetically Modified Corn: Potential Benefits and Risks"

Procedure

1. Read the background information about Bt corn on the next page.

2. When you finish reading, record in your science notebook the two or three questions about Bt corn that you would most like to have answered before you advise this country about growing Bt corn.

3. With your group, review all of your questions, and select the three or four that you think are most important. Record these questions on the top half of the chart paper.

4. With your group, decide who will read which one of the statements on the following pages made by the science panel members. Take turns reading your statements aloud to your group.

5. After each statement is read, record on Student Sheet 1.1, "Genetically Modified Corn: Potential Benefits and Risks," any benefits or risks mentioned in the statement.

6. Based on the information the scientific panel provided, decide if you would support growing genetically modified corn in this country. Be sure to consider the statements from all four scientists. In your science notebook, record your opinion and the evidence and your thinking that led you to your opinion.

7. Share your ideas with the class by conducting a walking debate. Your teacher will explain how to run the debate.

8. With your group, review the questions you listed on the chart you made for Step 3. Check which of those questions have been answered. With another colored pen, add to your chart three or four new questions you have about genetically modified corn and other genetically modified organisms. Be prepared to share any answers you found for your previous questions and your new questions with the class.

BACKGROUND INFORMATION

Bt Corn

COMMON SOIL BACTERIA called *Bacillus thuringeinsis (Bt)* produce a protein toxic to the larvae of certain insects, such as the European corn borer. This insect is found throughout Europe, North Africa, Canada, and most of the United States. A single generation of corn borers can reduce by as much as 5% the amount of corn a farm produces. In warm climates up to three generations of corn borers will attack a crop during one growing season, which causes an even greater percentage of crop loss. In the past, many farmers have sprayed chemical insecticides that kill corn borers and many other insects. Many of these insecticides pose health risks to farm workers, consumers, and bees and other beneficial insects. Also, the insecticides are expensive to buy and to spray on crops.

Beginning in Europe in the 1930s, farmers in many regions of the world have sprayed Bt bacteria on fields of plants as an insecticide. The Bt toxin is generally considered safe for people and wildlife. Its drawbacks are that it remains active for no more than a week after it is applied, and it is not effective against all insects.

In 1996, farmers in the United States began growing a new

a

b

The adult corn borer is a moth (a). The corn borer larvae bore into the plant and destroy the corn (b).

genetically modified corn plant, called Bt corn. This corn plant had the Bt gene from *Bacillus thuringeinsis* inserted into its cells. This gene provides information that causes the plant cells themselves to produce the Bt protein. As a result, the offspring of the modified plants are protected from the corn borer.

Today, genetically modified corn is one of four genetically modified crops—along with canola, cotton, and soybeans—grown in huge quantities. The table below shows the top 10 countries that grow genetically modified crops, which

crops they grow, and on how much land.

Today, the need for more food to meet the needs of growing populations has led many countries to consider growing genetically modified crops as a way to increase the amounts grown. People in various countries fear that such crops might harm humans, other organisms, and the environment. These concerns have led to debate about which is greater: the benefits or risks of genetically modified organisms. ■

Top 10 Countries Growing Genetically Modified Crops in 2008

COUNTRY	TYPE OF CROP	AREA (MILLIONS OF HECTARES)
United Sates	soybean, corn (maize), cotton, canola, squash, papaya, alfalfa, sugar beet	62.5
Argentina	soybean, corn (maize), cotton	21.0
Brazil	soybean, corn (maize), cotton	15.8
India	cotton	7.6
Canada	canola, corn (maize), soybean, sugar beet	7.6
China	cotton, tomato, poplar, petunia, papaya, sweet pepper	3.8
Paraguay	soybean	2.7
South Africa	corn (maize), soybean, cotton	1.8
Uruguay	soybean, corn (maize)	0.7
Bolivia	soybean	0.6

SOURCE: *International Service for the Acquisition of Agri-biotech Applications Brief 39-2008. http://www.isaaa.org/Resources/publications/briefs/39/executivesummary/default.html*

Panel Member #1

I think that planting genetically modified crops to improve yield and reduce the need for insecticides will be good for our people and safe for the environment. Bt corn has raised corn yields in the United States. Investigations of Bt corn at a leading university showed that it did not harm monarch butterflies in the field. Bt corn seed might be more expensive, but it may also save farmers money and labor, since they will not need to purchase and spray the insecticides that fight the corn borer. Research has shown that farmers growing Bt corn use fewer chemical insecticides to fight other organisms that attack corn. In addition, one researcher found that Bt corn has lower levels of a fungal toxin that is common in corn.

Because that toxin is harmful to children, Bt corn may be safer to eat than unmodified corn.

Bt corn is just one example of how genetically modified organisms might contribute to the food supply. For example, genetically modified disease- and drought-resistant crops have already been developed. Researchers are also working to improve the nutritional quality of such basic foods as rice through genetic modification. By increasing food production in our country, we can help to end hunger and malnutrition among our people. We would no longer have to import corn, which is more expensive than growing it. We could also make money by selling our corn to other countries.

Panel Member #2

I do not think we know enough about genetically modified crops for our country to invest in any of them at this time. Genetic engineering technology has not always resulted in improved crop yields. A study by the U.S.-based Union of Concerned Scientists found that Bt corn is the only genetically modified crop giving better yields, but the improvements were small. I'm also concerned that it will harm monarch butterflies and other organisms, or cause other environmental damage.

Many people think that changing just one or a few genes is unlikely to cause harm, because a single gene codes for just one protein. But I am concerned because one protein can have multiple effects in the organism. New discoveries in genetics suggest that the effects of inserting a gene from one organism into another organism's DNA are more complex than scientists once thought.

Finally, the continual exposure of insects to insecticides nearly always leads to the development of resistant insect populations. With Bt in the corn itself, the insects are constantly exposed to the toxin, and are more likely to become resistant than when farmers spray it on their crops just a few times. For these reasons, I urge caution. We must feed our children today without harming the environment for the children of tomorrow.

Panel Member #3

Humans have been breeding crops to develop desirable traits for thousands of years. Genetic engineering technology is a faster and more precise way to make these changes. Genetic modification allows scientists to insert beneficial genes from one species into another, and that's not possible with breeding. Several genetically modified organisms have been used for more than 30 years to produce medicines. One example is the modification of *Escherichia coli (E. coli)* bacteria to produce the human hormone, insulin. Before this was produced in 1978, insulin was extracted from pig pancreases, which was time-consuming and more expensive to produce. With the hunger we face, it's time to allow the growth of genetically modified crops here. Corn is a major food for people and livestock. Research shows that Bt corn is most cost-effective in areas like ours, where crop losses to corn borers are large. People in our country are starving, and researchers have shown that Bt corn does improve yields. Research also shows that with Bt corn we do not have to rely as much on chemicals to control insects in the cornfields. I am certain that genetically modified crops will contribute to a sustainable food supply, help our farmers make a better living, and let our children think about schoolwork instead of their empty stomachs.

Panel Member #4

I do not think genetically modified crops should ever be grown or eaten. The impact that they have on ecosystems and humans has not been fully explored. What if the plants breed with wild crops or other plants and spread the inserted genes? This has happened with some genetically modified crops. If it happened here it could be harmful for our native plants. Additionally, what impact will the proteins produced by the modified crops have on the health of humans or animals? There was a case of a soybean plant that was genetically modified to make it more nutritious by adding a gene for a Brazil-nut protein. A study published in the *New England Journal of Medicine* found that the nut protein produced by these soybeans caused allergic reactions in people allergic to Brazil nuts. As a result, the company that developed the modified soybean had to stop its work and not sell the soybeans. I am concerned that there might be other unintended consequences of planting such crops as Bt corn. Much more thorough scientific studies of each product are needed. These studies would divert resources from other approaches to sustainable agriculture, such as better soil management, relying on pests' natural enemies, and other ecologically balanced approaches to pest control.

Analysis

1. What is a genetically modified organism?

2. How might genetically modified food organisms affect each of the three pillars of sustainability:

   a. economic?

   b. social?

   c. environmental?

3. Did your initial ideas about Bt corn change? Explain your initial ideas. If they have changed, explain how and why. If they have not changed, explain why not.

4. Write a letter to the country's Office for Agriculture explaining your views on growing Bt corn. In your letter include

   a. a statement explaining your decision and the evidence and reasoning that led you to your conclusion.

   b. a description of the trade-offs of your decision. A **trade-off** is giving up something in order to gain something else.

5. Currently in the United States, federal law does not require foods containing genetically modified ingredients to be labeled as such.

   a. What would be the advantages of labeling foods that have genetically modified ingredients?

   b. What would be the disadvantages?

   c. Would you recommend labeling of foods that have genetically modified ingredients? Explain.

KEY VOCABULARY

gene

genetically modified organism

genetic engineering

trade-off

---

2 Creating Genetically Modified Bacteria

GLOW-IN-THE-DARK rabbits, pigs, and mice may sound like something out of a science fiction movie, but because of genetic modification, these animals actually exist. They were the results of scientists inserting a gene from the jelly species *Aequorea victoria* into their DNA. Genes code for the production of specific proteins. *Aequorea* jellies naturally glow in the dark because they have a gene that codes for green fluorescent protein.

The goal of inserting a gene from one organism into another is for the modified organism to make the protein coded by the inserted gene and express the new trait. For example, a certain gene in *Bacillus thuringiensis* bacteria produces the Bt pesticide protein. When this gene is inserted into corn, the resulting Bt corn produces the Bt pesticide. This production of a protein is called **gene expression.**

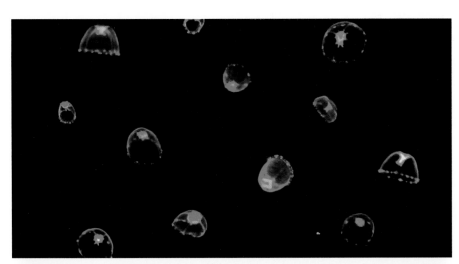

A gene from an Aequorea *jelly (a) has been inserted into the DNA of the mouse (b), causing it to glow.*

a

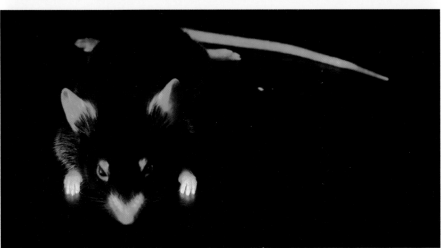

b

In order to produce a genetically modified organism, scientists insert the desired gene into the DNA of eggs from the target organism. Scientists often include the gene for an *Aequorea* jelly's green fluorescent protein, in addition to the desired gene. If they can successfully raise these eggs to adult organisms, and if that organism glows, scientists know that they have inserted the genes correctly. The green fluorescent protein acts like a marker that shows the genes have been inserted into the target organism and that the organism can express the trait.

In this activity, you will genetically modify a population of *Escherichia coli (E. coli)* bacteria. Geneticists study *E. coli* because, even though it is a simple organism, it uses the same cellular processes for gene expression as do more complex organisms. You will insert two genes into *E. coli:* one for green fluorescent protein (GFP), and one that will make the *E. coli* resistant to the antibiotic ampicillin. Because the plates on which you will grow the bacteria contain ampicillin (which normally kills *E. coli*), only the successfully modified *E. coli* will grow.

Challenge

▶ How do scientists genetically modify an organism?

MATERIALS

FOR THE CLASS

4–6   *E. coli* starter plates

tube of pGLO (GFP) plasmid

waste container holding 10% bleach solution

spray bottle of disinfectant

ultraviolet (UV) light

supply of paper towels

FOR EACH GROUP OF FOUR STUDENTS

container of crushed ice

2   microtubes containing 300 μL $CaCl_2$

inoculating loop

4   sterile pipettes

permanent marker

timer

2   Luria broth (LB)—ampicillin plates

2   spreaders

FOR EACH STUDENT

Student Sheet 2.1, "Genetic Modification Procedure"

Student Sheet 2.2, "*E. coli* Growth Observations"

Student Sheet 2.3, "Genetics Case Study Comparison"

3   sticky notes

safety goggles

Procedure

1. Follow your teacher's instructions for recording notes on this laboratory.

2. Read the entire procedure to familiarize yourself with the steps. After doing so, on Student Sheet 2.1, "Genetic Modification Procedure," write a summary of the purpose of this activity and the experimental design you will follow to transform the *E. coli* bacteria.

3. Sterilize your table surface with disinfectant. It is important to work on sterile surfaces during this investigation so that your bacteria do not become contaminated.

4. Label one of the microtubes containing $CaCl_2$ "+ pGFP," and label the other "Control." Place both tubes in your beaker of crushed ice.

5. With the inoculating loop carefully scrape about ¼-loop-full of *E. coli* bacteria from the starter plate. To prevent contamination touch only the handle of the loop. Be careful not to damage the agar plate while harvesting the bacteria.

6. Place the loop with the bacteria into the $CaCl_2$ solution in tube + pGFP, and twirl it back and forth in the liquid for a few seconds to be sure the bacteria have come off the loop. Remove the loop, and place it on a clean paper towel. Do not touch the loop—touch only the handle—to prevent contamination.

7. Your solution should turn cloudy with *E. coli*. If not, use a sterile pipette to mix the cells by gently suctioning the solution into the pipette and then pushing it back out into the microtube. Repeat the mixing 4 to 5 times. Place the pipette on the paper towel with the loop. Close the tube, and put the tube back on ice.

   Note: Touch only the bulb end of the pipette, to avoid contamination. Be careful to only suction the solution far enough to remove it from the tube; do not let any get into the bulb of the pipette. Do this gently to prevent any bubbles from forming in the solution.

8. Repeat Steps 5–7 for the Control tube. You may use the same loop and pipette, as long as they have been kept on a clean paper towel.

9. Obtain the pGFP plasmid according to your teacher's instructions. With a new pipette, transfer 10 µl of pGFP plasmid to the + pGFP tube. Close the tube. Mix the contents by flicking the tube vigorously with your forefinger several times, then tap the end of the tube on the table to make sure the contents are all at the bottom of the tube. Do NOT add plasmid to the Control tube.

10. Place both tubes on ice, and let them sit for 15 minutes.

11. Label the underside of your Luria broth (LB)–ampicillin plates with your group's initials and the date. Label one "+ pGFP" and the other "Control."

Safety

Be cautious when working with live organisms. If there are any spills, or if any substances come in contact with your skin, notify your teacher immediately, and wash with soap and water. Wash your hands at the end of the investigation. Do not look directly at the UV light source, as it might damage your eyes.

Follow the sterile technique procedures outlined in the box on the next page.

Sterile Technique Practices for Working with *E. Coli*

1. Keep all equipment away from your eyes and nose to avoid contact with bacteria.

2. Wipe all surfaces with a disinfectant solution before and after working with *E. coli.*

3. Wash your hands before and after any work with *E. coli.*

4. Treat all equipment that has been exposed to *E. coli* (pipettes, spreaders, microtubes, etc.) by soaking them in a 10% bleach solution for 10 minutes before placing them in the appropriate waste container.

5. To prevent overgrowth of *E. coli* do not over-incubate culture plates.

12. The next step is to shock the bacteria with heat. Heat shock causes the bacteria cells to take in the plasmid with the GFP gene. Rub your hands together rapidly to be sure they are warm. Remove both tubes from the ice, and hold them in your hands to incubate them. Shake your hands gently for 2–3 seconds to mix the fluid in the tubes. Incubate EXACTLY 3 minutes, and immediately put the tubes back on ice for 1 minute.

13. With a new sterile pipette transfer 100 μl of the mixture from the Control tube to the control plate. Use one of the spreaders to spread the liquid across the entire plate, taking care not to damage the agar. Discard the pipette in the waste container.

14. With another new sterile pipette and the other spreader, repeat Step 13 to transfer the contents of the + pGFP tube to the + pGFP plate.

15. Let the plates sit for 3 minutes to allow the agar to absorb the liquid that contains the bacteria.

16. Turn the plates upside down. Your teacher will give you instructions for storing the plates.

17. On Student Sheet 2.2, "*E. coli* Growth Observations," record your observations of each plate on the section of the Student Sheet designated, "time = 0 hours."

18. After 48 to 72 hours, observe the plates under a UV light. *Keep the lids on the plates. Do not look directly at the UV light source, as it might damage your eyes.* In your science notebook, record your observations of the plates your team prepared. Be sure to record the number of bacterial colonies on each plate, and to sketch each plate and the colonies.

19. Following your teacher's instructions, compare the results from your plates with the number of colonies on plates that other groups grew.

20. Dispose of all materials as instructed by your teacher, and sterilize your table surface.

21. Wash your hands thoroughly with soap and water.

22. Throughout this unit, you will read case studies about genetic modification. You will use the information you collect on Student Sheet 2.3, "Genetics Case Study Comparison," to answer Analysis Questions in a number of activities.

23. Follow your teacher's directions for reading the case study about biofuels. As you read, follow the "Read, Think, and Take Note" strategy. To do this:

    • Stop at least three times during the reading to mark on a sticky note your thoughts or questions about the reading. Use the list of guidelines below to start your thinking.

    • After writing a thought or question on a sticky note, place it next to the passage in the reading that prompted your note.

    • Discuss with your partner the thoughts and questions you had while reading.

24. Complete the information for "Biofuels from Bacteria" on Student Sheet 2.3, "Genetics Case Study Comparison."

Read, Think, and Take Note: Guidelines

As you read, from time to time, write one of the following on a sticky note:

• Explain a thought or reaction to something you read.

• Note something in the reading that is confusing or unfamiliar.

• List a word that you do not know.

• Describe a connection to something you learned or read previously.

• Make a statement about the reading.

• Pose a question about the reading.

• Draw a diagram or picture of an idea or connection.

CASE STUDY

Modifying Bacteria to Produce Biofuels

CITIES, HOMES, FACTORIES, cars, and trucks throughout the world are powered primarily by fossil fuels. Concerns about the availability of these fuels and the environmental impacts of producing and using them have led to a search for alternatives. One of these alternatives is a group of fuels called biofuels. **Biofuels,** including bioethanol and biodiesel, are compounds that are produced from renewable biological sources. Plants high in starch and sugar are made into ethanol, while vegetable oils and other fats are made into biodiesel. Both of these fuels may be burned in combustion engines in place of fossil fuels. Research on alternative fuels and the role of genetically modified organisms in producing them is rapidly expanding in the United States.

Scientists are currently working on ways to overcome several obstacles to the sustainable production of biofuels. They hope to improve the plants themselves to get high yields of fuel, and to improve the

Many farm machines at the Agricultural Research Service's Beltville Agricultural Research Center are running on a mixture of diesel fuel and biodiesel, which is made from soybean oil.

technology for extracting fuel from the plants. Much of the research focuses on the development of genetically modified microorganisms. Currently, most bioethanol is generated by fermenting corn or sugar cane with yeast or bacteria. Those crops, however, are also important food crops, and the starchy and sugary edible parts of these plants are the parts needed to make bioethanol. If too many farmers dedicate too much agricultural land to producing biofuel plants, supplies of basic foods will shrink. For this reason, scientists are trying to find efficient ways to make biofuels from the waste stalks and leaves of crops and from grasses that don't require the high-quality soil that food crops need.

The difficulty in making fuel from grasses and inedible parts of crops is that they contain two substances —lignin and cellulose—that are very hard to break down. These substances add strength to the plants' cell walls, but cause problems in the production of biofuels. The solution might be found in bacteria that live in such places as compost piles or in the digestive systems of termites and other organisms. Enzymes that break down wood and the tough parts of plants have been identified in these bacteria. A current approach scientists are pursuing is to insert genes from these bacteria into other

bacteria that grow well on the large scale needed for producing commercial ethanol. One such bacterium is the very well understood *E. coli*. Scientists are working on a genetically modified *E. coli* that can break the lignin and cellulose into sugars that can then be converted to ethanol.

Another potential use of genetically modified microorganisms is to improve the quality of the fuel produced from sugars. Typically, yeast or bacteria break down sugars and starch to produce ethanol, a two-carbon fuel. Ethanol's shortcomings, however, are that it doesn't have a

$$H-\overset{\displaystyle \overset{H}{|}}{\underset{\displaystyle \underset{H}{|}}{C}} - \overset{\displaystyle \overset{H}{|}}{\underset{\displaystyle \underset{H}{|}}{C}} - O - H$$

Ethanol is currently used as a fuel, but has some shortcomings.

high energy content, it binds to water, and it corrodes metals, including those with which storage tanks and cars' gas tanks are made. One research group has modified *E. coli* to produce fuels that have longer carbon chains and are similar to gasoline. These longer-chain alcohols store more energy than ethanol, are easier to separate from water, and perform better in engines.

(Continued on next page)

(Continued from previous page)

Currently, other types of microbes can produce these fuels, but the yield is low. The fuels can also be produced through breaking down the plant matter with chemicals, but this is expensive and requires a lot of energy. To harness *E. coli* to produce fuels scientists have deleted several genes in *E. coli* and replaced them with genes from other organisms. These efforts have been somewhat successful. The modified *E. coli* produces longer-chain alcohols, but not enough for commercial use. Some researchers are trying to determine how to balance each step of the reaction pathway in the *E. coli* to maximize production of the fuels. Other research is looking at performing a similar genetic modification in yeast and other microbes that are often used in converting plant material into other types of biofuel.

A third research group has genetically engineered *E. coli* that are able to both break down cellulose and turn that product into biodiesel and related compounds. They have done this by deleting two *E. coli* genes and adding genes from several other organisms. Although these modified *E. coli* produce less fuel than needed for commercial use, they produce enough that the results are promising.

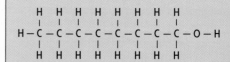

Longer chain alcohols, such as octanol, may perform better than ethanol as a fuel.

Some scientists question the safety of modifying bacteria and other microbes to produce biofuel. They think there has not been enough safety testing done on genetically modified organisms, and suggest that there may be unintended consequences for human health or the environment. Although the *E. coli* needed to make biofuels would be grown only in laboratories, there might be problems if some were accidentally transferred to other environments.

Alternatives to developing genetically modified organisms for producing biofuels include:

- Improving the fuel quality of plants by selective breeding.
- Weakening plants' cell walls through selective breeding.
- Improving the process of chemically breaking down plant matter.

Both scientific advances and policy decisions will play a role in decisions about pursuing these approaches to producing biofuels. ■

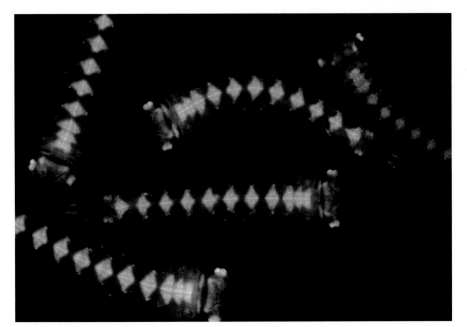

These mosquito larvae have been genetically modified with GFP. Scientists hope to one day genetically modify mosquitoes so they cannot carry the protozoa that cause malaria. This could save millions of lives.

Analysis

1. Analyze your work in this activity and that of the other groups, according to your teacher's instructions. Analysis should include a summary of the data collected and conclusions you and your group draw from the data about the bacteria on the plates. Explain possible sources of experimental error.

2. How would your results differ if you had not added ampicillin to any of the plates but kept all other variables the same?

3. What results would you expect if you had created a Luria–ampicillin plate containing *E. coli* that were not transformed?

4. What are the possible benefits and risks involved in developing genetically modified organisms to produce biofuels?

KEY VOCABULARY	
biofuel	**gene expression**
DNA	genetic modification
gene	

3 Mitosis and Asexual Reproduction

WHEN SCIENTISTS GENETICALLY modify an organism, it is important that they be able to predict how many of the offspring of the modified organism will contain the newly inserted gene. This prediction depends on how the organism reproduces. In this activity you will investigate how a single-celled organism, in this case *E. coli*, reproduces asexually.

In **asexual reproduction** it takes only one parent to produce offspring. The parent's cells undergo **mitosis,** in which a single cell divides to produce two identical daughter cells. When humans and other multicellular organisms grow, their new cells are also products of mitosis.

You will model mitosis and compare the genetic makeup of a parent cell and its daughter cells. Then you will predict the chance of an inserted gene being passed on to next generations through asexual reproduction.

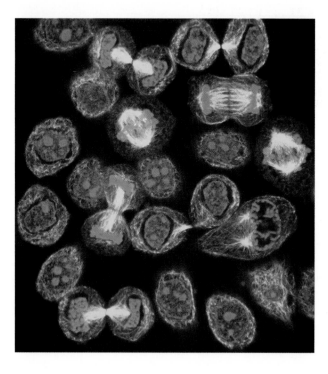

Some of these human cells are undergoing mitosis. At bottom left and top, the cells are in the last stages, and will soon form two daughter cells.

Challenge

▶ If a genetically modified cell undergoes mitosis, how likely is it that the daughter cells will contain the inserted gene?

MATERIALS

FOR EACH PAIR OF STUDENTS

    set of 2 pop-bead chromosome models

16 blue pop beads

16 green pop beads

2 orange pop beads

2 blue centromeres

2 green centromeres

    access to online mitosis simulation

FOR EACH STUDENT

    Student Sheet 3.1, "Mitosis"

Procedure

1. Observe the mitosis simulation on the *Science and Global Issues* page of the SEPUP website *(sepuplhs.org/sgi)*. Determine what happens to the genetic material of the cell at each phase.

2. On Student Sheet 3.1, "Mitosis," draw what happens to the chromosomes during each of the phases shown.

3. In your science notebook, write a description summarizing the key events of each stage of mitosis.

4. With your partner, use the pop-bead model chromosomes to show what happens when a cell with one pair of chromosomes undergoes mitosis. To do this:

   a. Make two strands of four blue pop beads, and attach them to the blue centromere. Repeat this process for green. This represents one pair of chromosomes.

   b. Simulate the replication of each chromosome during prophase. To do this, repeat Step 4a. With the centromeres, form the shape of a replicated chromosome as shown in the illustration on the next page. Note that the X shape is a replicated chromosome, and that the model demonstrates one pair of replicated chromosomes.

   c. Refer to Student Sheet 3.1, "Mitosis," to determine how to move the chromosomes as they would move through each phase—prophase, metaphase, anaphase, and telophase. Determine the genetic makeup of the cells that result.

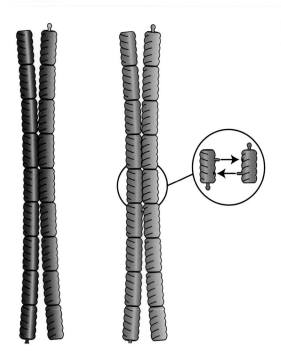

This model shows one pair of replicated chromosomes.

5. With your partner, discuss how the genetic makeup of the daughter cells compares to that of the parent cell. Write your conclusions in your science notebook.

6. Consider a cell that has been genetically modified and has had a gene inserted into one chromosome. Starting with a pair of nonreplicated chromosomes, replace one of the blue pop beads on one model chromosome with an orange pop bead. With your partner, repeat Steps 4 and 5 for your modified model chromosomes to demonstrate the replication of the modified chromosome.

7. Discuss with your group what the probability is that a daughter cell will receive an inserted gene from a genetically modified parent cell that undergoes mitosis.

   Be sure your discussion includes:

   • chromosomes

   • parent cell

   • daughter cell

   • gene

   Write your conclusions in your science notebook.

Analysis

1. Explain mitosis. In your explanation include the preparations that take place during interphase and each of the four phases of mitosis (prophase, metaphase, anaphase, and telophase).

2. In mitosis, how does each daughter cell's chromosomes compare to the chromosomes of the parent?

3. A friend of yours claims that every genetically modified single-celled organism that reproduces asexually would pass along the inserted gene to its daughter cells. Based on your work in this activity, is that claim valid? Explain.

4. Based on your answer in Procedure Step 7, what benefits and risks might the asexual reproduction of a genetically modified organism or cell pose?

KEY VOCABULARY	
asexual reproduction	cytokinesis
centrioles	daughter cell
centromere	**mitosis**
chromatid	parent cell
chromosomes	

4 Breeding Corn

FARMERS THROUGHOUT THE world grow crops and raise animals to sustain their families and communities, and to earn a living. Livestock and most crops reproduce by **sexual reproduction**—in which two parents contribute genetic material to the offspring. Farmers practice selective breeding to improve livestock and crops. In **selective breeding,** organisms with desirable traits are mated with the goal of producing even more desirable offspring. For example, farmers have bred apples for different colors, tastes, and types of consumption, such as baking, juicing, and eating. Before the development of biotechnology methods that allow scientists to alter plants and animals on a gene-by-gene basis, selective breeding was the only way people could develop varieties of crops and livestock that had traits they wanted or needed.

In this activity, you will explore the results of selectively breeding two varieties of corn.

Challenge

▶ How can information about the genetic makeup of plants help farmers breed plants for desirable traits?

MATERIALS

FOR EACH PAIR OF STUDENTS
    cardboard corn ears A and B
    set of P/p allele cards

FOR EACH STUDENT
    Student Sheet 4.1, "Traits and Heredity"

Breeding yellow-kernelled corn and purple-kernelled corn will produce a first generation of purple-kernelled offspring. Breeding those offspring will produce corn with kernels of both colors.

Procedure

1. Read the questions posed on Student Sheet 4.1, "Traits and Heredity." Fill in the "I think" column with a response to each question.

2. The figure below shows a cross between a corn plant that produces ears with purple kernels and a corn plant that produces ears with yellow kernels. The resulting offspring have ears with only purple kernels.

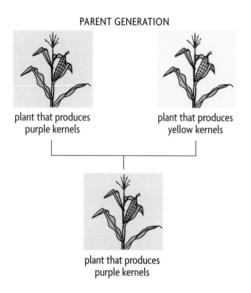

PARENT GENERATION

plant that produces
purple kernels

plant that produces
yellow kernels

plant that produces
purple kernels

With your group, discuss what you think is happening in the above cross. Share your ideas with the class, as directed by your teacher.

The corn shown above has been selectively bred to exhibit many kernel colors.

3. Read the information on the next page in the text box, "Basic Genetics," that you will need for the rest of the procedure. Record information in your science notebook, as instructed.

4. With your partner, and based on what you know about the heredity of traits, use the P and p allele cards to discuss why the corn kernels (offspring) were all purple. Discuss your ideas with the other pair in your group. Record a summary of your discussion in your student notebook.

5. Record your group's ideas from Step 4 in the second column of Student Sheet 4.1 in the "My group thinks" column. You will return to these questions later to see how your ideas and understanding of traits and heredity have changed.

6. **a.** A **Punnett square** is a tool that shows and helps predict the possible offspring when two organisms reproduce sexually. The Punnett square below shows a cross between a purple corn plant that has PP alleles and a yellow corn plant that has pp alleles.

	P	P
p	P p	P p
p	P p	P p

The alleles written along the top and side of the square are the alleles from each parent organism, in this case the purple corn and the yellow corn. The allele combinations inside the square show the possible combinations that could be found in the offspring of this cross.

b. Draw a blank Punnett square in your science notebook, and show what a cross would look like between two parent corn plants with the genes Pp. Note the allele combinations and what color the offspring would be for each combination.

7. Determine the predicted ratio of the different-colored offspring in the Punnett square you drew in Step 6b. How is this different from the ratio for the Punnett square shown in Step 6a?

BACKGROUND INFORMATION

Basic Genetics

- An organism has two copies of the gene for each of its traits. These copies are called **alleles.**

- Some traits are either **dominant,** meaning they will mask another version of the trait, or they are **recessive,** meaning that they will be hidden by a dominant trait.

- In scientific writing a dominant trait is represented with a capital letter, which is underlined to be easy to distinguish. A recessive trait is shown with a lower-case letter. For example, in corn the allele for purple kernel color is P, and the allele for yellow kernel color is p. The possible allele combinations for a corn plant are PP, Pp, or pp.

8. Read the scenario that follows.

   Shauna is a gardener who would like to produce bicolored (two-colored) corn like some samples she got from a friend. In her garden, she has corn with purple kernels and corn with yellow kernels, but no bicolored corn. Shauna begins by crossing the plants with yellow kernels with those with purple kernels. The offspring produced have all purple kernels, as shown in the Punnett Square in Step 6a. Help Shauna figure out what to do next to produce corn like corn ears A and B.

9. In your science notebook, make a data table like the one below.

10. Count the number of purple kernels and the number of yellow kernels on corn ear A. Record them in your data table.

Corn Breeding Data

	Number of purple kernels	Number of yellow kernels	Ratio of purple kernels to yellow kernels	Ratio rounded to the nearest whole number
Kernels on ear A				
Kernels on ear B				

11. Count the number of purple kernels and the number of yellow kernels on corn ear B. Record them in your data table.

12. With your group, discuss what the ratio of purple to yellow kernels tells you about the genetic information that was passed from the parent generation to each of these corn kernels. Remember: In corn, the trait for purple is dominant over the recessive trait for yellow.

13. From the data you recorded in Steps 10 and 11 calculate the ratio of purple kernels to yellow kernels. To do this, divide the number of purple kernels by the number of yellow kernels. Enter your results on the data table. Then divide the smaller number by itself, to produce 1. The ratio of purple to yellow kernels would be $x : 1$. Round the ratio to the closest whole numbers.

14. With your partner, discuss what the genes of the parent corn must have been to produce the corn kernels on ears A and B. Record your ideas in your science notebook.

15. Based on the ratio of kernels counted, Shauna constructed three Punnett squares to show the possible crosses she thinks may have produced the corn on ears A and B.

	$\underline{P}$	p
$\underline{P}$	$\underline{P}\,\underline{P}$	$\underline{P}\,p$
$\underline{P}$	$\underline{P}\,\underline{P}$	$\underline{P}\,p$

PUNNETT SQUARE X

PUNNETT SQUARE Y

PUNNETT SQUARE Z

16. Given the data you collected in Step 10, which of the three Punnett squares shown in Shauna's notes—X, Y, or Z—best describes the cross that produced ear A? Record your reasoning in your science notebook.

17. Given the data you collected in Step 11, which of the three Punnett squares—X, Y, or Z—best describes the cross that produced ear B? Record your reasoning in your science notebook.

18. Follow your teacher's instructions to discuss your ideas from Steps 16 and 17 with the class. Determine if your ideas agree. If not, discuss why, and try to come to agreement.

Analysis

1. How does a Punnett square show the possible results of a cross between two individuals?

2. Describe how your observations of offspring (corn kernels) allowed you to determine the genetic makeup of the two parents. Discuss how you used ratios in this process.

3. What do you predict will happen if a purple corn plant with the genes Pp is bred with a corn plant with purple kernels and the genes PP? Explain your answer, and include a matching Punnett Square.

4. How could scientists use selective breeding to help solve a sustainability challenge such as breeding a crop that can survive drought?

KEY VOCABULARY	
allele	**selective breeding**
dominant	**sexual reproduction**
Punnett square	trait
recessive	

5 Genes and Traits

IF YOU EXAMINE a family photograph of relatives from three or four generations, you may notice similar traits among the people, such as a certain eye or
hair color. When people began growing crops and breeding animals, they noticed
patterns in the traits of parent plants and animals and their offspring. These patterns of traits passing from one generation to the next helped farmers decide
which animals to breed and which seeds of which plants to grow to obtain the
qualities they wanted in their farm products. More recently, scientists began
studying these patterns in human families to track and understand such traits as
those that cause genetic diseases.

In the previous activity, you modeled the possible combinations of traits passed
on to sexually reproduced corn plants. In this activity, you will learn more about
the mechanism of **heredity,** the passing of genetic traits from one generation to
the next.

Challenge

▶ What can we infer about genes and traits based on heredity patterns?

*Due to many generations
of selective breeding,
domestic carrots (Daucus
carota) (on the right) show
many traits that differ
from those of wild carrots
(on the left).*

Procedure

1. The reading below involves a strategy called Stopping to Think questions. Occasionally, in between paragraphs, there will be a question. As you read, stop and answer these questions in your mind. They can help you determine the main ideas of the reading. Follow your teacher's instructions on further exploration of these questions in discussions.

Reading

Early Breeding Practices

Farmers learned thousands of years ago that by selecting which parent plants and animals to breed, those parents would produce offspring with characteristics people wanted. Through this selective breeding, farmers' improvements in farm products have helped sustain human communities. The potato, for example, was first discovered as a food source in South America more than 10,000 years ago. Native South Americans who started farming potatoes quickly learned that they would lose fewer potatoes to disease if they grew several kinds. Through selective breeding, potato farmers around the world now grow thousands of varieties. A few traits of those varieties are size, color, and how long they can be stored. Such progress in agriculture led to the modern study of heredity.

STOPPING TO THINK QUESTION 1

Why is the study of heredity and traits important?

Gregor Mendel was a 19th century monk, teacher, and scientist, who set out to systematically explore the relationship between traits and heredity. He worked mainly with pea plants, which he could grow easily and which showed several traits clearly. Among the pea traits Mendel analyzed were seed color (yellow or green) and stem length (long or short). Over several years, he conducted carefully controlled experiments and kept detailed records of the traits inherited by off-spring from parent pea plants. A summary of Mendel's findings is shown in the table on the following page.

Mendel's Results for Three Generations of Pea Plant Crosses

	FLOWER COLOR	SEED COLOR	SEED SURFACE	POD COLOR

Original cross	purple × white	green × yellow	wrinkled × smooth	green × yellow
F₁ generation	all purple	all yellow	all smooth	all green
F₂ generation	705 : 224 (purple : white)	6,022 : 2,001 (yellow : green)	5,474 : 1,850 (smooth : wrinkled)	428 : 152 (green : yellow)

Mendel crossed hundreds of pea plants, and observed and counted phenotypes of traits related to seeds, pods, and flowers in thousands of offspring. The **phenotype** of an organism is its physical characteristics, which result from the organism's genes and their interaction with the environment. For example the color of some flowers depends on both the genes they carry and the soil conditions in which they are grown. He then analyzed the results and applied his knowledge of statistics to figure out the patterns associated with individual genes and the probability of such patterns occurring.

Painting of Gregor Mendel working with pea plants

As he looked at the data, Mendel noticed an interesting relationship. With seed color, if the original cross (parent generation) was a purebred green seed with a purebred yellow seed, he found that all of the offspring (F_1 generation) had yellow seeds. When he bred the F_1 seeds together, their offspring (F_2 generation) still had many yellow seeds, but some were green. Calculating the ratio of the two traits in the F_2 generation, he obtained a ratio very near to 3:1. This means that for every one green-seeded plant, there were approximately three yellow-seeded plants in the third generation. For example, for color in 8,023 pea seeds he calculated the ratio of yellow to green seeds as

$$\frac{6{,}022 \text{ yellow}}{2{,}001 \text{ green}} = \frac{3.01 \text{ yellow}}{1 \text{ green}}$$

This is almost exactly a 3:1 ratio of yellow : green.

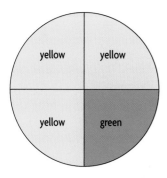

Mendel observed that the green-color trait was absent in the F_1 generation, but reappeared in the third generation, and that the probability of the seeds of an F_2 generation plant having the trait was one in four—that is, about one green-seeded plant for every four plants produced overall. Mendel found the same ratio for several other characteristics involving the same number of generations. The 3:1 ratio was the clue to how the parents' genes combine in their offspring. Based on his analysis, he proposed three principles of heredity:

- Each characteristic that appears in the F_1 generation is the dominant version of the trait. A dominant trait, when present in an individual, will always appear in that individual. The trait that is "hidden" in the F_2 generation is called recessive. It can be present but does not appear if there is a dominant trait masking it.

- Every plant has two copies, alleles, of the gene for each trait.

  Note: The terms "allele" and "gene" were proposed long after Mendel's research.

- Every offspring receives only one allele for each trait from each parent.

STOPPING TO THINK QUESTION 2

Look at the information presented in the table, "Mendel's Results," on the previous pages. Based on these results, which allele for each trait is a) dominant? b) recessive? What evidence supports your claim?

The work of Mendel and other scientists has provided evidence that supports his basic ideas about heredity. Today, scientists know that heredity is controlled through genes. A **gene** is a segment of an organism's genetic material, or DNA. Each gene is present in an individual in two versions, called alleles. We now know that when organisms reproduce sexually, each parent donates a gamete. A **gamete** is a sexual reproductive cell, such as a sperm or an egg, which contains genetic material of the organism. The gamete from each parent carries one allele for each trait. During sexual reproduction the two gametes, one from the female and one from the male, fuse together and create a new cell with two alleles for each trait. This new cell eventually grows into a fully developed organism.

Consider the corn ears in the last activity. You worked with two alleles for corn color—purple and yellow. Each kernel (offspring) received one allele for color from each parent to make a complete set of two alleles. This genetic makeup for an organism is its **genotype.**

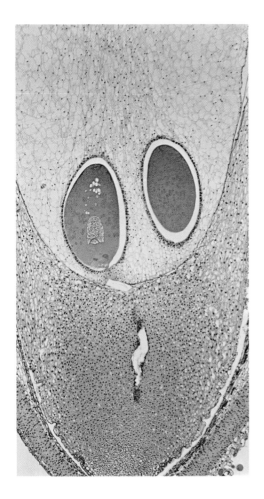

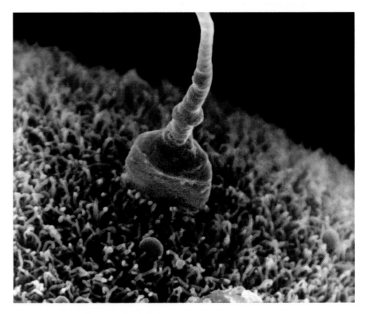

In sexual reproduction, a gamete from a male parent carrying one allele for every trait fuses with the gamete of a female parent, also carrying one allele for every trait as shown in the ovule of a plant at left and in the human sperm and egg above. Once fused, the fertilized egg contains a complete genetic set of alleles—one from each parent.

In the simplest cases, there are two types of alleles, and the gene can produce only two traits, one of which is dominant over the other. An example of this in Mendel's pea plants is flower color. Based on the results of breeding plants with purple flowers with plants with white flowers, Mendel inferred that a pea plant having two copies of the allele for the white color trait will have white flowers, while a plant with two copies of the allele for the purple color will have purple flowers. However, a pea plant with one allele for the purple color and one allele for the white color will always have purple flowers. This evidence led to the conclusion that the purple flower trait is dominant and the white trait is recessive.

For corn kernel alleles, we can designate <u>S</u> for smooth and s for wrinkled. The allele pair—whether <u>SS</u>, <u>S</u>s, or ss—is the kernel's genotype. Genotypes that have two identical alleles, such as <u>SS</u> or ss, are called **homozygous.** The prefix homo means "same." Genotypes with two different alleles, such as <u>S</u>s, are referred to as **heterozygous.** The prefix hetero means "different." The kernels with homozygous recessive alleles will express the recessive phenotype (ss = wrinkled kernels), those with homozygous dominant alleles will express the dominant phenotype (<u>SS</u> = smooth kernels), and kernels with heterozygous alleles will express the dominant phenotype (<u>S</u>s = smooth kernels).

	homozygous dominant	homozygous recessive	heterozygous
phenotype			
genotype	<u>S</u> <u>S</u>	s s	<u>S</u> s

STOPPING TO THINK QUESTION 3

If <u>P</u> represents the dominant purple allele for corn color and p represents the recessive yellow color allele, what letters would represent a kernel that has the following genotypes:

- *Homozygous purple?*
- *Homozygous yellow?*
- *Heterozygous purple?*

Since the time of Mendel's work, scientists have continued to explore patterns of heredity in organisms. For some traits, the patterns follow the rules of simple dominance, as Mendel observed. However, some traits are not so simple.

Consider flower color in snapdragons. When red snapdragons are crossed with white snapdragons, pink flowers result, as shown in the Punnett square below.

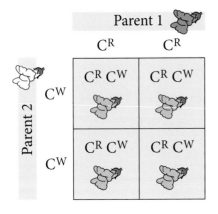

SNAP DRAGONS:
A CASE OF INCOMPLETE DOMINANCE

This is called **incomplete dominance,** and it occurs when neither trait is dominant. The result is a blending of the two traits that produces a third trait. In humans, the trait for curly hair shows a type of incomplete dominance. If a person inherits one allele for straight hair and one allele for curly hair, he or she will have the intermediate trait, wavy hair.

STOPPING TO THINK QUESTION 4

What are the possible phenotypes and genotypes of offspring from a cross between a pink snapdragon and a white snapdragon? What percentage of each phenotype and genotype would you expect to find?

A third type of dominance occurs when more than one trait is dominant, and each is expressed instead of the two blending into one trait. This is called **codominance.** Blood type in humans is a trait that exhibits codominance. Humans who have the allele for type A red blood cell proteins and the allele for type B red blood cell proteins will have red blood cells that express both proteins, type AB blood. This means that the traits produced by the A and B alleles are equally dominant, or codominant. However, there is a third blood trait, type O, which is recessive to both A and B. The box on the next page explains codominance and human blood types in more detail.

BACKGROUND INFORMATION

Codominance of Human Blood Types

Human Blood Type Alleles

ALLELE	CODES FOR PHENOTYPE	RED BLOOD CELL SURFACE PROTEINS
I_A	Type A surface proteins on red blood cells	
I_B	Type B surface proteins on red blood cells	
i	No surface proteins on red blood cells	

THERE ARE THREE possible alleles for human blood type; each person carries two alleles of the gene, which may be two of the same, or any combination of two out of the three possible alleles.

Figure 1 shows the red blood cells of a person who has type A blood and has the genotype I_AI_A.

1

Figure 2 shows the red blood cells of a person who has type A blood and has the genotype I_Ai.

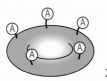

2

Figure 3 shows the red blood cells of a person who as type B blood and has the genotype I_BI_B.

3

Figure 4 shows the red blood cells of a person who has type AB blood and the genotype I_AI_B.

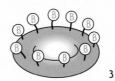

4

Figure 5 shows the red blood cells of a person who has type O blood and the genotype ii.

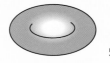

5

NOTE: *Cell surface proteins not drawn to scale.*

STOPPING TO THINK QUESTION 5

If a child has type O blood, what blood types might his or her parents have? Explain.

If a parent with type A blood and the genotype $I_A i$ and a parent with B blood and the genotype $I_B i$ have children, four possible phenotypes may result, as shown in the Punnett square below.

	I_A	i
I_B	$I_A I_B$	$I_B i$
i	$I_A i$	$i i$

An understanding of genes, alleles, and recessive and dominant traits allows scientists to predict the outcome of many genetic crosses. This information is the basis for both selective breeding and modern biotechnology research. Some traits are determined by only one gene, as illustrated in the cases above. A majority of traits are determined by a combination of many genes. Then again, many traits are also determined by the interaction of one or more genes with environmental conditions. For example, both genes and nutrition determine size in dogs. A Chihuahua that is poorly fed will be smaller than a well-fed Chihuahua. However, because of their genes a Chihuahua cannot be the size of a Great Dane no matter how well it is fed. There are also genes that control more than one phenotype. For example, if a gene controls the production of an enzyme needed by multiple organs, one mutation in that gene that changes the enzyme could affect each organ that uses the enzyme. For most traits, an organism's phenotype is determined by multiple genes and a combination of environmental conditions.

Analysis

1. Explain the difference between an organism's phenotype and its genotype. Include an example in your answer.

2. Explain the difference between simple dominance, incomplete dominance, and codominance.

3. Think back to the Bt corn you considered in Activity 1, "A Genetically Modified Solution?" When an organism is genetically modified, which of the following is changed: genotype, phenotype, both, or neither? Explain.

4. The following is a list of a few traits in plants and animals. Determine if the traits described are examples of simple dominance, codominance, or incomplete dominance. Explain your reasoning.

Trait	Description	Type of dominance and reasoning
Feather color in chickens	The feathers of a species of chicken can be black, white, or "erminette." Erminette chickens have both black feathers and white feathers, but not gray feathers.	
Sweet pea tendrils	When sweet pea plants with tendrils (structures that grow from the stem and help the plant attach and climb) are crossed with sweet pea plants without tendrils, all of the resulting sweet peas have tendrils.	
Rabbit hair length	Longhaired rabbits crossed with shorthaired rabbits produce off-spring that have medium-length hair.	

KEY VOCABULARY

allele	**homozygous**
codominance	**incomplete dominance**
dominant	**phenotype**
gamete	Punnett square
gene	recessive
genotype	selective breeding
heredity	trait
heterozygous	

6 Breeding Corn for Two Traits

WHEN FARMERS BREED plants, they often are trying to produce plants with more than one new and specific trait. The more traits they try to introduce, the more complicated the breeding becomes.

In Activity 4, you considered the heredity in corn of one trait: kernel color. In this activity, you will explore patterns of heredity for two traits: kernel color and texture. You will examine the results of a cross between two purple smooth-kernelled corn plants. This type of cross is referred to as a **dihybrid cross.** You will complete Punnett squares to predict the heredity of these two traits and compare the predicted and actual results.

Challenge

▶ How do scientists predict the results of crossing corn for two kernel characteristics: color and texture?

MATERIALS

FOR EACH PAIR OF STUDENTS
P/p and S/s Allele Cards
cardboard corn ears C and D

FOR EACH STUDENT
3 sticky notes
Student Sheet 2.3, "Genetics Case Study Comparison," from Activity 2

Procedure

Part A: Breeding Corn

1. In the crosses that you are about to work with, you will examine kernel color and shape. Note the following:

    Kernel color: You will consider two possible alleles—purple ($\underline{P}$) and yellow (p). Purple is dominant over yellow.

    Kernel texture: You will consider two possible alleles—smooth ($\underline{S}$) and wrinkled (s). Smooth is dominant over wrinkled.

2. With your partner use the $\underline{P}$/p and $\underline{S}$/s Allele Cards to model the gametes that might be produced by a parent with purple and smooth kernels and the genotype $\underline{P}p\underline{S}s$ (heterozygous for both traits). Record each possible gamete in your science notebook. (Remember, each gamete should include one of the alleles for the gene for color and one of the alleles for the gene for smoothness.)

3. In your science notebook, make a copy of the Punnett Square shown below. Write the possible allele combinations you determined in Step 2 on your Punnett square in place of the dotted blanks.

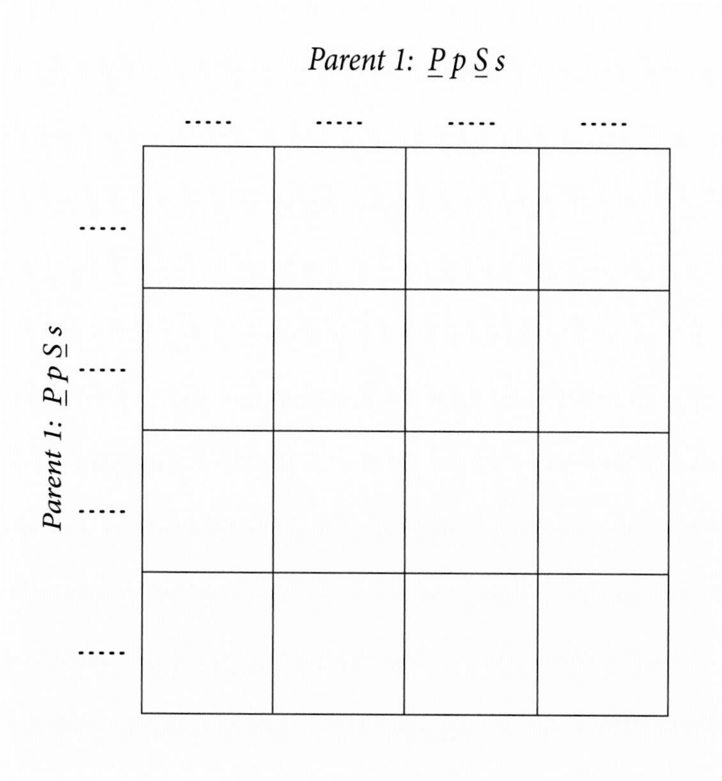

Parent 1: $\underline{P} p \underline{S} s$

4. Complete the Punnett square for the cross described in Step 3.

5. Base your answers to the following questions on your Punnett square. Record your answers in your science notebook. According to your Punnett square:

   • How many genotypes are possible in the kernels produced by the cross in Step 4?

   • How many phenotypes are possible in the kernels produced by the cross in Step 4? List them in your science notebook.

6. From your Punnett square predict the ratio of phenotypes predicted for the cross performed in Step 4. Express your ratio in this form:

   # purple smooth : # purple wrinkled : # yellow smooth : # yellow wrinkled

7. In your science notebook make a data table like the one below.

Corn Cross Offspring: Color and Smoothness

	Number of purple smooth kernels	Number of purple wrinkled kernels	Number of yellow smooth kernels	Number of yellow wrinkled kernels
Ear C				
Ear D				

8. Obtain ear C from your teacher. This ear is the result of a cross between two of the PpSs plants you worked with in Steps 3–6. Count, and record in your data table the number of each of the four kernel types found on ear C. Determine ratios by dividing all numbers by the least amount in each row and reducing to the lowest ratio.

9. How closely did the ratios of phenotypes from ear C in your data table correspond to the ratios predicted by the Punnett square? With your partner, discuss possible reasons for any differences.

10. Imagine you have several corn plants that have produced only purple smooth kernels. You want to determine whether these plants are homozygous (PPSS) for the dominant purple and smooth kernel traits. What type of crosses could you do to find out if your plants are homozygous?

With your group, develop a plan.

- Record your plan for the cross in your science notebook.

- Construct a data table to show the ratio of kernel phenotypes.

- Construct a Punnett square to show the possible results if the plants are homozygous <u>PPSS</u>.

- Include a description of the possible results and an interpretation of what they indicate.

11. Imagine that the way you carried out the procedure you proposed for Step 10 produced corn ears similar to ear D. Obtain ear D from your teacher. Count and record the number of each type of kernel found on ear D.

12. Analyze the data (color and smoothness of each kernel) from ear D to determine if the parent plants are homozygous or heterozygous for the two traits. Explain your answer in your science notebook.

Part B: Golden Rice Case Study

13. Individually read the case study on the next pages. As you read, follow the literacy strategy, "Read, Think, and Take Note."

14. Share your thinking with your group. Place your sticky notes on the table in front of you. Look for connections between your notes and those of others in your group.

   Hint: Were there common questions people asked? Were people unfamiliar with the same words? Did people react differently to statements in the reading?

15. Place your sticky notes in your science notebook. Below them write a short summary of what your group discussed and any conclusions the group came to.

16. Record the appropriate information from the Golden Rice case study on Student Sheet 2.3, "Genetics Case Study Comparison."

CASE STUDY

Golden Rice

EVERY DAY 3,000 people in the world die from having too little vitamin A in their bodies. Half a million infants become permanently blind each year from the same deficiency. Some geneticists claim to have found a solution, but others argue that what those geneticists are doing is more problematic than helpful.

Vitamin A is essential for the human body to function. Proper functioning of the immune system, vision, gene transcription, and bone metabolism all rely on vitamin A. The human body converts beta-carotene—a pigment found in carrots, leafy green vegetables, sweet potatoes, and many other foods—into vitamin A.

To combat vitamin A deficiency, experts in biotechnology have developed a way to deliver vitamin A to more people through rice. For more than 3 billion people, white rice is their main food.

The geneticists have inserted genes from plants with high levels of beta-carotene into the gene sequence of rice plants. These are the genes that cause the plants to produce beta-carotene, and the hope is that the rice will now produce beta-carotene. In their first attempts to genetically modify the rice, they inserted a daffodil gene. This modification, however, did not produce enough beta-carotene in the rice to meet a human body's daily needs.

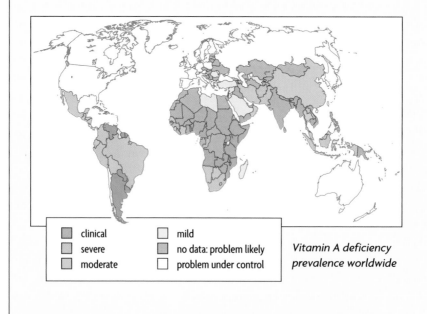

■ clinical	■ mild	
■ severe	■ no data: problem likely	
■ moderate	□ problem under control	

Vitamin A deficiency prevalence worldwide

In their second attempt, geneticists used a maize (corn) gene. The resulting strain of genetically modified rice, called Golden Rice 2, may succeed in reducing the numbers of people with vitamin A deficiency. The rice still has to be tested to determine how well the human body can absorb the beta-carotene in the rice. One concern is that the rice still may not contain enough beta-carotene. Another is that human bodies need protein and fat in their diets for converting beta-carotene to Vitamin A. Malnourished people, however, only rarely eat protein and fat.

Some groups object to the possible use of Golden Rice 2 to address Vitamin A deficiency. They argue that vitamin A deficiency would be better treated by increasing people's consumption of foods that naturally contain beta-carotene.

Eating more leafy greens, sweet potatoes, and other beta-carotene rich foods would alleviate other nutritional deficiencies as well. In addition, there are concerns that there has not been sufficient long-term testing for potential health side effects from genetically modified foods on humans and other organisms.

There are also objections to farming Golden Rice 2 because of the potential for cross-pollination with existing crops. Many rice farmers, particularly in areas where vitamin A deficiency is high, save and then plant their rice's seed from one season to the next, instead of buying new seed. They would have to buy genetically modified rice seed, which is expensive for them, unless the seed is donated by international aid agencies. ■

White and golden rice

Analysis

1. Compare the Punnett squares you constructed in Activity 4, "Breeding Corn," with the Punnett squares you constructed in this activity. By answering the following questions, show how the possible outcomes of a cross for one trait helps in analyzing two traits.

   a. How did you need to change the Punnett square to consider two traits?

   b. How would you need to change the Punnett square if you were to consider three traits?

2. Use the terms below to describe the information given in the Punnett square.

	R	r
R	R R	R r
r	R r	r r

   a. Genotype

   b. Phenotype

   c. Offspring

   d. Allele

3. In what ways might the planting and consumption of "golden rice" affect the sustainability of a community? Discuss it in terms of all three pillars of sustainability: economic, social, and environmental.

KEY VOCABULARY	
allele	phenotype
dihybrid cross	Punnett square
gamete	selective breeding
genotype	trait

7 Breeding Better Rice

RICE PROVIDES MORE than 20% of the calories consumed worldwide, and in some countries accounts for more than 90% of the agriculture. A grain of rice is the seed of the *Oryza sativa* plant. There are more than 100,000 varieties, differing in texture, color, grain length, and taste. To grow rice takes a lot of water. Some varieties, however, suffer damage in floods, while others are flood-tolerant and can be submerged in water for up to two weeks and remain unharmed.

Imagine you are a university professor studying food crop genetics. Your team specializes in selective breeding to produce crops with specific traits. The team has been studying flood tolerance and flavor in rice strains and is working with two strains of rice plants, which are described in the table below.

Rice Strains

STRAIN	AROMATIC (PLEASANT AROMA AND FLAVOR)	FLOOD-TOLERANT
1	yes	no
2	no	yes

Your team would like to selectively breed a variety of rice that tastes good and can be grown in flood-prone areas of the world.

This photograph shows 12 types of rice, each with a different genotype and phenotype. They vary in taste, nutritional value, optimal growing conditions, and other characteristics.

Challenge

▶ What trade-offs are involved in selectively breeding a desirable strain of rice?

MATERIALS

FOR EACH PAIR OF STUDENTS
2 yellow allele cards (A)
2 yellow allele cards (a)
2 green allele cards (F)
2 green allele cards (f)

FOR EACH STUDENT
Student Sheet 7.1, "Breeding Rice—Class Data"
Student Sheet 2.3, "Genetics Case Study comparison," from Activity 2

Procedure

Part A: The First Generation of Rice

1. Your research team breeds plants from Strain 1 with plants from Strain 2. After cross breeding the plants and allowing the offspring (F_1 generation) to grow, you find that none of these offspring are aromatic, but 100% are flood-tolerant. Based on these results, determine which traits are dominant and decide

   a. whether A or a represents the aromatic trait.

   b. whether F or f represents the flood-tolerant trait.

   Write your responses and your key to the alleles in your science notebook.

2. **a.** Based on the team's results, what is the genotype for both traits (aromatic and flood-tolerant) for the parent plant from Strain 1?

   b. Based on the team's results, what is the genotype for both traits (aromatic and flood-tolerant) for the parent plant from Strain 2?

3. Based on the genotypes you determined above for the parent plant from Strain 1 and the parent plant from Strain 2, what genotypes do you predict for the F_1 offspring described in Step 1? Construct a Punnett square to model your prediction.

4. Compare your work with the work done by the other pair in your group. If there are differences, discuss why the results do not agree.

Part B: The Second Generation of Rice

Now that you have determined the genotypes of the parent and F_1 generations, you will simulate the results (F_2 generation) of a cross between two F_1 generation plants. The goal is to produce rice that contains both desired traits.

5. Prepare a Punnett square to show all of the possible F_2 generation genotypes that could result from breeding two plants from the F_1 generation.

   a. What types and ratio of phenotypes would you expect from the cross?

   b. What percentage of the offspring do you predict will have the desired traits?

6. Create the chart shown below in your science notebook. Make rows for 10 offspring.

F_2 Generation Rice Plants

Offspring	Genotype (aromatic gene, flood gene)	Phenotype (aromatic trait, flood trait)
1		
2		

7. With your partner, simulate a cross between two F_1 generation rice plants. Each person should place four allele cards—$\underline{A}$, a, $\underline{F}$, and f—face down on the table and mix them up. Now, each of you takes one of the green cards and one of the yellow cards. Pair your two cards. You now have a gamete from one of the parent rice plants, and your partner has a gamete from the other parent rice plant. Individually your cards are the alleles. Lay your cards face up.

8. The four cards that are face up represent the genotype of an F_2 generation plant. Record the phenotype and genotype in your chart.

9. Reset by placing the cards you turned over back in the original pile and mixing them up.

10. Repeat Steps 7–9 until you have phenotypes and genotypes for 10 F_2 generation plants.

11. Add all of your results to the results of the other pair in your group, and record the data for the 20 offspring on Student Sheet 7.1, "Breeding Rice—Class Data."

12. Fill in the data from all the other groups on Student Sheet 7.1, and add the numbers of each type of gamete.

13. Discuss the class's results according to your teacher's instructions.

Part C: Selective Corn Breeding Case Study

14. Individually read the case study on selective breeding at right. Follow the literacy strategy, "Read, Think, and Take Note," as you read.

15. After reading, share your thinking with your group. Place your sticky notes on the table in front of you. Look for connections between your sticky-note comments and those of others in your group.

    Hint: Were there common questions people asked? Were people unfamiliar with the same words? Did people react differently to statements in the reading?

16. Place your sticky notes in your science notebook. Below them, write a short summary of what your group discussed and any conclusions the group came to.

17. Record the appropriate information from this case study on Student Sheet 2.3, "Genetics Case Study Comparison."

Corn is the most widely grown crop in the United States.

CASE STUDY

History of Selective Corn Breeding

TODAY, THE UNITED STATES grows more corn than any other crop, and produces much more corn than any other country in the world. In 2009, farmers in the United States planted 90 million acres of corn and harvested 13.2 billion bushels, worth billions of dollars. The largest percentage of this corn is for feeding to livestock. The remainder is for humans' consumption, corn-based biofuel, and other products. The following is a list of some of the products derived from corn: corn, corn meal, corn oil, corn starch, high fructose corn syrup, fuel alcohol, beverage alcohol, and corn feed. The ups and downs of corn-crop yields from year to year have a major impact on the U.S. economy and the availability and cost of food. Growing all of this corn also has a major environmental impact.

Corn has been grown in southern Mexico for more than 6,000 years. Both anthropological and genetic evidence suggest that corn is descended from the wild grass teosinte. Teosinte is native to Mexico and parts of Central America, and produces small hard kernels that people once cooked and ate. Some scientists think that the selective

(Continued on next page)

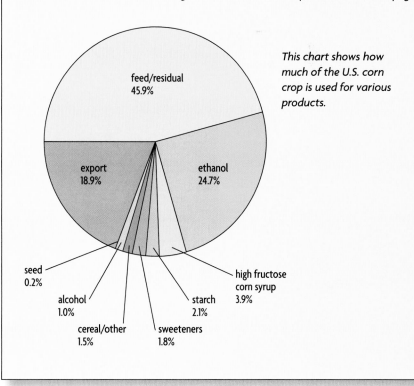

This chart shows how much of the U.S. corn crop is used for various products.

feed/residual
45.9%

ethanol
24.7%

export
18.9%

seed
0.2%

alcohol
1.0%

cereal/other
1.5%

sweeteners
1.8%

starch
2.1%

high fructose
corn syrup
3.9%

(Continued from previous page)

Teosinte plant

leaves of teosinte have high sugar content, and may have been chewed like chewing gum. People farming teosinte began to purposefully select and breed plants with desirable traits. They cultivated plants that produced more kernels per cluster and were resistant to drought and disease. Over the centuries, farmers continued to select and breed the plants that had traits that best suited their needs. As humans took the plants throughout North America, they selected plants that grew faster in the shorter summers and could withstand drought, while farmers who carried corn to the Caribbean islands selected plants that could withstand heavy rainfall. Today, because of human manipulation,

breeding of teosinte by native Mexican farmers eventually produced plants that we would recognize today as corn.

The differences between corn and teosinte are remarkable. Teosinte produces ears with a few seeds that each have a hard outer coating and are easily separated. In contrast, the corn you are familiar with produces hundreds of kernels per ear. These kernels are much larger, softer, and sweeter than teosinte kernels. Without human cultivation, current-day corn kernels would remain attached to the cob, and would not be dispersed or able to produce new plants.

At some point humans started to farm teosinte for food and other purposes. Anthropologists hypothesize that mashed dried kernels were used as a type of baby powder and as a healing substance. The

At the top is a Teosinte ear (Zea mays ssp mexicana); at the bottom, an ear of modern corn. In the middle is the F1 hybrid of these two species from the University of Wisconsin-Madison.

with as little as 5 inches of rain in a season, others thrive in as much as 150 inches of rain in a growing season.

Corn became a key crop in the United States in the mid-1800s as settlers' push westward vastly increased farmlands. Farmers continued to selectively breed corn for desirable traits. Some developed plants with low moisture in their kernels so they would be less likely to rot when stored for the winter. Since each farmer owned a limited amount of land and wanted to maximize the yield from each plant, they bred plants that produced more ears per plant. In the 1920s, farmers began to control which plants pollinated each other, and to improve their selection process, allowing

there are hundreds of varieties of corn. One type may be 2 feet tall while another grows to 12 feet tall; ears range from 1 to 18 inches long; and while some types grow

(Continued on next page)

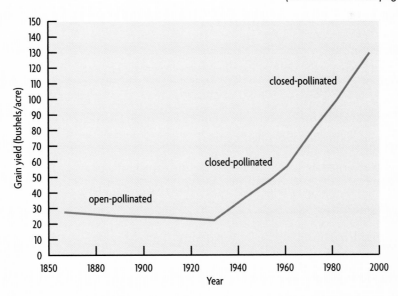

MODIFIED FROM: Lamkey, K. R. and J. W. Edwards. (1999.) *The quantitative genetics of heterosis.* Retrieved June 2010 from http://www.agron.iastate.edu/corn/Lamkey/Publications/PDF/heterosis.pdf, p. 2.

(Continued from previous page)

them to increase the amount of grain produced per plant. This is shown in the graph below. By the middle of the century such controlled pollination, instead of natural pollination by wind, rain, and birds, began to show much higher yields. Today, an average corn plant in the United States produces up to 800 kernels per ear of corn.

Today, farmers and agricultural scientists across the globe continue to breed corn to produce for certain purposes, such as feed corn or biofuel corn. New genetic technologies may lead to further improvements in selective breeding. One such development is the mapping of the corn genome completed in 2009. This map provides the location of each gene within corn's genetic material. It is hoped that this information will help model the results of crosses in laboratories. As this technology is further developed, it could significantly reduce the time it normally takes to selectively breed corn with a new trait. More breeding innovations may also help relieve sustainability challenges by enhancing not only the yield of corn for human consumption, but corn's use in other products, such as biofuel, textiles, and renewable fibers. ■

Analysis

Apply the data on Student Sheet 7.1, "Breeding Rice—Class Data," to answer Questions 1 and 2.

1. Based on the class's data, what is the ratio of the phenotypes expressed by the second-generation (F_2) offspring?

2. What fraction and percentage of the second-generation (F_2) offspring had the desired aromatic and flood-tolerance phenotype?

3. Based on what you have learned in this activity, describe and explain the procedure the university research team might follow to produce rice plants that are all aromatic and flood-tolerant.

4. In this activity, you considered breeding rice for two desired traits. Imagine that you would like to selectively breed rice for three or more traits. How would this affect your breeding efforts?

5. Look at the class's data on Student Sheet 7.1, "Breeding Rice." Compare the ratio of genotypes produced by the class with the ratio predicted by the Punnett square in Procedure Step 5 of Procedure Part B. Did the results follow those predicted by the Punnett square? Explain why the predicted outcome might be different from the actual outcome.

6. Examine the following table, listing the reproductive characteristics of three organisms. In the context of selective breeding, explain why a geneticist would need to understand each of these characteristics.

Reproductive Characteristics of Selected Organisms			
ORGANISM	MODE OF REPRODUCTION	AGE OF SEXUAL MATURITY	TOTAL POSSIBLE NUMBER OF OFFSPRING PRODUCED PER REPRODUCTIVE CYCLE
Rice plant	sexual reproduction	2–3 months	50 grains (seeds)
Corn plant	sexual reproduction	2–3 months	Up to 800 kernels (seeds) per ear Sweet corn has been bred to produce up to 6 ears per plant.
Cow	sexual reproduction	1 year	1

KEY VOCABULARY

allele	Punnett square
gamete	selective breeding
genotype	trait
phenotype	

8 Interpreting Pedigrees

SCIENTISTS ARE STUDYING *a recently discovered risk factor for heart disease, known as factor Z. Scientists have developed a test for factor Z, which they are currently using in a small island community with a high incidence of heart disease. In this community, where much of the population is related, a high percentage of the people also test positive for factor Z. Scientists have evidence that factor Z is likely a genetically inherited trait. The people on the island have agreed to participate in a study of the genetic basis of factor Z.*

In this activity, you will analyze data collected over several generations to determine the genetic mechanism of this trait. The mechanism of inheritance will be dominant, recessive, or sex-linked recessive.

Challenge

▶ What information can geneticists obtain by analyzing a pedigree?

MATERIALS

FOR EACH PAIR OF STUDENTS
  Family Risk Factor Data card
  card with additional risk factor data

FOR EACH STUDENT
  Student Sheet 8.1, "Family Pedigrees"

Procedure

Part A: How to Read a Pedigree

1. When geneticists want to track a trait over several generations, they often use a diagram called a pedigree. Similar to a family tree, a **pedigree** shows generations and relationships among biological parents and offspring. It also tracks which of those individuals have a specific trait. Shown on the next page is a pedigree tracing the appearance of black coats in a family of mice. With your partner, discuss the information shown in the pedigree and in the background information box below it.

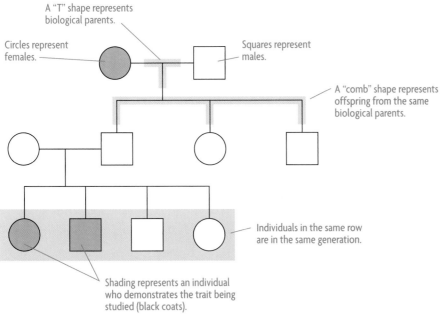

A "T" shape represents biological parents.

Circles represent females.

Squares represent males.

A "comb" shape represents offspring from the same biological parents.

Individuals in the same row are in the same generation.

Shading represents an individual who demonstrates the trait being studied (black coats).

SAMPLE PEDIGREE

BACKGROUND INFORMATION

Sex-linked Traits

THE ALLELE FOR a **sex-linked** trait is carried on one of the sex chromosomes. In humans, most other mammals, and some other organisms, females' sex chromosomes are X and X. In these organisms the males have only one X chromosome, and the other chromosome in the pair is a Y chromosome. Because males have only one allele for each sex-linked trait on the X chromosome, all alleles on the X chromosome are expressed in males, even if the trait is recessive. Sex-linked traits carried on the X chromosome are sometimes referred to as X-linked traits. There are only a few sex-linked traits on the Y chromosome in humans.

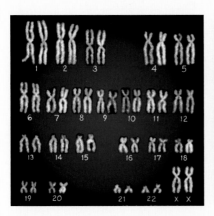
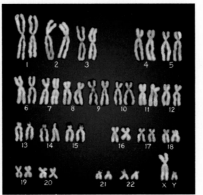

In humans, most sex-linked genes are carried on the X chromosome. These karyotypes show human female (left) and male (right) chromosomes.

2. Scientists think that factor Z may be one of the following types of genetic traits: dominant, recessive, or sex-linked recessive. With your group, discuss what it would mean over several generations for the populations that have factor Z if it were

a. a dominant trait.

b. a recessive trait.

c. a sex-linked recessive trait.

Write your ideas in your science notebook.

3. Pedigree A below shows where Huntington's disease appeared in several generations of one family. People who suffer from Huntington's disease are afflicted with severe muscle degeneration and dementia, usually starting in middle age. With your partner examine pedigree A. Record in your science notebook your answers to the following questions:

a. What patterns do you notice about which offspring have the trait? Can you tell from the pedigree which parents passed the allele for the trait to the affected offspring?

b. What evidence do you have that suggests the trait is dominant, recessive, or sex-linked recessive?

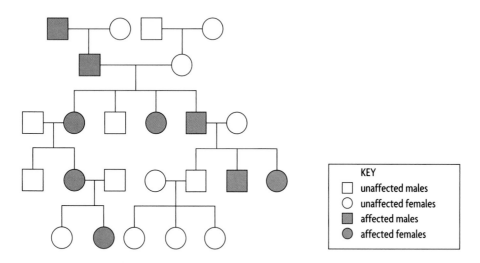

PEDIGREE A: HUNTINGTON'S DISEASE
Shading indicates that the individual is affected by Huntington's disease.

4. With your group, repeat Step 3 for pedigrees B and C shown below.

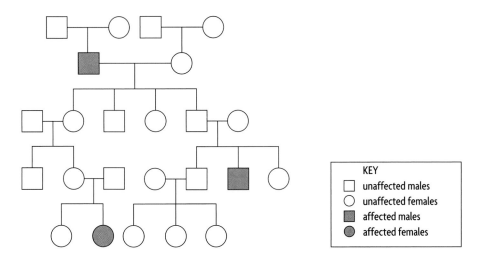

PEDIGREE B: PKU
Shading indicates the individual has PKU, or phenylketonuria. PKU, if not treated, causes mental retardation, seizures, and brain damage in the people who are afflicted by it.

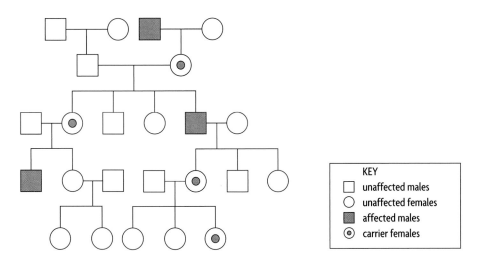

PEDIGREE C: HEMOPHILIA
Shading indicates individual with hemophilia: small circle (○) indicates an individual is a carrier of the trait, but is not afflicted. Generally a carrier can only be identified through genetic testing. Hemophilia is a disease that prevents a person's blood from clotting or coagulating properly. In a severe case, if a hemophiliac who is not receiving clotting treatment is injured, even slightly, the bleeding might not stop for hours, days, or longer and can be fatal. Carriers show no symptoms of the disorder.

5. Based on your conclusions, with the other pair in your group, compare the inheritance of dominant, recessive, and sex-linked recessive traits. Record your comparisons in your science notebook.

Part B: Using Pedigrees to Investigate Factor Z

6. In an attempt to determine what type of genetic mechanism causes factor Z, the genetic research scientists have interviewed families from two of the island's communities where there is a high number of people testing positive for factor Z. The scientists plan to create a pedigree showing who in each family expresses factor Z. Obtain a Family Risk Factor Data card for one of the families from your teacher. Take only one card for yourself and your partner, and together review the information on that card.

7. From the information on your Family Risk Factor Data card, fill in the pedigree for your assigned family on Student Sheet 8.1, "Family Pedigrees," including a key and indicating who in the family tests positive for factor Z. Be sure to use only the data shown on your card.

8. With your partner, discuss whether factor Z is a dominant, recessive, or sex-linked recessive trait.

9. Write a hypothesis in your science notebook stating whether the trait is dominant, recessive, or sex-linked recessive. Support your hypothesis with evidence from your pedigree and the Family Risk Factor Data card. If you determine that it is NOT one of these three mechanisms, cite evidence to support your reasoning.

10. Compare your pedigree and hypothesis with those of the other pair in your group, who have data on a different family. Discuss the similarities and differences between your data and hypotheses.

11. Predict the traits that would be exhibited in their offspring if Lynn, from the Sabah-Inde family, or Jackie, from the Brune-Pala family, had three children with an unaffected male, and if the trait were

    a. recessive.

    b. X-linked recessive.

12. Obtain an additional risk factor data card for your assigned family from your teacher. Does this additional data support your hypothesized mechanism for factor Z? Explain.

13. As a group,

    a. reach a consensus about the genetic mechanism of factor Z.

    b. revise your hypothesis if necessary to express the ideas of your group.

Analysis

1. What types of information does a pedigree give us?

2. Examine the pedigree below for grain plants with a trait for a high amount of protein. What can you determine about the trait based on the pedigree?

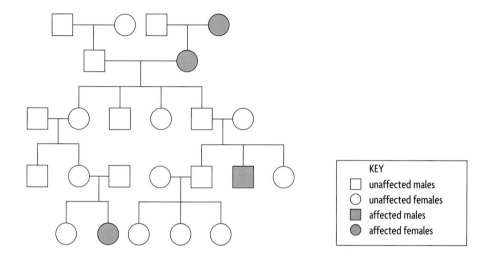

3. How do farmers and agricultural geneticists use the information provided by a pedigree to breed desirable traits in an agricultural crop?

4. Below is a pedigree for cattle that has been genetically modified to produce a human protein that helps prevent blood clots in humans. Using the information in the pedigree, answer the following questions:

   a. What type of inheritance mechanism—dominant, recessive, or sex-linked recessive—is shown in the pedigree? Support your answer with evidence.

   b. From the information in the pedigree from generation 3, can you determine if the gene is still present in the cow population? Explain why or why not.

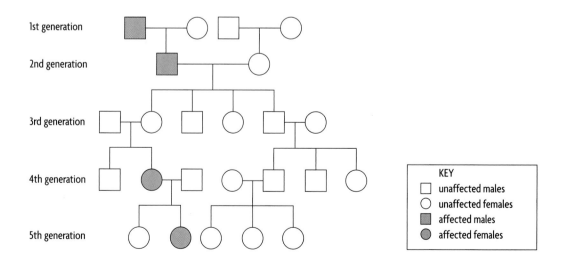

5. Imagine a population of endangered songbirds that are part of a captive breeding program at a zoo. If this population is known to have individuals with a genetic disease, how might an understanding of the mechanism of inheritance of this disease help scientists sustain this population?

6. Pedigrees for three traits—parasite resistance in biting flies, abnormal immune cell receptors in guinea pigs, and white eyes in fruit flies—are shown below. With your partner, determine the inheritance mechanism—dominant, recessive, or sex-linked recessive—that you think is supported by the pedigree. Write your answers in your science notebook. Include evidence to support your conclusions.

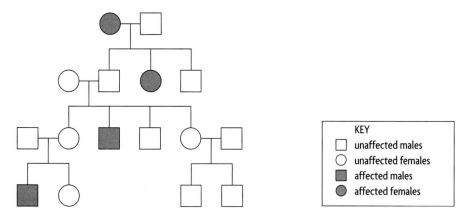

PEDIGREE 1: PARASITE RESISTANCE IN BITING FLIES

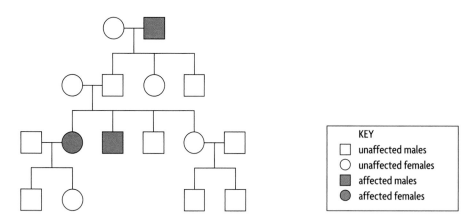

PEDIGREE 2: ABNORMAL IMMUNE CELL RECEPTORS IN GUINEA PIGS

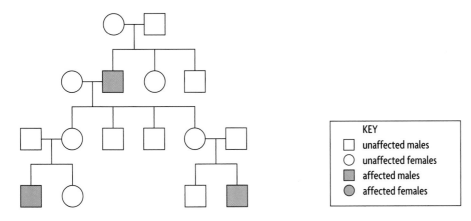

PEDIGREE 3: WHITE-EYED FRUIT FLIES

KEY VOCABULARY

allele	recessive
carrier	**sex-linked**
dominant	sex-linked recessive
pedigree	

9 DNA Isolation

As you explored in earlier activities, the process of making a genetically modified organism begins by identifying a desirable trait in another organism. The second step is to isolate the specific piece of DNA—the gene—that codes for that trait. Genes are made of **deoxyribonucleic acid (DNA),** a molecule that is present in every cell of every living organism.

In this activity, you will isolate DNA in various organisms by following a laboratory procedure developed by a team of scientists who isolated DNA from spinach. They published their results, and now other scientists are building on their work.

Challenge

▶ How is DNA isolated from an organism?

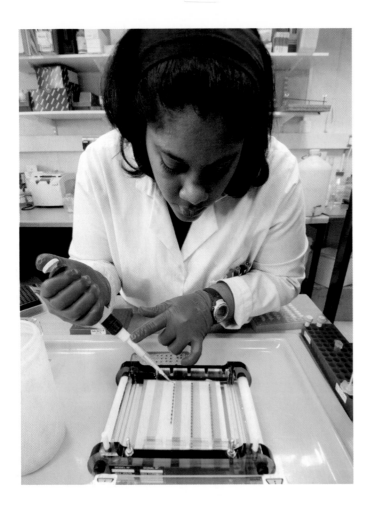

MATERIALS

FOR EACH GROUP OF FOUR STUDENTS

   bottle of cell lysis solution (detergent solution)

   bottle of chilled DNA precipitation solution (100% ethyl alcohol)

FOR EACH PAIR OF STUDENTS

2   test tubes

2   short SEPUP graduated cylinders

   dropper

   funnel

   sealable plastic bag

   square of cheesecloth

   timer

   organism sample (approximately 5 g)

FOR EACH STUDENT

   Student Sheet 9.1, "DNA Isolation Procedure"

Procedure

1. With your group, read the entire Procedure and the Spinach DNA Isolation Protocol to familiarize yourself with the steps. After doing so, summarize the purpose of the isolation steps on Student Sheet 9.1, "DNA Isolation Procedure."

2. Your teacher will assign you an organism to work with. With your group, follow the Spinach DNA Isolation Protocol to isolate DNA from your assigned organism.

3. Your teacher will explain how to share your results with the class.

Spinach DNA Isolation Protocol

1. Place the spinach sample into a plastic bag, seal the bag, and with your fingers mash the sample into a uniform pulp.

2. Add 10 mL of cell lysis solution to the bag, and reseal it, pushing out most of the air. Gently squeeze the mixture (without creating bubbles) for 1 minute.

3. Filter the mixture to separate the solids from the liquids. To do this:

   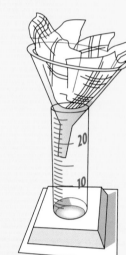

   a. Set up the filtering equipment. Place a funnel in a graduated cylinder, as shown at right. Place a piece of cheesecloth in the funnel.

   b. Slowly pour the mixture into the funnel. Let the liquid drip into the cylinder for approximately 5 minutes. (Be careful not to allow any solids to fall into the cylinder.)

4. Remove the funnel from the graduated cylinder.

5. Fill a test tube approximately half-full with DNA precipitation solution. Pick up the test tube, and hold it at a 45° angle. Using a dropper, slowly add the filtered liquid down the inside surface of the side of the test tube until both solutions fill ¾ of the test tube.

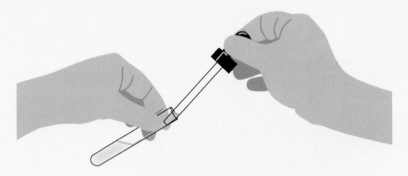

6. Let the solutions in the test tube sit for at least 3 minutes. A white layer of DNA should appear at the boundary between the two solutions.

Analysis

1. What was the purpose of mashing the sample in the plastic bag?

2. Describe the purpose of the cell lysis solution and the DNA precipitation solution.

3. Explain why it is important that scientists record detailed and specific procedures.

4. Compare the properties of DNA isolated from different organisms. What similarities did you observe?

5. How is the mechanism for isolating DNA from an organism connected to the mechanism for genetically modifying that organism?

KEY VOCABULARY	
cell	gene
deoxyribonucleic acid (DNA)	isolation

10 Modeling DNA Structure

DNA IS THE genetic material of all living organisms. Like proteins, carbohydrates, and lipids, DNA is a polymer—a large molecule made of many repeating subunits, called monomers. The subunits of DNA are nucleotides.

DNA contains information that codes for life's processes. Understanding the chemical structure of DNA allows scientists to understand how DNA codes for proteins. Scientists also need to understand the structure of DNA to determine how to isolate a specific desirable or undesirable gene from an organism.

In this activity, you will model the structure of DNA and explore how it provides information that directs the processes in a cell.

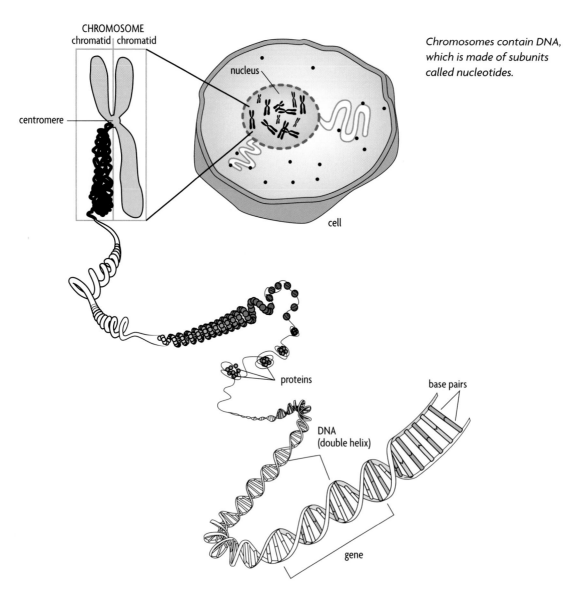

Chromosomes contain DNA, which is made of subunits called nucleotides.

Challenge

▶ What is the molecular structure of DNA?

MATERIALS

FOR EACH GROUP OF FOUR STUDENTS
    set of colored pencils

FOR EACH PAIR OF STUDENTS
    bag containing DNA model kit pieces
        36   black deoxyribose sugars pentagons
        36   white phosphate tubes
              various orange, yellow, blue, and green nitrogenous base tubes
        18   white hydrogen bond rods

Procedure

1. DNA is made of repeating subunits called nucleotides. A **nucleotide** is made of a sugar, a phosphate group, and a nitrogen-containing base. Identify each of these in the figure below.

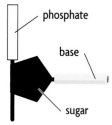

The nucleotide shown is composed of a deoxyribose sugar, a phosphate group, and a nitrogenous base.

2. There are four different nucleotides in DNA. These four vary only by which of the four bases they contain. The four bases are adenine, cytosine, guanine, and thymine. With your partner, use the DNA model kit to construct a DNA nucleotide as shown in the figure above.

Key for DNA Model Nitrogenous Bases	
NITROGENOUS BASES	**COLORED TUBE**
Adenine (A)	• Orange
Cytosine (C)	• Blue
Guanine (G)	• Yellow
Thymine (T)	• Green

3. Continue to build and connect a single chain of eight nucleotides, using any sequence of bases.

4. DNA occurs in its natural state as two strands linked down the middle by hydrogen bonds. Identify the two strands and the location of the hydrogen bonds in the figure below.

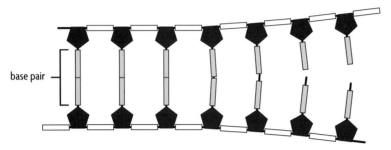

A **base pair** is two nucleotides in double-stranded DNA connected by hydrogen bonds.

BACKGROUND INFORMATION

Discovering the Structure of DNA

IN THE 1950S, discovering the structure of DNA became a subject of intense scientific investigation and rivalry. Several research groups competed to be the first to find the answer. These groups included the laboratory of Linus Pauling (who had earlier determined the structure of proteins) at the California Institute of Technology; scientists at Cambridge University in England; and another group of scientists at Kings' College of the University of London.

James Watson and Francis Crick of Cambridge University won the race. In 1953, after careful analysis of structural and chemical data—much of which was provided by Maurice Wilkins and Rosalind Franklin at Kings' College—Watson and Crick published a scientific paper that proposed that DNA is made of two strands spiraling to form a double helix. This structure not only accounts for the chemical makeup of DNA, but also allowed Watson and Crick to predict how DNA replicates when a cell divides. Their discovery opened up the field of molecular biology, which provides insights into the molecular basis of genetics, development, evolution, and other biological processes. Watson, Crick, and Wilkins were awarded the Nobel Prize in 1962, for their breakthrough. Unfortunately, Rosalind Franklin did not share in the prize because she had died in 1958, and the Nobel Prize is not awarded to someone who has died. The story of these scientists and their work is the subject of a number of books and articles.

5. In the mid-1940s, Erwin Chargaff, an Austrian scientist, analyzed the percentages of each of the four nitrogenous bases in DNA. A summary of his findings is shown in the table below. With your group, review the data, and search for patterns. Discuss what these patterns might suggest about the nucleotides in DNA.

Percentages of DNA Nucleotides in Selected Organisms

SOURCE OF DNA	ADENINE (A)	CYTOSINE (C)	GUANINE (G)	THYMINE (T)
Human	30.2%	18.8%	18.8%	32.2%
Rat	28.6%	21.6%	21.4%	28.4%
Sea Urchin	31.2%	19.1%	19.2%	30.5%
Salmon	29.2%	20.8%	21.9%	28.1%

6. Based on your conclusions from the data in Step 5, construct a second strand of DNA that pairs with the strand you built in Step 3.

7. Connect the two strands down the middle with hydrogen bonds.

8. With colored pencils sketch the resulting double-stranded DNA model in your notebook. On your sketch, label the following:

- Phosphate group
- Deoxyribose sugar
- DNA nucleotide
- Nitrogen base
- Hydrogen bond
- Base pair
- Sugar–phosphate backbone

9. At this point, your piece of DNA should resemble a ladder. Watch as your teacher connects several DNA models and demonstrates the shape of a DNA molecule.

10. With your group, look at the series of DNA models shown in the figures on the next page. Compare your DNA Model with the DNA in each image. Discuss what each model demonstrates about the structure of DNA. Record your ideas in your science notebook.

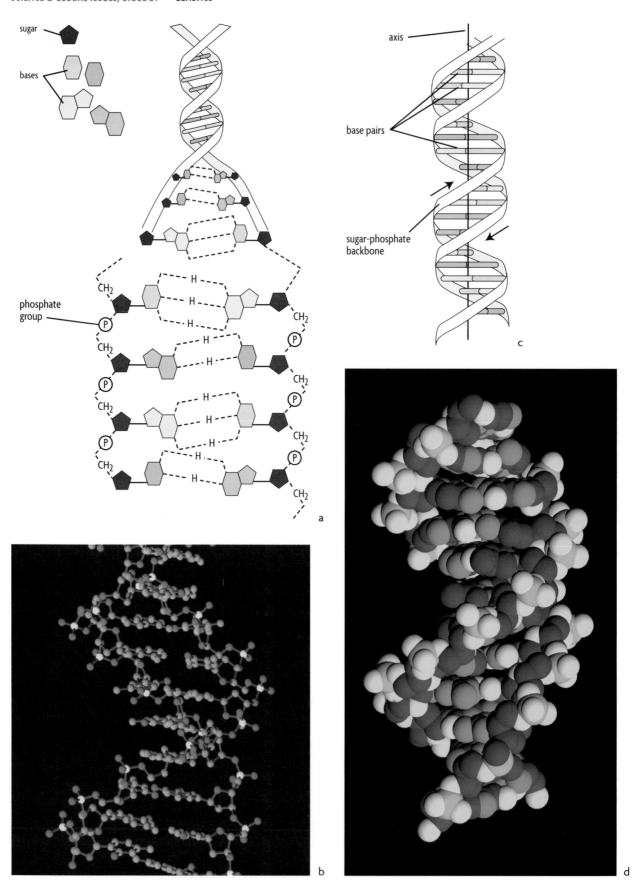

These images represent double-standed DNA in various levels of detail.

11. With your partner, identify the following in the images of DNA shown on the previous page:

- Phosphate group

- Deoxyribose sugar

- DNA nucleotide

- Nitrogen base

- Hydrogen bond

- Base pair

- Sugar–phosphate backbone

Analysis

1. How would you describe the structure of DNA to a 10-year-old?

2. What nucleotide sequence would bond with the following strand?
   5' ATCGCC 3'

3. Arrange the following cell structures from the smallest to the largest, left to right:
   DNA
   chromosomes
   gene
   cell

4. The table below shows the number of base pairs in the DNA of selected organisms. From the data in the table, what can you say about the amount of DNA contained in the cells of these three organisms?

Amount of DNA in an Average Cell of Selected Organisms	
ORGANISM	NUMBER OF BASE PAIRS
E. Coli	4.7 million
Corn (Zea Mays)	2.5 billion
Human (Homo sapiens)	3.3 billion

KEY VOCABULARY

base pair	hydrogen bond
double helix	**nucleotide**
deoxyribonucleic acid (DNA)	sugar–phosphate backbone

11 Genomics

U NDERSTANDING THE PHYSICAL characteristics and molecular structure of
DNA is a start to understanding the connections between an organism's
genotype and phenotype. But these are only two pieces of the puzzle. By sequencing an organism's genetic material, and mapping the DNA contained in that material, scientists have begun to understand the bigger pictures, including the
evolution of organisms and the genetic causes of some human diseases. In this
activity, you will read about the field of genomics.

Challenge

▶ How has genomics contributed to our understanding of heredity?

MATERIALS

FOR EACH STUDENT
Student Sheet 11.1, "Three-level Reading Guide: Genomics"

Procedure

1. Complete the reading below. When you have finished, complete Student
   Sheet 11.1, "Three-level Reading Guide: Genomics."

Reading

DNA: Information for Life

Every organism contains genes, which, along with environmental factors, control
every process necessary for life. Scientists are only beginning to understand how
phenotypes arise from genotypes, but they do know that genes play a central role.
These genes are coded in molecules of DNA. Since the 1944 discovery of DNA as the
molecule of heredity, scientists have investigated how the information encoded in
DNA directs the way cells reproduce, grow, and function. Even viruses, which are
not cells, contain genetic material in the form of either DNA or RNA, the same
genetic code used by organisms. This basic understanding is helping us tackle issues
related to sustainability. In recent years, new biotechnology tools have helped scientists explore DNA and genes in ways never before possible.

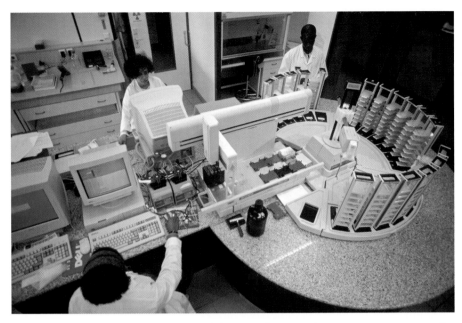

These researchers are monitoring the amplification of DNA. In this process, many copies of a DNA strand are made and used to sequence the DNA. By sequencing the order of the DNA, scientists hope to learn more about how the DNA determines an organisms's traits.

Scientists are using DNA from many organisms including people, corn, and termites to learn more about the connections between an organisms's phenotype and genotype.

The Field of Genomics

The complete sequence of an organism's genetic material is called its **genome**. **Genomics** is the study of this sequence and its organization. Since the role of DNA as genetic material was first discovered, scientists have learned a tremendous amount about it. Genomics aims to determine the sequence of bases in an organism's DNA, where the genes are located in that sequence, and how genes work together along with environmental factors to produce different phenotypes. Genomics research also determines which sections of genomes do not code for genes. In fact, current research indicates that in a typical eukaryotic genome, only 1%–5% codes for genes. Genomics has helped scientists to read the information in the DNA and begin to figure out its role in determining an organism's traits.

As you learned in Activity 10, "Modeling DNA Structure," DNA is a very long double-stranded molecule made of nucleotide subunits. Each nucleotide contains a sugar, a phosphate group, and one of four nitrogenous bases—adenine (A), thymine (T), cytosine (C), and guanine (G). The number and sequence of these bases varies from species to species. Variations in the size of genomes of several species are shown in the table below.

Selected Genome Sizes

ORGANISM OR VIRUS	ESTIMATED SIZE OF GENOME (BASE PAIRS)	ESTIMATED NUMBER OF GENES	NUMBER OF CHROMOSOMES
Amoeba *(Amoeba dubia)*	670 billion	Unknown	Unknown
Human *(Homo sapiens)*	3.2 billion	20,000–25,000	46
Mouse *(Mus musculus)*	2.6 billion	20,000–25,000	40
Fruit fly *(Drosophila melanogaster)*	137 million	13,000	8
Mouse-ear cress plant *(Arabidopsis thaliana)*	100 million	25,000	10
Roundworm *(Caenorhabditis elegans)*	97 million	19,000	12
Yeast *(Saccharomyces cerevisiae)*	12.1 million	6,000	32
Bacteria *(Escherichia coli)*	4.6 million	3,200	1
Bacteria *(Haemophilus influenzae)*	1.8 million	1,700	1
Rotavirus	18,555	11	—
Human immunodeficiency virus (HIV)	9,749*	9	—

This number represents single nucleotides, not base pairs, because the genome for HIV is single-stranded.

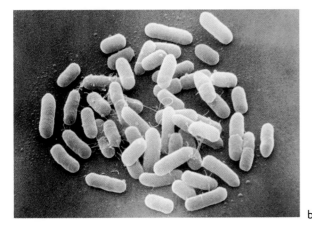

Scientists have sequenced the genomes of many organisms, including mice (a), E. coli (b), and A.Thaliana (c), which are frequently used in research.

Sequencing and Mapping a Genome

Analyzing an organism's genome involves several steps, each of which requires biotechnology tools developed over the past 30 years. First, scientists must isolate the DNA from the many other molecules in a cell of the organism. Next, they make multiple copies of the DNA through a process called polymerase chain reaction (PCR). They then sequence the DNA to determine the total number and order of each base. With this information, scientists can look for the locations of specific genes within the sequence. This is called gene mapping. They can also begin to identify which sections of the DNA do not code for genes. When sequencing and mapping are finished, scientists have the genome of the organism.

THE KEY STEPS TO ANALYZING A GENOME

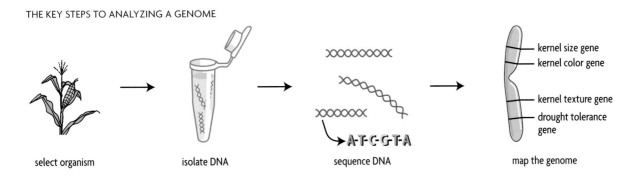

select organism   isolate DNA   sequence DNA   map the genome

kernel size gene
kernel color gene
kernel texture gene
drought tolerance gene

ATCGTA

The History of Genomics

In 1972, molecular biologist Walter Fiers and his research team at the University of Ghent in Belgium completed the first sequence of an individual gene in an RNA virus. In 1976, Fiers and his team sequenced the complete genome of the same virus. A year later in 1977, Frederick Sanger in the United Kingdom and Allan Maxam and Walter Gilbert in the United States independently developed sequencing methods that allowed scientists to sequence longer stretches of DNA or RNA. In 1977, Sanger published the first complete sequence of a DNA viral genome. Although the genome of a virus is very small compared to those in such organisms as plants and animals, these were major accomplishments.

TIMELINE OF SELECTED DNA GENOME SEQUENCING PROJECTS

As time progressed, scientists developed faster and cheaper technology for sequencing genomes. This allowed them to map and sequence the genomes of a wide range of viruses and organisms. On the previous page is a timeline of the completion of major genome sequencing projects. As more and more genomes were sequenced, the amount of information available for new directions in research increased rapidly. Scientists can now search for the location of genes within a genome, explore how genes work together, and compare genomes both within a population of organisms and between species.

The Human Genome Project

A monumental achievement was the sequencing of the human genome. In 1990, the United States Department of Energy and the National Institutes of Health co-sponsored the international Human Genome Project, with partner countries including the United Kingdom, Japan, France, and Germany. As stated on the project's website, the goals of the project were to

- *identify* all the approximately 20,000–25,000 genes in human DNA.
- *determine* the sequences of the 3 billion chemical base pairs that make up human DNA.
- *store* this information in databases.
- *improve* tools for data analysis.
- *transfer* related technologies to the private sector.
- *address* the ethical, legal, and social issues that may arise from the project.

It took 14 years of data collection and analysis to determine the human genome sequence. In 2000, the first rough draft of the human genome was published. Overall, the project determined basic information about the human genome, as shown in the box below. Before the completion of the Human Genome Project, it often took researchers years to identify genes associated with a disease or phenotype. With the information made available by the Human Genome Project, this can now be done much more rapidly.

Findings from the Human Genome Project

- The human genome contains 3.2 billion nucleotide base pairs.
- The total number of genes in the human genome is 20,000–25,000. This is much lower than numbers predicted previously, which estimated 80,000–100,000 human genes.
- Genome sequences are 99.9% the same from one person to the next.
- Only 2% of DNA codes for the synthesis of proteins.

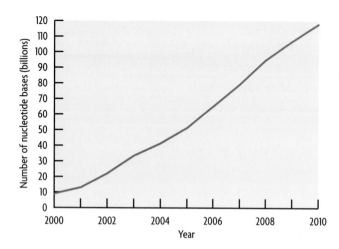

The number of nucleotide bases sequenced increased dramatically between 2000 and 2010.

The Human Genome Project was historic in many ways. It was the first major global project in which all results were made public. The entire human genome sequence was released in an online database. Researchers developed ways to catalog the vast amounts of data so that it could be easily used in future research projects. In addition, committees of scientists, ethicists, attorneys, and policy makers worked together to write guidelines for the use of human genetic data.

The techniques and information developed through the Human Genome Project have inspired a host of new projects that explored the connection between an organism's genome and its phenotype. One was the HapMap project that compared the DNA sequences of people from around the world. HapMap scientists collected DNA samples from populations having Asian, African, or European ancestry. They sequenced specific regions of each person's genome and entered the information into a database freely available to all researchers. With these data scientists are studying the similarities and differences between the populations sampled. From this information, they hope to study human variation and determine which specific gene sequences in human populations contribute to diseases.

Genomics and Sustainability

Since its first applications in the 1970s, genomic technology has advanced rapidly. Scientists have devised ever better equipment and methods for sequencing the genomes of most major model research organisms, and they continue to sequence and map more genomes each year. Genomics data are now freely available to researchers worldwide.

Advances in genomic technology have led to investigations beyond medical applications in a wide range of areas, such as alternative energy sources, ecosystem biodiversity, and evolution. Sample projects include:

* **ALTERNATIVE ENERGY:** Scientists have sequenced the genomes of bacteria found in termite digestive tracts. These bacteria break down the cellulose in the wood that termites ingest. From this information scientists hope to find ways to easily break down cellulose to produce ethanol for biofuel.

- **ECOSYSTEM BIODIVERSITY:** A team of scientists circumnavigated the world by sea, taking ocean water samples every 200 miles. They sequenced the DNA found in each sample to construct a genomic profile of each sample and chart the biodiversity and dynamics of the ecosystems of the world's oceans. Similar investigations of the genomic profiles of organisms in terrestrial and other aquatic ecosystems worldwide are also under way.

- **EVOLUTION:** Scientists continually add new material to the database of genomes from living and extinct species. With that information they can compare species and organisms of the same species to investigate evolutionary relationships. This is called comparative genomics.

- **HUMAN HEALTH:** The Human Genome Project so far has identified and sequenced the genes for such diseases as cystic fibrosis, types of blindness and deafness, and certain cancers. This information helps identify individuals' risk for a disease and could help develop therapies and cures for various conditions.

Genomics may help scientists understand the evolution of species, such as these two Hawaiian honeycreepers.

The Future of Genomics

The Human Genome Project is complete, but our understanding of how genes are read, how they interact, how they are influenced by environmental factors, and how they produce both normal human traits and disease is far from complete. Many years of additional work and international collaboration are needed to understand the human genome.

Mapping genomes and understanding the role of genetic information in all realms of life presents astounding possibilities. This information combined with extensive further research about the interaction of genes with the environment, may lead to a much more sophisticated understanding about how phenotypes arise. For example, scientists might apply this research to answer questions that may contribute to sustainable solutions for societal problems, such as

- How does a cancer patient's genome affect which anti-cancer drugs are most likely to be effective in that patient?
- How can understanding genetic risk factors for disease lead to more effective methods of disease prevention and treatment?
- How can microbes be engineered to help clean up toxic wastes?

Analysis

1. What is genomics?

2. How has the field of genomics developed over the past 40 years?

3. Describe the Human Genome Project and its major accomplishments.

4. How can genomic research help scientists understand the mechanisms of heredity?

5. What types of sustainability challenges have scientists researched using genomics?

KEY VOCABULARY	
DNA	**genomics**
gene	nucleotide
genome	

12 DNA Replication

IN ACTIVITY 10, "Modeling DNA Structure," you learned about the work of Watson, Crick, Wilkins, and Franklin that led to the discovery of the structure of DNA (deoxyribonucleic acid). Based on their proposed structure of DNA, Watson and Crick also hypothesized how DNA is replicated. **Replication** is the process by which DNA is copied within each cell. Without replication, cells would not be able to make and then pass on to daughter cells copies of chromosomes and the genes they carry.

In the late 1950s, several hypotheses that described DNA replication had been proposed. To test these hypotheses, two American scientists, Matthew Meselson and Franklin Stahl, performed an experiment with the bacteria *E. coli.*

In this activity you will read about the three hypotheses that Meselson and Stahl tested, weigh the evidence that they gathered from their experiments, and decide which DNA replication hypothesis their results support.

Challenge

▶ How does DNA replicate?

MATERIALS

FOR EACH PAIR OF STUDENTS

bag containing DNA model kit pieces

  36   black deoxyribose sugars pentagons

  36   white phosphate tubes

        various orange, yellow, blue, and green nitrogenous base tubes

  18   white hydrogen bond rods

access to online simulation, "DNA Replication"

FOR EACH STUDENT

Student Sheet 12.1, "Investigating DNA Replication"

Procedure

1. With your group, read the description and examine the images of each of the three possible hypotheses for DNA replication below. Discuss the differences between the three hypotheses, and in your science notebook summarize the result of replication according to each hypothesis.

Hypothesis 1: Conservative DNA Replication

The original DNA strand "unzips" down the center. Individual nucleotides link together to make a copy of each strand. The new strands unbind from the original strands, allowing the original strands to bind back together.

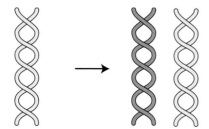

original DNA double helix   conservative DNA replication

Hypothesis 2: Semi-conservative DNA Replication

The original DNA strand "unzips" down the center. Individual nucleotides link together to make a copy of each strand. The DNA formed contains one old and one new strand.

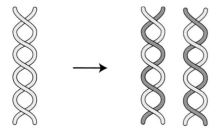

original DNA double helix   semi-conservative DNA replication

Hypothesis 3: Dispersive DNA Replication

The original DNA strand "unzips" down the center. Individual nucleotides link together to make a copy of the original strand. The original pieces and the new pieces join in random combinations.

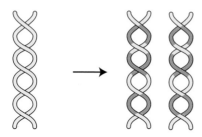

original DNA double helix   dispersive DNA replication

2. With your group, construct a DNA model to show the result of replication described by each of the three hypotheses. Start by assembling a double-stranded sequence of DNA that is three nucleotides long and contains the nucleotide sequence ATG on one of its strands.

   Note: Refer to Activity 10, "Modeling DNA Structure," if you need help assembling the DNA.

3. With your group decide which of the three proposed replication methods you think is correct. Record your choice and the reasoning for it in your science notebook.

4. Find the "Replicating DNA" simulation on the *Science and Global Issues* page of the SEPUP website *(sepuplhs.org/sgi)*. With your partner, complete the simulation, referring to Student Sheet 12.1, "Investigating DNA Replication," to guide you.

Analysis

1. Describe how DNA replicates.

2. How does identifying alternate hypotheses help scientists design and analyze experiments?

3. Return to the list of ideas your class generated at the beginning of this activity to explain ways DNA might replicate. How did your ideas change?

KEY VOCABULARY		
DNA	**replication**	
nucleotide		

13 Meiosis and Sexual Reproduction

As **YOU LEARNED** in Activity 5, "Genes and Traits," Gregor Mendel explained the results of his pea plant crosses by saying that each parent contributed a unit of information to each offspring. These units of information came to be known as genes. Mendel knew that the genes had to be in the male and female sex cells—the sperm (or pollen) and the egg. For the next 50 years, scientists did not know where in the cell the genes were located, but they continued to breed improved crops and livestock.

As microscope technology improved, scientists discovered small dark structures in cells that they named chromosomes. As scientists watched the behavior of chromosomes during the formation of sex cells, or gametes, they made a significant observation: in the sex cells the number of these chromosomes was reduced to half the normal number in other cells. They realized that the chromosomes must carry the genes. The process that results in this halving of the chromosome number is called meiosis. **Meiosis** is the process of cell division that occurs in developing sex cells. In human males, meiosis occurs in those cells that differentiate into sperm in the testes. In human females, meiosis occurs in the cells that differentiate into eggs in the ovaries. It is only after egg and sperm are joined at fertilization that the full number of chromosomes the new offspring needs is restored.

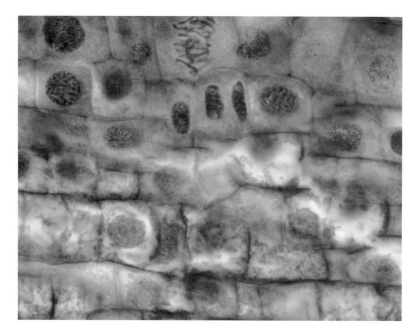

Onion root tips undergo mitosis to make new cells. The new daughter cells are identical to the parent cell.

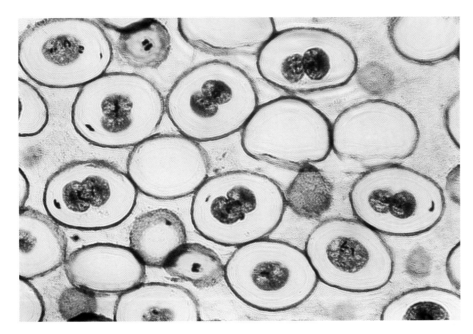

These Ascaris (roundworm) cells are undergoing meiosis. This produces gametes (sex cells) with half the number of chromosomes of the parent cells.

Challenge

▶ How do chromosomes divide during the formation of egg and sperm cells?

MATERIALS

FOR EACH PAIR OF STUDENTS

    set of 2 pop-bead chromosome models

16 blue pop beads

16 green pop beads

2 orange pop beads

2 blue centromeres

2 green centromeres

    colored pencils

    access to online meiosis simulations

FOR EACH STUDENT

    Student Sheet 13.1, "Meiosis"

    Student Sheet 13.2, "Mitosis and Meiosis Comparison"

3 sticky notes

    Student Sheet 2.3, "Genetics Case Study Comparison," from Activity 2

Procedure

Part A: Modeling Meiosis

1. Observe the meiosis simulation on the *Science and Global Issues* page of the SEPUP website *(sepuplhs.org/sgi)*. Determine what happens to the genetic material of the cell at each phase.

2. On Student Sheet 13.1, "Meiosis," draw what happens to the chromosomes during each phase shown.

3. In your science notebook, write a description summarizing the key events of each stage of meiosis.

4. With your partner, use the pop beads to model chromosomes and show what happens when a cell with two chromosomes—one pair—undergoes meiosis. To do this:

   a. Make two strands of four blue pop beads and attach them to the blue centromere. Repeat this process for green. This represents one pair of chromosomes.

   b. Simulate the replication of each chromosome during prophase I. To do this, repeat Step 4a. Use the centromeres to form the shape of the replicated chromosome shown below. Note that the X shape is a replicated chromosome, and so the model demonstrates one pair of replicated chromosomes, with a total of four sister chromatids.

5. **Crossing over** is a phenomenon that might happen, but only during prophase in meiosis I. During crossing over, homologous chromosomes exchange portions, as shown below. With the pop-bead model demonstrate crossing over between the replicated chromosomes you built in Step 4b. In your science notebook, describe crossing over.

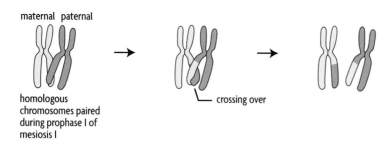

6. Move the chromosome models through each remaining phase of meiosis to show what occurs as they move through prophase, metaphase, anaphase, and telophase of meiosis I and II, and the cells that result. In your science notebook, use colored pencils to sketch the chromosomes at each stage.

7. Repeat Steps 4–6 with the following modification:

   Model a chromosome in a cell that has been genetically modified to contain a new gene. Take an orange pop bead, and switch out one segment of one chromosome. With your partner work with your pop-bead model chromosomes and your understanding of meiosis to determine:

   • What is the probability that a daughter cell will receive a gene that was inserted into one chromosome in a parent cell?

   In your discussion, incorporate the terms that follow:

   DNA   daughter cell
   chromosome   gene
   parent cell

8. Share your model and your reasoning from Step 7 with the other pair in your group. Discuss any differences in your ideas.

9. In your science notebook, write an answer to the question posed in Step 7. Incorporate each of the terms from the list above in your writing.

10. Return to the computer simulation on the *Science and Global Issues* page of the SEPUP website *(sepuplhs.org/sgi)*. Proceed to the page comparing mitosis and meiosis, and complete the simulation.

11. In your science notebook, write a description summarizing the similarities and differences between mitosis and meiosis.

Part B: Fast-growing Salmon Case Study

12. Individually read the case study on the following pages. As you read, use the literacy strategy, "Read, Think, and Take Note." To do this:

    • Stop at least three times during the reading to mark on a sticky note your thoughts or questions about the reading.

    • After writing a thought or question on a sticky note, place it next to the passage in the reading that prompted your note.

13. Share your thinking with your group. Place your sticky notes on the table in front of you. Look for connections between your notes and those of others in your group.

    Hint: Were there common questions people asked? Were people unfamiliar with the same words? Did people react differently to statements in the reading?

14. Place your sticky notes in your science notebook. Below them write a short summary of what your group discussed and any conclusions your group came to.

15. Record the appropriate information from this case study on Student Sheet 2.3, "Genetics Case Study Comparison."

CASE STUDY

Fast-growing Salmon

THE AQUACULTURE INDUSTRY has long been on the lookout for ways to grow fish faster while spending less money. Industry leaders hope to meet the increasing demand for fish, increase profits, and reduce the environmental impact of fishing. In recent years they have teamed up with genetic scientists to find ways to speed up fishes' growth rates. Geneticists are currently researching methods to genetically modify a number of farmed fish species, including members of the salmonid family (salmon and trout) and other commercially important species like catfish and tilapia.

One promising idea involves inserting a growth-hormone gene from the Pacific chinook salmon *(Oncorhynchus tshawytscha)* into the Atlantic salmon *(Salmo salar)*. Like humans, salmon produce a growth hormone that signals their bodies to grow. Normally the fish grow at a certain rate, depending on environmental conditions, including food availability. If the genetic modification works as intended, the growth rate of the genetically modified fish should increase so that they grow large enough to be sold four times faster than unmodified salmon. Geneticists have succeeded in producing this genetically modified salmon, but, along with success, there has been controversy.

One concern about genetically modified salmon is that if they escape from their net pens, they could breed with wild salmon and make those salmon less fit. Wild female salmon are most likely to mate with larger males. Studies have shown that in some fish species females mate more frequently with the genetically modified males. Studies of genetically modified fish have also shown that in some species genetically modified males breed offspring that do not survive as well in the wild and are

A gene from the Pacific Chinook salmon, above, has been inserted into the Atlantic salmon, right, to make them grow much faster than unmodified salmon.

more likely to be eaten by predators. This also prevents the unmodified, wild males from having as many mating opportunities, which depletes the wild populations of fish.

A group of scientists at Purdue University in Indiana created a computer model to examine what would happen if 60 genetically modified fish were released into a population of 60,000 wild fish. They used a species of fish called medaka. The computer model predicted that if the genetically modified medaka and wild medaka successfully reproduced, within 30 generations the wild fish would be extinct. One option to prevent genetically modified fish from disrupting wild populations is to make them sterile. Salmon eggs

may be treated just after fertilization so that they grow into sterile adult fish, but this technique is not always 100% effective.

Another concern is how much genetically modified salmon eat. Some studies show that they eat the same amount as wild salmon, and therefore would not out-eat the wild fish if they escaped. Other studies, however, have shown that genetically modified salmon eat up to three times as much as the wild fish.

Researchers continue to investigate the possible damage genetically modified salmon might do to wild populations, and how to prevent these kinds of problems. As of 2009, genetically modified salmon have not been approved for commercial sale in the United States. ■

Net pens for growing farmed salmon are often built along the migration routes of wild salmon, which poses a problem if the farmed salmon escape.

Analysis

1. How do the daughter cells that result from meiosis compare to the parent cell?

2. Draw meiosis I and II, starting with the parent cell shown below. What possible allele combinations could form in gametes produced from these cells?

3. Explain how crossing over can affect the genetic makeup of the gametes an organism produces.

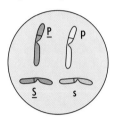

4. A salmon is genetically modified in a laboratory by inserting one gene into one chromosome of a pair. The salmon escapes, and breeds with a wild, unmodified salmon. Would you expect all of the offspring to be genetically modified? Explain your reasoning.

KEY VOCABULARY	
chromosome	gene
crossing over	**meiosis**
daughter cell	mitosis
DNA	parent cell
gametes	

14 Genes and Chromosomes

As **you have** observed in the previous activities, the behavior of chromosomes in cells helps to explain the behavior of genes that are passed from one generation to the next. Understanding the behavior of chromosomes is also fundamental to learning how inserting genes into an organism might affect the function of the organism's genome.

Challenge

▶ How do genes and chromosomes behave during meiosis and sexual reproduction?

MATERIALS

FOR EACH STUDENT
Student Sheet 14.1, "Three-level Reading Guide: Genes and Chromosomes"

Procedure

1. Refer to Student Sheet 14.1, "Three-level Reading Guide: Genes and Chromosomes," to guide you as you complete the following reading.

Humans have 46 chromosomes and the same sequence of genes. Variations in the alleles for same genes, along with environmental factors, cause variation in human phenotypes.

Reading

Chromosomes Carry Genes

In each cell of a living organism, DNA carries the genetic information in the sequence of its nitrogen bases. The DNA is wrapped with proteins into structures called chromosomes. A gene is the section of DNA in a chromosome that contains information that influences one or more traits.

The number of chromosomes in each cell of an organism depends on the species. Bacteria, such as *Escherichia coli (E. coli),* have one circular chromosome that contains about 4,500 genes. In addition, some bacteria also have one or more smaller plasmids that carry a small number of genes. In comparison, a human body cell contains 46 chromosomes, carrying 20,000–25,000 genes. This means that most human chromosomes carry hundreds of genes. Every cell in the human body except for the sex cells contains the same set of 46 chromosomes.

In eukaryotes (organisms with a nucleus in each cell), the chromosomes are present in pairs. Each chromosome in a pair is similar to its partner in size and the genes it carries, except for the chromosome pair that determines the organism's sex. The image at right, called a karyotype, illustrates the 23 pairs of chromosomes in the cell of a human male. Notice that chromosomes in pairs 1–22 are identical in size and shape. The two chromosomes of pair 23 are the sex chromosomes—they determine the individual's sex. In human males, pair 23 has one X chromosome and one Y chromosome. These two chromosomes differ in size and shape. If this were a karyotype for a human female, pair 23 would contain two X chromosomes.

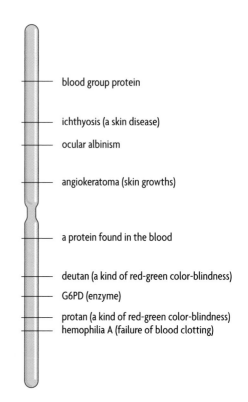

- blood group protein
- ichthyosis (a skin disease)
- ocular albinism
- angiokeratoma (skin growths)
- a protein found in the blood
- deutan (a kind of red-green color-blindness)
- G6PD (enzyme)
- protan (a kind of red-green color-blindness)
- hemophilia A (failure of blood clotting)

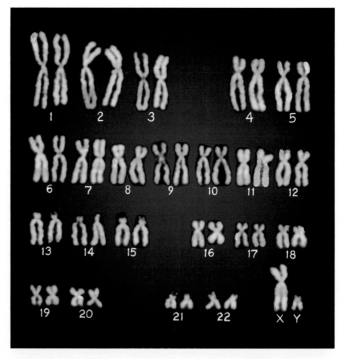

The map of the human X chromosome, top, shows the location of several specific genes and the traits they influence. This male karyotype, above, shows the X chromosome and smaller Y chromosomes present in male cells.

Growth and Reproduction

For organisms to grow and reproduce, cells must divide to form offspring cells, called daughter cells. As you know, during mitosis the chromosomes are divided evenly between the two new cells to produce two daughter cells that are identical to the parent cell. This occurs regularly for cell growth and tissue repair in somatic cells (body cells, but not reproductive cells) in multicellular organisms, such as humans, and in single-celled organisms, such as *E. coli.* In this way, cells in the body of a multicellular organism, except for the sex cells, are exact copies of the parent cell.

How and why are gametes different from the rest of the cells in an organism? The answer lies in the processes of meiosis and sexual reproduction. Sexual reproduction occurs when a male sperm fertilizes a female egg. If these sex cells had a full set of chromosomes, each generation would have twice the number of chromosomes as its parents. Meiosis produces gametes (egg or sperm) that have half as many chromosomes as other cells in the body to prevent this from happening.

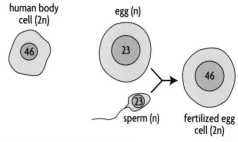

SEX CELLS AND FERTILIZATION

A gamete is **haploid** because it has one set of chromosomes. This is referred to as n chromosomes. Human gametes contain 23 chromosomes (n = 23). A somatic (nonreproductive) cell is **diploid** (has 2n chromosomes) because it has pairs of chromosomes. When a human haploid egg and haploid sperm unite by fertilization, they form a diploid cell with 46 chromosomes (23 pairs). Below is a table showing the number of chromosomes found in several organisms.

Number of Chromosomes in Several Organisms		
ORGANISM	DIPLOID (2n) CHROMOSOMES FOUND IN SOMATIC CELLS	HAPLOID (n) CHROMOSOMES FOUND IN SEX CELLS
Human	46	23
Corn	20	10
Rye plant	14	7
Common fruit fly	8	4
Garden snail	54	27
Gorilla	48	24
Elephant	56	28

Chromosomes and Genes

In the beginning of this unit, you modeled the process of crossing corn plants with such traits as purple or yellow and smooth or wrinkled kernels, which shows independent assortment. When Gregor Mendel was first developing his theories on genetics, he proposed that there is a law of independent assortment. Independent assortment means that it is equally likely for a PpSs corn plant to produce any of four kinds of gametes: PS, Ps, pS, and ps.

Now that scientists have determined that genes are sections of chromosomes, we know that genes on the same chromosome usually stay together during meiosis. These are called "linked genes," and they don't usually show independent assortment. The combination of traits they influence is passed on to the next generation together. For example, in fruit flies the genes for body color and eye color are found on the same chromosome. Therefore, a parent with a grey body and yellow eyes would pass on this combination of genes to its offspring.

In the figure on the next page, "Chromosomes and Meiosis," the red chromosomes represent ones inherited from the female parent, while the blue ones represent those inherited from the male parent. When the chromosomes line up before division, the paternal and maternal chromosomes in the pair line up randomly and separate independently of each other. This is called independent segregation of the chromosomes. Independent segregation of chromosomes explains the behavior of genes that follow Mendel's law of independent assortment. It also accounts for the fact that genes that are linked on the same chromosome don't follow the law of independent assortment, also shown on the next page.

Sexual reproduction and human variation

What happens in meiosis also helps explain why siblings are not identical. In Activity 13, "Meiosis and Sexual Reproduction," you observed the variations in gametes produced by one parent due to both independent segregation and crossing over of chromosomes. New combinations of chromosomes from two different parents produce offspring with a combination of traits from both parents. Notice that the offspring formed by fertilization inherits one set of chromosomes from each parent. This explains why an offspring only inherits one allele for each gene from each parent.

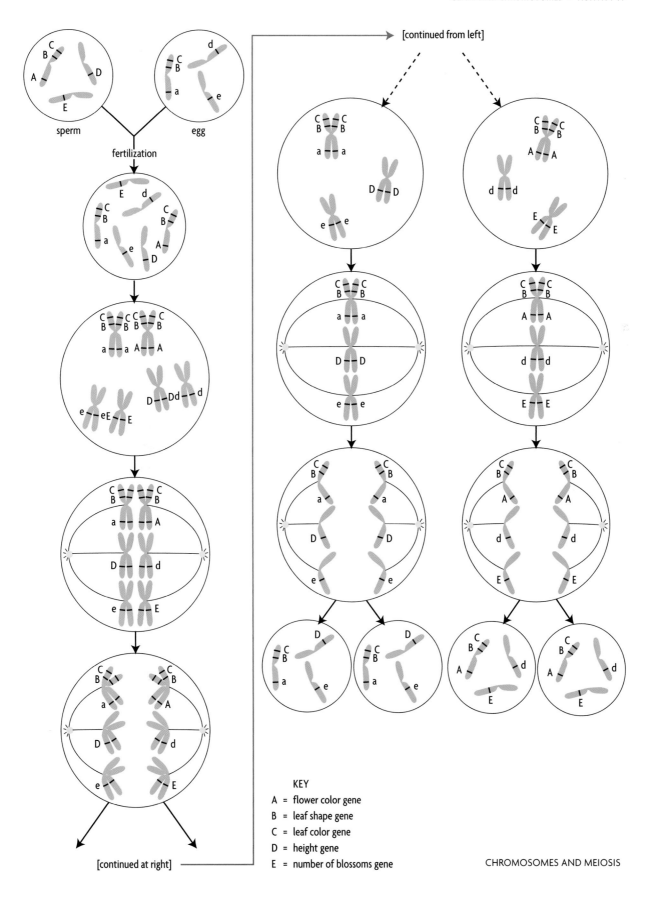

[continued from left]

sperm

egg

fertilization

[continued at right]

KEY

A = flower color gene
B = leaf shape gene
C = leaf color gene
D = height gene
E = number of blossoms gene

CHROMOSOMES AND MEIOSIS

Another source of chromosomal variation in gametes occurs during a process called crossing over. This only happens during meiosis I when chromosomes exchange segments at their ends, as shown in the figure below. Crossing over happens quite frequently and substantially increases the genetic variation of gametes an individual can generate.

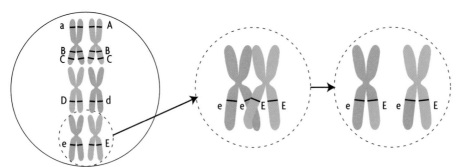

These two chromosomes have exchanged segments of their DNA, through crossing over or a cross-over event. Each chromosome now has DNA from both the maternal and paternal parent.

Abnormal meiosis

Meiosis does not always go perfectly. Several human genetic conditions result when errors during meiosis lead to abnormalities in chromosome number, shape, or size. Genetic specialists use karyotypes to test for chromosome abnormalities. To make a karyotype, the white blood cells are separated from a sample of the patient's blood. These cells are placed in a solution with a substance that causes them to divide. Then, another substance is added to stop the cell division in metaphase, when the chromosomes are at their most condensed and easy to see. The cells are then squashed on a microscope slide, stained with a special dye, and photographed. The images of the chromosomes are then arranged in pairs according to size and shape.

One of the most common errors that occurs in meiosis is nondisjunction. **Nondisjunction** is the failure of chromosomes to separate during cell division. If this happens, a gamete can form with an extra chromosome or missing chromosome. Most nondisjunctions result in gametes that either cannot participate in fertilization, or they produce zygotes that do not survive past the initial stages of cell division. In human fertilizations, however, there are instances where chromosomal abnormalities appear in an offspring, as shown in the chart of chromosome-related syndromes on the next page.

Chromosome-Related Syndromes

SYNDROME NAME	CHROMOSOMAL ABNORMALITY	COMMON EFFECTS
Down syndrome	Three copies of chromosome 21 (trisomy 21)	Delayed physical and mental development, heart defects
Klinefelter syndrome	Males have extra X chromosome (XXY)	Learning difficulties, sometimes sterility, higher risk for some forms of cancer and heart disease
Prader-Willi syndrome	Missing part of chromosome 15	Reduced muscle tone, short stature, learning difficulties, chronic hunger
Turner syndrome	Females missing all or part of an X chromosome	Short stature, sometimes sterility, sometimes do not enter or complete puberty

The phenotypes produced by these conditions vary. For example, the effects of Down syndrome, one of the most common chromosome abnormalities, are usually mild to moderate, but sometimes severe. Educational interventions and good health care often improve the outlook for affected individuals. Today, most individuals with chromosomal abnormalities live full and productive lives.

Analysis

1. Explain the relationship between genes, chromosomes, and DNA.

2. A species of snail has 24 chromosomes—12 pairs—in each somatic cell. How many chromosomes are there in a snail egg cell? A snail sperm cell?

3. How does the number of chromosomes in gametes of an organism that reproduces sexually differ from the number of chromosomes in its other cells? Explain.

4. Describe how each of the following increases human variation:

   a. Independent segregation of chromosomes during meiosis

   b. Crossing over

5. Define nondisjunction and explain its effect on a sex cell.

6. The chromosomes pictured below are from a fruit fly that is heterozygous for two traits. How many kinds of gametes could form if this were in a male? A female?

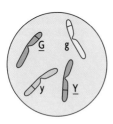

7. Consider your answer to Question 6. Explain how crossing over could affect the gametes that result.

8. If the fruit fly from Question 6 also had a gene on that chromosome that was genetically modified to produce red spots on its body, and it mated with a wild fruit fly that was not genetically modified, what would you expect to see in the offspring?

KEY VOCABULARY

chromosome	karyotype
crossing over	law of independent assortment
diploid	meiosis
gamete	mitosis
gene	**nondisjunction**
haploid	somatic cell

15 Evaluating Genetically Modified Organisms

IN THIS UNIT you have read about countries or groups that have considered supporting the development and application of genetically modified organisms to help address sustainability problems. For example, in the first activity you evaluated evidence to determine if a country should grow genetically modified corn to feed hungry people. Central to making a decision about genetically modified organisms is collecting evidence about the organism and weighing the trade-offs of its use.

In this activity, you will research and collect evidence to evaluate potential benefits and problems of a genetically modified organism in solving a specific sustainability issue. You will prepare a poster explaining the possible benefits, risks, and trade-offs associated with the use of the organism. The class will then evaluate the evidence you collected to make a recommendation about the organism.

The growth and harvest of GM organisms has been proposed as a potential solution for many sustainability issues, such as overfishing. However, some people feel the benefits are not worth potential risks.

Challenge

▶ What are the benefits and trade-offs of using genetically modified organisms?

MATERIALS

FOR EACH GROUP OF FOUR STUDENTS

access to a library and the Internet

supplies for making a poster

FOR EACH STUDENT

Student Sheet 15.1, "Evaluating Genetically Modified Organisms"

Student Sheet 15.2, "Poster Template"

Literacy Student Sheet 6, "Discussion Web"

Student Sheet 2.3, "Genetics Case Study Comparison," from Activity 2

Drought and crop failure are sustainability issues in many areas worldwide.

These researchers are measuring the growth of wheat exposed to elevated atmospheric carbon dioxide levels. Many researchers are concerned that higher levels of atmospheric carbon dioxide will lead to future sustainability issues.

Procedure

Part A: Gathering Information

1. With your group make a list of the concerns often associated with genetically modified organisms. To help you generate ideas, refer to Student Sheet 2.3, "Genetics Case Study Comparison."

2. Discuss your ideas with the class, as directed by your teacher.

3. With the class, make a list of questions that must be answered if a community is to responsibly evaluate the environmental, social, and economic effects of using a genetically modified organism.

4. Review Student Sheet 15.1, "Evaluating a Genetically Modified Organism," which contains a list of topics and questions to guide your research on your assigned organism. Add to the Student Sheet any questions from Step 3 that are not listed.

5. Your teacher will assign your group a sustainability issue and a genetically modified organism to research.

6. Decide who in your group will research each of the items listed on Student Sheet 15.1. Divide the topics among yourselves, making sure each person will contribute evidence to the group poster.

7. Your teacher will provide instructions and a timeline for completing your research.

Part B: Preparing the Poster

8. As a class, view several examples of posters, and develop a list of criteria for making an effective poster. Keep in mind that the goal of the poster is to offer evidence-based information to help inform a decision on whether or not a genetically modified organism should be used.

9. Working with the criteria the class created in Step 8, decide how your group will represent the information you gathered on your poster. To do this

   • review the poster template on Student Sheet 15.2, "Poster Template."

   • decide how you will fit your information into the template.

10. Prepare your poster.

Part C: Informational Poster Session

11. Your teacher will explain how to present your poster to the class during the poster session.

12. As you review other groups' posters, write down on Literacy Student Sheet 6, "Discussion Web," two to three key points from each poster you view.

13. Based on the information you recorded on Literacy Student Sheet 6, decide if you would support the use of each genetically modified organism discussed in the poster session. In your science notebook record your opinion, and the evidence and your thinking that led you to your opinion.

14. Share your ideas with the class by conducting a walking debate. Your teacher will explain how to run the debate.

Analysis

1. Based on the posters you viewed, what questions should communities ask when considering the sustainability factors involved in using a genetically modified organism?

2. Based on your research, would you recommend that a community adopt the use of your assigned genetically modified organism? In your recommendation explain the evidence that supports your decision, and the trade-offs associated with that genetically modified organism.

KEY VOCABULARY

gene   trade-off

genetic modification

16 Protein Synthesis: Transcription and Translation

GENES CARRY THE information that, along with environmental factors, determines an organism's traits. How does this work? Although the complete answer to this question is complex, the simple answer is that genes, along with the influence of environmental factors, direct the production of proteins in cells, and the types of proteins in a cell determine the cell's and organism's structure and function. When scientists set out to genetically modify an organism, their goal is to insert a gene or genes that code for a protein that is not normally in that organism.

While genetically modified organisms produce a protein or proteins that the original organism would otherwise not produce, the process for making the proteins is the same for any and all cells. This process is **protein synthesis.** Protein synthesis has two phases, shown in the figure below. In the first phase, the information contained in DNA is converted into a messenger molecule called messenger ribonucleic acid, or mRNA. The scientific word for this conversion is **transcription.** In eukaryotic cells transcription takes place in the nuclei. The second phase of protein synthesis is **translation,** and this happens on ribosomes in the cytoplasm of a cell. In this phase, the code in the mRNA messenger molecule is translated by transfer RNA (tRNA), which carries the amino acids used to make a protein molecule. In this activity, you will view a computer simulation of both transcription and translation. You will see that these processes occur similarly in both genetically modified and unmodified organisms.

PROTEIN SYNTHESIS

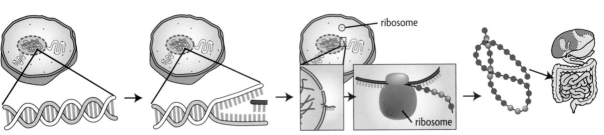

DNA resides in the nucleus.

Transcription: DNA is used as a template to make RNA.

Translation: RNA is used as a template to make proteins.

Protein is used by the organism. For example, an enzyme could be used by the digestive system.

Challenge

▶ How does a cell make proteins with the information from DNA?

MATERIALS

FOR EACH PAIR OF STUDENTS

      set of 10 Transcription and Translation Cards (A–J)

      access to online protein synthesis simulation

      bag containing DNA model kit pieces

        36   black deoxyribose sugars pentagons

        36   white phosphate tubes

             various orange, yellow, blue, and green nitrogenous base tubes

        18   white hydrogen bond rods

      bag containing transcription model kit pieces

         9   purple ribose sugar pentagons

         5   purple uracil nitrogenous base tubes

      bag containing translation model kit pieces

         3   purple tRNA molecules (diamond, oval, rectangle)

         3   black amino acids (diamond, oval, rectangle)

         2   gray polypeptide bond tubes

FOR EACH STUDENT

      Student Sheet 16.1, "Transcription and Translation"

      Student Sheet 2.3, "Genetics Case Study Comparison," from Activity 2

  3 sticky notes

Procedure

Part A: Transcription and Translation

1. With your partner spread out the 10 Transcription and Translation cards in front of you on the table. Look closely at the cards. Discuss what each card shows and how the images on the cards differ.

2. To make a protein, a cell must convert the information contained in DNA into a messenger molecule. Then the code in the messenger molecule is translated into a string of amino acids that will make a certain protein. Place the cards in the order that you think shows this process. Record the order of the cards on the back of Student Sheet 16.1, "Transcription and Translation."

3. The first stage of protein synthesis is transcription. During transcription, the information in DNA instructs the cell to make a messenger molecule, mRNA. With your partner, visit the *Science and Global Issues* page of the SEPUP website *(sepuplhs.org/sgi),* and go to the protein synthesis simulation. Student Sheet 16.1, "Transcription and Translation," will guide you through the simulation.

4. Look at the order in which you placed the cards in Step 2. Based on what you viewed in the animation, was your ordering of the cards correct? If necessary, discuss with your partner any changes you need to make, and rearrange the cards to reflect the correct order of events in transcription. On the back of Student Sheet 16.1, "Transcription and Translation," record the revised order of cards.

5. Based on what you observed in the animation and the information on the cards, fill in the transcription section of Student Sheet 16.1, "Transcription and Translation."

6. The second stage of protein synthesis is translation. During translation, the information in the messenger molecule mRNA translates into a chain of amino acids that will make a protein. Return to the *Science and Global Issues* page of the SEPUP website *(seuplhs.org/sgi)* and the protein synthesis simulation. Again, Student Sheet 16.1, "Transcription and Translation," will guide you through the simulation.

7. Look at the order in which you placed the cards in Step 4. Based on what you viewed in the simulation, was your ordering of the cards correct? If necessary, discuss with your partner any changes you need to make, and rearrange the cards to reflect the correct order of events in translation. On the back of Student Sheet 16.1, record the revised order of translation cards.

8. Based on what you observed in the animation, and the information provided on the cards, fill in the translation section of Student Sheet 16.1, "Transcription and Translation."

9. From the information you recorded on Student Sheet 16.1, in your science notebook write a description of what is shown on each card. Be sure to include

   a. the name of each molecule involved.

   b. a description of what each molecule does.

Part B: Mutations

As you saw in Part A of this activity, DNA is a template that provides information for creating messenger RNA. The information in mRNA is then converted into an amino acid sequence, which is then turned into a protein. Occasionally during this process a mutation occurs. **Mutations** are changes in the sequence of nucleotides in a strand of DNA. In this part of the activity, you will investigate the effect of DNA mutations on protein synthesis.

Mutations can be harmful, neutral, or beneficial. Certain strains of E. coli *bacteria have mutations that allow them to withstand extreme temperatures.*

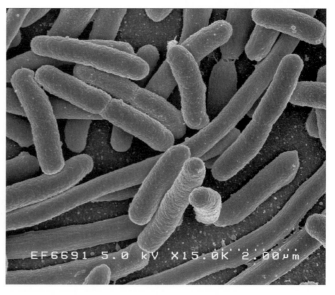

10. Copy the table below into your science notebook.

Mutation	DNA sequence resulting from DNA mutation indicated in table	mRNA transcript	Amino acid sequence	Effect on amino acid sequence
Original strand	5' TACCTAGCCAGTCGG 3'			
Base insertion (frameshift)				
Base deletion (frameshift)				
Substitution				
Three-base insertion				

11. With your partner, select the appropriate pieces of the Protein Synthesis Model, and build a single strand of DNA with the following sequence of bases:

5' TACCTAGCCAGTCGG 3'

Use the Protein Synthesis Model Key below to identify each molecule.

PROTEIN SYNTHESIS MODEL KEY

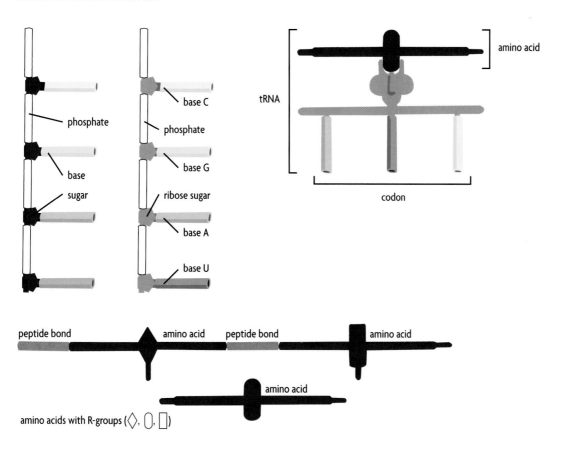

12. Work through the steps to translate and transcribe the DNA. Record your results in your data table, using the information in the chart on the next page to identify the amino acids.

Second letter

First letter		U		C		A		G		
U		UUU UUC	Phenyl-alanine	UCU UCC UCA UCG	Serine	UAU UAC	Tyrosine	UGU UGC	Cysteine	U C
		UUA UUG	Leucine			UAA UAG	Stop codon Stop codon	UGA UGG	Stop codon Tryptophan	A G
C		CUU CUC CUA CUG	Leucine	CCU CCC CCA CCG	Proline	CAU CAC	Histidine	CGU CGC CGA CGG	Arginine	U C A G
						CAA CAG	Glutamine			
A		AUU AUC AUA	Isoleucine	ACU ACC ACA ACG	Threonine	AAU AAC	Asparagine	AGU AGC	Serine	U C
		AUG	Methionine Start codon			AAA AAG	Lysine	AGA AGG	Arginine	A G
G		GUU GUC GUA GUG	Valine	GCU GCC GCA GCG	Alanine	GAU GAC	Aspartic acid	GGU GGC GGA GGG	Glycine	U C A G
						GAA GAG	Glutamic acid			

13. The chart Selected DNA Mutations on the next page describes types of DNA mutations. According to your teacher's instructions, explore how each type of mutation affects the production of an amino acid sequence. To do this

  a. as described by each row in the Selected DNA Mutations chart, sequence the DNA mutations.

  b. work through the steps to translate and transcribe the DNA. Record in your data table the amino acid sequence that results.

  c. repeat Steps 13a and b for each type of mutation listed in the chart, starting each time with the original strand of DNA from Step 10.

14. Compare the amino acid sequence that resulted from each mutation to the original sequence. Based on your work, what can you say about the effect of DNA mutations on the production of amino acid sequences and proteins? Summarize your ideas in your science notebook.

Selected DNA Mutations

CATEGORIES OF DNA MUTATIONS	CHANGE IN DNA	CHANGE TO DNA MODEL
Base insertion (frameshift)	One nucleotide is inserted into the DNA sequence.	Insert a thymine after the first cytosine.
Base deletion (frameshift)	One nucleotide is deleted from the DNA sequence.	Delete the first cytosine.
Substitution	One nucleotide is substituted for a different nucleotide.	Change the first cytosine to a thymine.
Three-base insertion	Three nucleotides are added or deleted to the DNA sequence.	After TAC, insert three additional nucleotides, CTG.

Part C: Gene Therapy Case Study

15. Individually read the case study on the following pages. As you read, follow the literacy strategy, "Read, Think, and Take Note."

16. Share your thinking with your group. Place your sticky notes on the table in front of you. Look for connections between your notes and the notes of others in your group.

    Hint: Were there common questions people asked? Were people unfamiliar with the same words? Did people react differently to statements in the reading?

17. Place your sticky notes in your science notebook. Below each, write a short summary of what your group discussed and any conclusions you came to.

18. Record the appropriate information from this case study on Student Sheet 2.3, "Genetics Case Study Comparison."

CASE STUDY

Seeing the Results of Gene Therapy

This researcher is in the process of sequencing DNA from an organism.

NORMALLY YOU WOULD not think of a baseball player and the owner of a basketball team working together, but the Chicago Cubs' first baseman Derrek Lee and Boston Celtics owner Wycliffe Grousbeck have teamed up for an unusual reason. Both men have a child who suffers from a rare genetic disease, Leber's congenital amaurosis (LCA), that causes blindness. In 2007, they started a foundation to help those affected in the United States to undergo genetic testing. Because, an estimated 3,000 people in the United States have this disease, the name of the foundation is Project 3000. The foundation works with victims of LCA and raises money for research to identify the genes responsible for LCA and to find ways to treat it.

In most cases, the disease begins in infants, and victims are usually

completely blind by age 20. So far there are no treatments for LCA, which is caused by a recessive genetic trait. Researchers have been working to create a gene therapy to treat the disease and restore at least partial sight to children and adults with LCA.

Developing these techniques is not easy. Scientists have been working on various gene therapies for more than 15 years and, as of 2010, there is no method of gene therapy that has been approved for use as a common (no longer experimental) medical treatment. Scientists must ensure that they are targeting the correct cells, that they are correcting the right gene, that the gene is producing the desired protein, that the correction is permanent, and that there are no harmful side effects.

Researchers have not yet determined the best methods of gene therapy. Many of the most promising methods target the various stages of protein synthesis. Some

Research scientists compare mice with one gene removed (left) to normal mice (right) as part of studying possible effects of gene therapy.

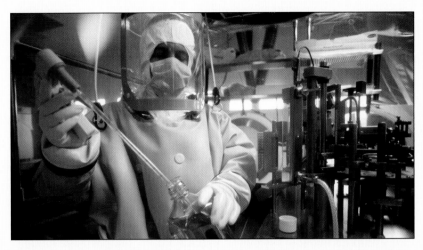

Researchers are working on methods for using viruses and bacteria to introduce therapeutic genes into patients.

of the techniques that are being explored are:

1. Targeting the mRNA and repairing the specific section of the mRNA that has the non-functioning gene

2. Preventing the transcription of a specific gene

3. Preventing the translation of a specific gene

In the case of gene therapy for LCA, scientists have run into problems with the treatment not working over the long term. The therapy has also triggered immune system responses, similar to severe allergic reactions, in some patients. The first clinical trials of gene therapy for LCA were halted in 2003, when a patient unexpectedly developed a cancer-like condition. In addition, research is finding that more and more disorders are based on the functioning of multiple genes, making therapies ever more difficult to create. With all the challenges that gene-therapy scientists face, researchers at the National Eye Institute were excited to report in September 2008, that they had successfully completed a gene transfer procedure in three young adults with LCA. All three patients showed partially restored vision over a 90-day study period. Dr. Samuel G. Jacobson of the University of Pennsylvania was the principal investigator of the study. While he was very pleased with the results, he acknowledged that there is still much work to be done. The study is currently being expanded to include more patients, and to further examine the safety and long-term effectiveness of the current therapy. ■

373

Analysis

1. Define protein synthesis and describe how it works.

2. Copy the chart below in your science notebook. Fill in the chart to determine the amino acid sequence that results from the transcription and translation of the following nucleotide sequence:

5' TACTCGGCATTGTGA 3'

Nucleotide	Transcription mRNA	Translation Amino Acid
5'		
A		
T		
G		
T		
C		
G		
G		
C		
A		
T		
T		
G		
T		
G		
A		
3'		

3. Predict the results of a two-base insertion or deletion to a strand of DNA that codes for a protein. How is this different from a three-base insertion or deletion?

4. One night while watching TV you hear a newscaster say, "DNA mutations cause damaged proteins." Based on your work in Part B, how would you respond to this claim?

5. Describe the relationship between gene therapy and protein synthesis.

KEY VOCABULARY

amino acid	replication
DNA	RNA
mRNA	**transcription**
mutation	**translation**
protein	tRNA
protein synthesis	

17 Cell Differentiation and Gene Expression

IN MOST HUMAN cells, the nucleus contains a full set of 23 pairs of chromosomes, which carry 20,000–25,000 genes. These genes are identical from cell to cell. In Activity 16, "Protein Synthesis: Transcription and Translation," you learned that genes are transcribed to produce RNA, and that this RNA is in turn translated to produce proteins. If all cells in the same organism have the same genes, why don't they all make the same proteins?

Some proteins are made by almost every cell because they are needed for basic cell functions. Other proteins are made by only one type of cell or small groups of cells. Only white blood cells, for example, make antibodies, the proteins that help the body fight infections. Each of the more than 220 kinds of specialized cells in the human body makes a characteristic group of proteins.

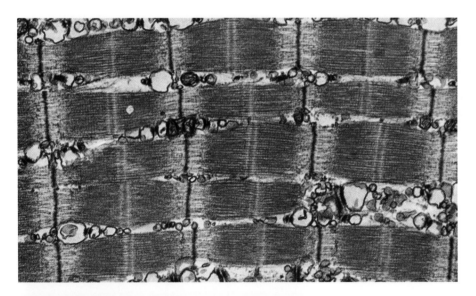

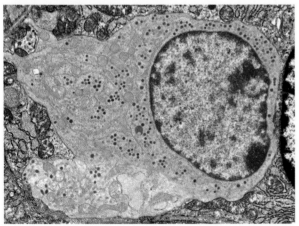

Although the two human cells shown have the same genes in their nuclei, they are specialized to make different proteins. The skeletal muscle cells, top, are specialized for voluntary muscle movement, while the thyroid cell, left, makes large amounts of thyroid hormone.

In each cell, only some of the genes are active, or **expressed.** The activity of genes in a cell is called **gene expression.** In this activity, you will explore how some genes are turned on and off by molecules called transcription factors. These molecules control the transcription of DNA into RNA.

Challenge

▶ How does the same set of genes direct the activities of 220 human cell types?

MATERIALS:

FOR EACH GROUP	FOR EACH STUDENT
set of 14 Cellular Event Cards	model of human chromosome 2
FOR EACH PAIR OR STUDENTS	model of human chromosome 11
3 colored pencils (blue, brown, and orange)	4 silver binder clips
	7 red paper clips
	7 green paper clips
	Student Sheet 17.1, "Chromosome Map"
	Student Sheet 2.3, "Genetics Case Study Comparison," from Activity 2
	3 sticky notes

Procedure

Part A: Gene Expression in Differentiated Cells

1. You will look at a small number of genes on two human chromosomes: chromosome 2 and chromosome 11. Identify these chromosomes in the diagram below.

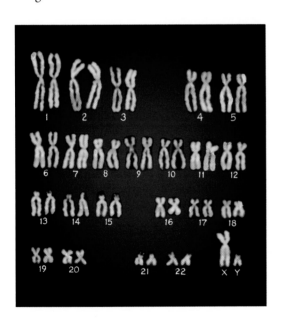

Human male karyotype

2. You will investigate the expression of only 11 of the approximately 25,000 human genes. Review the proteins these 11 genes produce and their functions in the two tables below.

Selected Genes on Human Chromosome 2

PROTEIN PRODUCED BY THE GENE	FUNCTION
Actin, smooth muscle type	Most cells produce actin for cell movement and cell division, but muscle cells produce large amounts of specific types of actin for muscle contraction.
AGA enzyme	Breaks down fats and some toxic substances
Cellular respiration enzyme	Catalyzes reactions for aerobic respiration in the mitochondria
Lactase enzyme	Required for digestion of lactose, the sugar in milk
Protein synthesis initiator	Controls the beginning of protein synthesis
Ribosome protein S7	Needed by ribosomes, which are essential for protein synthesis

Selected Genes on Human Chromosome 11

PROTEIN PRODUCED BY THE GENE	FUNCTION
Cell growth controller	Prevents cells from dividing unless more cells are needed, helps prevent certain cancers
DNA repair	Repairs damage to DNA and helps to prevent certain types of cancer
Fat and protein breakdown enzyme	Catalyzes one step in the breakdown of proteins and fats in the diet so they can be used for energy
Hemoglobin B	Carries oxygen to the cells throughout the body
Insulin	A hormone that regulates the metabolism of sugars and fats

3. Each member of your group will look at gene activity in one of four kinds of specialized cells shown below. With your group, decide what kind of cell each of you will investigate.

Cell Type

Cell Type
Beta cell in the pancreas
Developing red blood cell
Intestinal lining cell
Smooth muscle cell in the digestive system

4. Read the table below. It shows which of the 11 genes on chromosomes 2 and 11 are expressed in your cell.

Genes Expressed in Four Types of Human Cells

PROTEIN PRODUCED BY THE GENE	BETA CELL IN PANCREAS	DEVELOPING RED BLOOD CELL	INTESTINAL LINING CELL	SMOOTH MUSCLE CELL IN THE DIGESTIVE SYSTEM
Actin, smooth muscle type	−	−	−	+
AGA enzyme	−	−	−	−
Cell growth controller	+	+	+	+
Cellular respiration enzyme	+	+	+	+
DNA repair protein	+	+	+	+
Fat and protein breakdown enzyme	+	+	+	+
Hemoglobin B	−	+	−	−
Insulin	+	−	−	−
Lactase	−	−	+	−
Protein synthesis initiator	+	+	+	+
Ribosome protein S7	+	+	+	+

Key: + = active gene, − = repressed gene

5. Based on the information in the table above:

   a. On Student Sheet 17.1, "Chromosome Map," find the chromosomes for your cell. Draw a single, dark brown line in the position of each gene that is not expressed in your cell type. These genes are still present, but they are never expressed in your cell, and are permanently turned off, or **repressed.** Your teacher will help you with the first example.

   b. On Student Sheet 17.1, "Chromosome Map," draw a single, dark blue line in the position of any gene that is expressed *only* in your cell type. This is one of a number of genes that produce specialized proteins that help your cell perform its role in the human body.

   c. On Student Sheet 17.1, "Chromosome Map," draw a single, dark orange line in the position of any gene that is expressed in *all four* cell types. This is a gene that produces proteins that nearly all cells need if they are to function.

   d. Compare the chromosomes for your cell on Student Sheet 17.1, "Chromosome Map," with the others in your group. Copy the diagrams from their cells onto Student Sheet 17.1 to have a full set of diagrams.

6. Obtain a model of chromosomes 2 and 11. Place a silver binder clip over each gene that is permanently repressed in your cell type. This silver binder clip represents a specific **transcription factor,** a molecule that controls the transcription of DNA into RNA. This particular repressor permanently turns off genes that your cell does not need.

Part B: Differentiated Cells at Work

7. Prepare a table like the one below, in your science notebook.

Gene Expression

Cellular event	Affected gene and result

8. Shuffle the deck of Cellular Event Cards, and place it in the middle of your table. Put your models of chromosome 2 and chromosome 11 nearby.

9. Select one member of your group to start. That person will draw a card from the top of the deck and read it to the group.

10. Based on the information on the card, each member of the group determines which genes in their cells are activated to make proteins at this time, and which genes in their cells are repressed at this time. Follow directions on the card to place transcription factors that determine whether the genes are expressed, or temporarily repressed. These transcription factors include both activators (green paper clips) and repressors (red paper clips) that bind to portions of the DNA that regulate the gene. Place the paper clips on the appropriate gene on your model chromosomes.

    Key: Transcription activator = green paper clip
            Transcription repressor = red paper clip

11. For your cell, record the event, the affected gene, and the result in the table in your science notebook.

12. The next person, clockwise, in your group selects the next card from the top of the deck. Repeat Steps 10–11.

13. Continue selecting cards and determining which genes are affected until your teacher tells you to stop.

14. Compare your cell's chromosome 2 to those of the other members of your group. Discuss and record in your science notebook any similarities and differences you observe in the genes that are expressed and repressed.

15. Compare your cell's chromosome 11 to those of the other members of your group. Discuss and record in your science notebook any similarities and differences you observe in the genes that are expressed and repressed.

16. Discuss with your group

    a. the types of transcription factors that the paper clips represent.

    b. the types of changes in the cell or its environment that led to the need to turn the genes on and off.

Part C: Terminator Technology Case Study

17. Individually read the case study on the next pages. As you read, follow the literacy strategy, "Read, Think, and Take Note."

18. Share your thinking with your group. Place your sticky notes on the table in front of you. Look for connections between your sticky notes and the notes of others in your group.

    Hint: Were there common questions people asked? Were people unfamiliar with the same words? Did people react differently to statements in the reading?

19. Place your sticky notes in your science notebook. Below them, write a short summary of what your group discussed and any conclusions you came to.

20. Record the appropriate information from this case study on Student Sheet 2.3, "Genetics Case Study Comparison."

CASE STUDY

Terminator Technology

WITH GENETICALLY MODIFIED plants, one concern often raised is that they may spread engineered genes into plant populations that are not genetically modified. This can happen when genetically modified (GM) plants crossbreed with non-GM plants and produce hybrids, and may have unintended consequences in non-GM plant populations. For this reason, the United States Department of Agriculture and a private biotechnology company teamed up in the early 1990s to develop genetic use restriction technology, or GURT. GURT is a type of genetic modification that allows people to control gene expression in GM plants, thus earning it the nickname "terminator technology." By engineering GM plants that contain both a set of desired traits and GURT, scientists hope to develop plants that do not spread engineered genes to non-GM populations.

Two main types of GURT have been developed. The first type causes the GM plants to produce sterile seeds. It does this by activating and repressing a series of genes related to seed development. The advantage of this type of GURT is that the genetic modification cannot be passed on to other generations of plants, since the plant cannot reproduce. It is also financially advantageous for the company or group that owns the patent for the GM plant because it ensures that the seeds from one generation cannot be saved and grown again in the following years. Farmers would have to buy new seed each year.

The second type of GURT controls the phenotype of the GM plant. The genetically modified

GURT was developed to help prevent GM plants, such as the rice at left, from breeding with non-GM plants, such as the rice at right, when the GM rice is planted in fields.

plants would only express the GM gene if the plant were treated with a specific chemical. When the chemical is applied to the plants, the gene for the GM trait is activated. This approach allows seed growers and farmers to control when the GM genes are expressed. It also means that if the GM plants were to cross-breed with non-GM plants, the GM gene would not be expressed unless the chemical was reapplied.

As with any form of technology there are benefits and draw-backs. While scientists have identified genes that can be acti-vated and repressed, field trials have shown that the control of gene expression in GURT plants has not been 100% effective. This means that the seeds will not always be sterile, or that the GM gene is expressed even though the chemical has not been applied. Scientists are also unsure of the long-term perfor-mance of terminator technology. They do not yet know what will happen several generations down the line if GURT plants crossbreed with non-GM plants.

Farmers, environmentalists, indigenous-peoples' groups, and some governments have objected to the application of terminator technology for a number of reasons. One is that the farmers who want such plants need to purchase seeds and the activating chemi-cals from the seed companies each year. Many farmers around the world save seed from one generation of plants to produce the next year's crops. While the terminator technology addresses the fear of gene spread, farmers might not be able to afford to pay for new seeds each year.

Because so many objections were raised, several coun-tries, including India and Brazil, have passed laws prohib-iting the planting of GURT seeds. In 2006, the United Nations Convention on Biological Diver-sity recommended halting all field-testing and commercial release of terminator technology, citing concerns about inade-quate research on the unin-tended spread of the genes into

GURT would prevent gene spread, but would not allow farmers to save seeds from one year's crop to plant the next year's.

non-GM populations of plants. As of mid-2010, seeds engi-neered to have terminator abili-ties were still not commercially available. However, research in the development, use, and safety of terminator technology continues. ■

Analysis

1. Compare the following in your group's four cell types:

   a. Chromosomes

   b. Genes

   c. Expression of the genes to produce proteins

2. What kinds of genes were permanently inactivated in some cells? Why were these genes inactivated?

3. Explain why some proteins are made by nearly all cells, and give two examples.

4. What cellular mechanisms caused short-term changes in gene expression in the cell you investigated?

5. For your cell explain how gene expression related to the cell's ability to perform its function in the body.

6. How does terminator technology work?

7. **a.** What kinds of problems is GURT intended to solve?

   b. What are the pros and cons of GURT?

KEY VOCABULARY	
chromosome	**repressed (gene)**
expressed (gene)	**transcription factor**
gene expression	

18 Which Corn is Genetically Modified?

THE GENETICS LABORATORY *you work for has been hired to help solve a dilemma. In your community is a corn silo that holds corn from several farms in the same area. To export the corn, it must be certified as not genetically modified. Local officials hired your lab to test the corn, and it turned out that some kernels in the silo contained a gene from* Bacillus thuringeinsis (Bt), *which is only found in genetically modified Bt corn. Now your lab must trace back the genetically modified corn to determine which farm or farms were growing Bt corn.*

If a gene does not affect the physical appearance of an organism, how do we determine the presence of an engineered gene? One method is through DNA fingerprinting. While all organisms contain DNA, every individual organism contains a unique pattern of DNA sequences called a "DNA fingerprint." DNA fingerprints, like those shown below, allow scientists to compare the DNA of one organism to another.

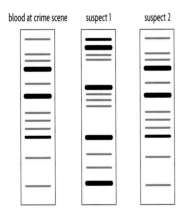

Comparing the DNA fingerprints of blood found at a crime scene to blood samples from two suspects allows investigators to determine if one of the suspects was at the crime scene.

In DNA fingerprinting enzymes cut a sample of an organism's DNA into small pieces, which are then separated, based on their weight, through a process called **gel electrophoresis.** The lighter the DNA, the further it will move through the gel in a fixed amount of time. Pieces of the same size form a band in the gel. The more pieces of the same size, the thicker the band will be. Only samples from the same individual (or identical twins) will have an identical pattern of bands in their DNA. In this activity, you will use gel electrophoresis to analyze DNA samples from several farms. This procedure will allow you to find the source of the Bt corn.

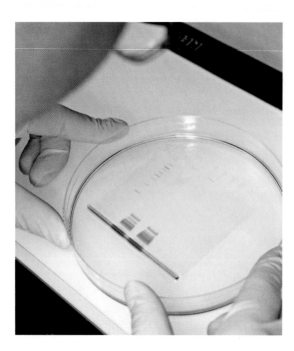

The DNA in this gel has been stained with a blue dye to make the banding pattern easy to see.

Challenge

▶ Which samples contain genetically modified corn?

MATERIALS

FOR EVERY TWO GROUPS OF FOUR STUDENTS

    electrophoresis chamber with lid and power supply

    electrical outlet

FOR EACH GROUP OF FOUR STUDENTS

    575 mL of electrophoresis buffer solution (sodium bicarbonate solution)

    agar gel in electrophoresis tray

    tray for carrying gel

    30-mL bottle of DNA samples from each of the following:

        sample of farm A corn

        sample of farm B corn

        sample of farm C corn

    30-mL bottle of Bt DNA

    30-mL bottle of glycerin

    30-mL bottle of water

    SEPUP chemplate

  4 pipettes

  4 SEPUP stir sticks

    cup of water

    paper towels

FOR EACH STUDENT

    safety goggles

    Student Sheet 2.3, "Genetics Case Study Comparison," from Activity 2

  3 sticky notes

Procedure

Part A: Analyzing DNA Samples

1. Follow your teacher's instructions for recording notes on this laboratory.

2. Watch carefully as your teacher demonstrates how to set up the electrophoresis chamber and run the samples in the agar gel.

3. According to your teacher's instructions, set up an electrophoresis chamber. Two groups will share this chamber. Place your gel in the chamber. As shown by your teacher, pour approximately 575 mL of buffer solution against the side of the electrophoresis chamber to the fill line in the chamber.

4. With your group, prepare each of the four DNA samples to be loaded into the gel—farms A, B, and C, and a control sample of Bt DNA. To prepare the samples, place 2 drops of each DNA sample into their own cup in the SEPUP chemplate. To each sample, add 2 drops of glycerin and 2 drops of water.

5. Stir the contents of each cup with a clean SEPUP stir stick. Be sure to use a fresh stir stick for each cup to prevent cross-contamination of the samples.

6. With a clean pipette transfer each DNA sample from the SEPUP tray into one well in the gel. Place sample A into well 1. Place sample B into well 2, and so on. To do this hold the pipette that contains the DNA sample directly above the well. With both hands slowly lower the tip of the pipette into the buffer solution, as shown by your teacher.

7. When both group's gels are ready, carefully place the lid of the electrophoresis chamber in place, as shown by your teacher. Make sure to put the lid on the chamber in the correct orientation, as shown by your teacher.

8. Without moving the chamber, check that the lid is on securely. Plug in the power cord to start the flow of electricity.

9. Allow the gel to run for 30 minutes, or until you see the samples separate in the gel.

10. Disconnect the power. Carefully take off the lid of the electrophoresis chamber. Remove your group's gel, while holding it level, and place it in the tray for carrying the gel.

11. Compare each lane of the gel to the lane that contains the control sample of the Bt DNA. With your group discuss the results. Draw a sketch of the results in your science notebook.

12. With your group, discuss the conclusions you might draw based on the electrophoresis results. In your discussion, explain the evidence that supports your conclusions.

Part B: Virus-resistant Papaya Case Study

13. Individually read the case study beginning on the next page. As you read, follow the literacy strategy, "Read, Think, and Take Note."

14. Share your thinking with your group. Place your sticky notes on the table in front of you. Look for connections between your sticky notes and the notes of others in your group.

    Hint: Were there common questions people asked? Were people unfamiliar with the same words? Did people react differently to statements in the reading?

15. Place your sticky notes in your science notebook. Below each, write a short summary of what your group discussed and any conclusions you came to.

16. Record the appropriate information from this case study on Student Sheet 2.3, "Genetics Case Study Comparison."

The papaya shown at top is healthy. The one at bottom has ringspot virus.

CASE STUDY

Virus-resistant Papaya

FOR YEARS, THE papaya ringspot virus has destroyed papaya crops in Central American and equatorial countries of the world. Once the virus infects a plant, an entire crop of papayas can be ruined. Traditional methods to handle the disease include isolating papaya orchards to prevent disease transmission, breeding naturally virus-resistant trees, and cross-protection. Cross-protection treats the papaya trees with a mild form of the virus, so that the trees develop immunity to it. All of these techniques have had limited success, and often work best when combined. When nothing works, the farmers' only choice, if they want to continue to grow papaya trees, is to move and start new plantations in a virus-free area.

In 1998, a scientist at Cornell University in New York State sequenced the genome of the papaya virus. Once the genome was completed, the gene that encodes for a protein in the coat of the virus was identified and isolated. Scientists used a gene gun to transport the gene and implant it in papaya seedlings. These GM seedlings grew up to be papaya plants that produced the papaya virus protein. Because the plants produced the virus coat protein, the trees developed immunity to infection by the virus, similar to the way a vaccine works. This

protects the crops from ringspot virus, and keeps the crop profitable. Since the development of the genetically modified papaya, many papaya plantations in Hawaii have successfully grown papaya crops without outbreaks of ringspot infection.

(Continued on next page)

A healthy papaya tree

(Continued from previous page)

A major concern with genetically modified food is that a person who eats it might have an allergic reaction to the engineered protein. This has happened in other genetically modified crops where genes from one species were inserted into another. For example, a soy plant was modified with a Brazil nut gene in the mid-1990s. In testing the genetically modified soy, it was determined that the modified soy could cause severe allergic reactions in people who were allergic to nuts, and so the project was terminated. Papayas, on the other hand, have been exposed to the ringspot virus for years, which causes them to contain the coat protein. This means that humans have been ingesting the coat protein for years, and thus far there are no documented cases of allergic reaction to the genetically modified papaya.

Non-GM papaya crops in Hawaii have become contaminated by unintentional breeding with GM-papaya crops. Some studies have shown widespread contamination of non-GM papaya crops with the modified gene. This is a problem for Hawaiian farmers because some countries, including those in the European Union, will not allow import of GM crops. Scientists are currently researching the extent of the contamination, and ways to prevent its spread. Many farmers and scientists also worry that if everyone grows GM papaya, there will only be one type of papaya grown. This makes the crop susceptible to devastating losses if a disease were to infect the crop. If all of the plants have the same genome, none would be resistant to the disease. This problem occurs whenever breeding leads to most crops having very similar genomes, even when they are not genetically modified. ∎

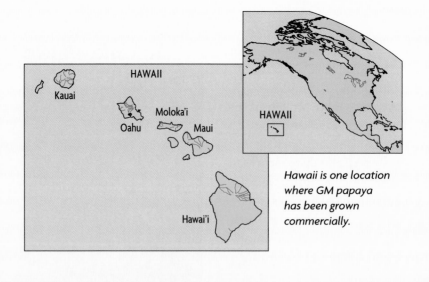

Hawaii is one location where GM papaya has been grown commercially.

Analysis

1. Look at the DNA electrophoresis results below.

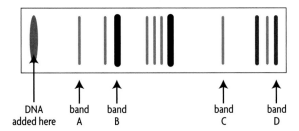

   a. Which single labeled band represents the smallest pieces of DNA? Explain how you can tell.

   b. Which of the labeled bands represents the most common-sized piece of DNA in this sample? Explain how you can tell.

2. Based on your DNA electrophoresis results, prepare a report to the city that hired you to test corn. In the report state your conclusion about which samples have been genetically modified, and explain the evidence that supports your conclusion.

3. DNA electrophoresis is one way to test for a gene in a DNA sample. Additional tests are shown in the table below. A company is deciding which test they will use to certify that the foods they manufacture do not contain genetically modified ingredients. Which test(s) would you recommend they use? In your answer, explain at least two trade-offs associated with your recommendation.

Genetic Modification Detection Tests					
TEST	**WHAT IT DETECTS**	**SPEED OF TEST**	**EASE OF USE**	**RELIABILITY**	**COST**
DNA electrophoresis	Inserted gene	1–2 hours	Must be conducted in a laboratory	high	$$$
ELISA protein plate	Amount of protein present	20 minutes	Can be conducted in non-laboratory setting	high	$$
ELISA protein strips	If the protein is present	5 minutes	Can be conducted in non-laboratory setting	low to moderate	$

4. Policies about labeling genetically modified (GM) foods, such as GM papaya, vary from country to country. Brazil, China, Russia, and Saudi Arabia require labeling of all GM foods and products. Japan requires GM labeling for some products but allows voluntary labeling of others. The United States has a voluntary labeling policy. Certain countries will only import foods that are certified 100% GM free. In countries where labeling is mandatory, consumers often will not buy products that are not certified GM-free. What are the trade-offs of labeling genetically modified foods? Explain at least two trade-offs.

KEY VOCABULARY

DNA   **gel electrophoresis**

19 Biopharming Edible Vaccines

As you read in Activity 1, "A Genetically Modified Solution?" scientists have been using genetically modified *E. coli* for more than 30 years to manufacture proteins for medicinal and industrial purposes. In the early 1990s, pharmaceutical researchers began working with genetically modified organisms to insert vaccines against diseases into the foods we eat. Their goal was to find a way to engineer a cheap, easy way to vaccinate people without needles. In many developing countries, making sure that people get their shots has been difficult because there are not enough qualified personnel and equipment. An edible vaccine contained in food would help to address these problems.

Throughout this unit you have been learning about genetic modification techniques—the same ones that are involved in the research on edible vaccines. In this activity you will read about how these techniques can be combined to engineer genetically modified organisms that are edible and carry vaccines.

Scientists are researching ways to genetically modify plants, such as this lettuce, to create edible vaccines.

Challenge

▶ What are the benefits and trade-offs of genetically modifying crops to contain edible vaccines?

MATERIALS

FOR EACH PAIR OF STUDENTS
set of 8 Genetic Modification of Lettuce Cards

Procedure

1. Spread the Genetic Modification of Lettuce Cards out on the table in front of you. Each card shows a step required to genetically modify lettuce. With your partner discuss what each card shows.

2. You performed processes similar to those shown on the cards in Activity 2, "Creating Genetically Modified Bacteria," Activity 9, "Isolating DNA," and Activity 18, "Which Corn Is Genetically Modified?" With your partner look back in your science notebooks and this book to identify which of these three activities correlate to which cards. Note that an activity may correlate to just one or to multiple cards, and some cards discuss processes you have not studied.

3. Copy the table below into your science notebook, and write your ideas from Step 2 in the table.

Card	Summary of step	Activity from Genetics unit

4. With your partner, arrange the cards in the correct order for genetically modifying lettuce. Record the predicted order in your science notebook, and add any new information to the KWL chart (What do I Know? What do I Want to Know? What did I Learn?) that your class started at the beginning of the activity.

5. Complete the reading that follows. As you read, record any new information or questions you have in your KWL chart.

6. When you finish the reading, review the order of the cards with your partner. Revise the order to reflect the information given in the reading. Refer back to the text if necessary.

7. Compare the card order with the other pair in your group. Discuss any differences in the way you have ordered the cards, and come to an agreement about the order. Record the final order your group decides on in your science notebook. Add any new information to your KWL chart.

Reading: Edible Vaccines

Imagine there was a way to be vaccinated against hepatitis B simply by eating a bowlful of lettuce instead of getting a shot. Currently most vaccines come in the form of an injection given by a doctor, nurse, or skilled technician. The vaccines must be kept refrigerated, and some of the shots hurt more than others. Edible vaccines, such as a vaccine in lettuce, would eliminate these problems. Vaccine lettuce is just one example of a genetically modified organism engineered by scientists working in the growing field of molecular farming, also known as biopharming. They are researching ways to insert genes into plants and animals. These genes would cause the organisms to produce proteins for pharmaceutical purposes.

Making an Edible Vaccine

Vaccines have been successful weapons against diseases since the 1800s. They have nearly eradicated polio and smallpox around the world and have prevented millions of children from getting measles, mumps, and rubella. Most vaccines are based on a protein from the virus that causes the particular disease, which triggers an immune system response in our bodies. The virus protein in the vaccine is not enough to actually cause the disease. Instead, when the vaccine is injected the immune system responds the same way it would to fight the disease, eventually making the person immune to the disease.

Creating an edible vaccine from a genetically modified organism relies on the same principles as making other genetically modified organisms. Scientists must first isolate the DNA from the disease agent. Just as you did in Activity 9, "Isolating DNA," scientists lyse (break down) the cell membrane with a detergent and then apply alcohol to precipitate (separate) out the DNA from the other material.

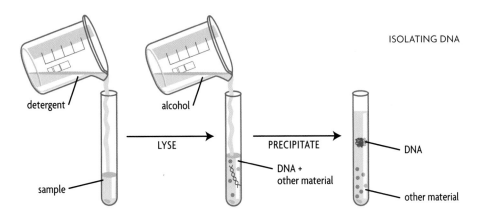

After the DNA is isolated, scientists extract the correct gene from the DNA and make copies of that gene. To do this, they use a process called PCR (polymerase chain reaction). The gene is heated to separate the DNA double helix strand, and then an enzyme and single nucleotides are added. Each separated strand is copied to form a double-stranded segment of DNA. This process is repeated through many cycles to make multiple copies of the gene. The diagram below shows the eight copies produced by three cycles of PCR. After 20 cycles over one million copies of the gene will be produced.

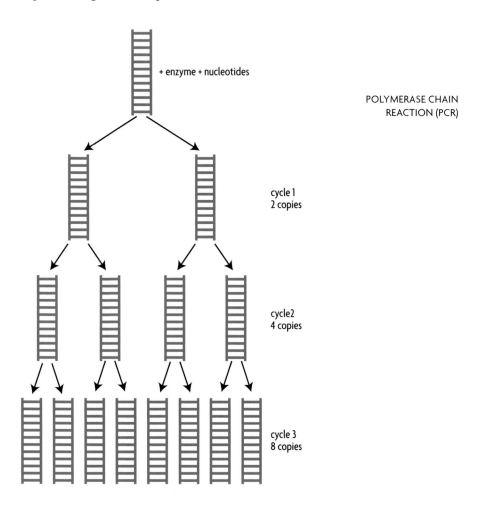

+ enzyme + nucleotides

POLYMERASE CHAIN
REACTION (PCR)

cycle 1
2 copies

cycle2
4 copies

cycle 3
8 copies

Once the gene has been copied, geneticists engineer a DNA construct. A DNA construct is a piece of DNA that is made of three specific parts: a start region, the desired gene, and a selectable marker. Antibiotic resistance is a common selectable marker. When you transformed E. coli in Activity 2, "Creating Genetically Modi-fied Bacteria," ampicillin resistance was the selectable marker. This meant that only E. coli cells transformed with the green fluorescent protein (GFP) protein would grow in Petri dishes with ampicillin in them. In other words, only the bacteria that had taken in the DNA construct containing the ampicillin resistance gene and the gene to make them glow would grow on the ampicillin plates. Bacteria that had not taken up the construct would not grow. Scientists also add a start region, which signals where gene transcription should begin.

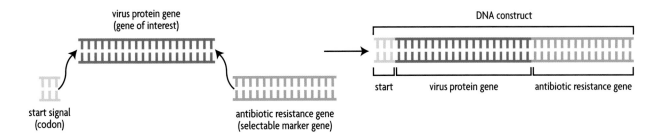

When all of these steps have been completed, scientists insert the DNA construct into the target organism. This can be done in several ways. In Activity 2, "Creating Genetically Modified Bacteria," you worked with a DNA plasmid, a ring of DNA found in bacteria. With bacteria, scientists use enzymes to insert the DNA construct into plasmids. Then the plasmid is introduced to the bacteria, which infects the target organism, bringing along the DNA construct. There are several methods for transmitting the DNA construct into the target organism, three of which are shown in the figure below.

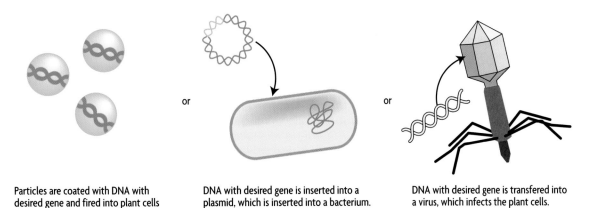

Particles are coated with DNA with desired gene and fired into plant cells using a gene gun.

DNA with desired gene is inserted into a plasmid, which is inserted into a bacterium. The bacterium infects the plant cells.

DNA with desired gene is transfered into a virus, which infects the plant cells.

After the DNA construct is inserted into the DNA of the target organism, the newly modified organism is grown to mature size. Researchers test for the presence of the new gene using electrophoresis, as you did in Activity 18, "Which Corn Is Genetically Modified?" Scientists also perform a second, more sensitive test, Southern blotting (named for molecular biologist Edward M. Southern), to confirm that the virus protein gene is being created by the cells and is present in the modified organism.

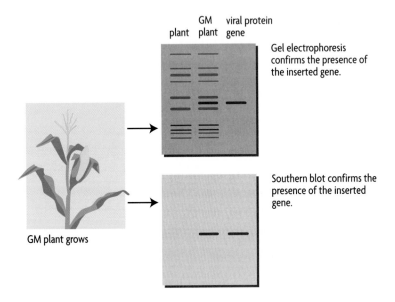

GM plant grows

Gel electrophoresis confirms the presence of the inserted gene.

Southern blot confirms the presence of the inserted gene.

If the modified organism produces the virus protein gene, clinical trials are conducted to see if the protein produces the desired vaccine effect. For example, in the vaccine lettuce that was modified to contain the hepatitis B protein gene, scientists first tested the modified lettuce on mice. The mice were fed the modified lettuce, and then tested to see if their immune systems responded to the hepatitis B protein. Once it was determined that the process does work in mice, similar tests were performed on human subjects. Today, testing and research are continuing and will go on until scientists determine if the lettuce consistently and safely produces the desired result in humans.

Benefits and Trade-offs of Edible Vaccines

The concept of producing edible genetically modified organisms to deliver vaccines has many benefits. Unlike traditional vaccines, many of the plants being tried in this process require little refrigeration, if any. It is easier to grow large amounts of the modified organisms than to produce large amounts of the injectable vaccine. The lettuce could be farmed anywhere that there is adequate soil, sun, and water. Because production does not involve expensive equipment or laboratories, it would cost less than traditional vaccines. There is no need for sterilized needles, or for trained medical staff to administer the vaccine.

There are also drawbacks to edible vaccines. Because organisms naturally vary, the dosage of the vaccines may be uneven. This is important because if there is not enough of the vaccine, the immune system will not respond. If there is too much of the vaccine in the organism, the body tolerates the vaccine but the immune system does not respond properly. Also, the edible vaccines still have to be delivered to where they are needed, which is the same problem with the traditional vaccines. Many of the locations where vaccines are most needed are remote areas that are difficult to reach and do not have the farmland needed to grow edible vaccines. Another concern that has been raised is that if the modified organisms are accidentally introduced into regular food crops, there could be unintended consequences.

Several edible vaccines are in the early stages of being tested on humans. Corn and potatoes have been modified to produce a vaccine against a harmful strain of *E. coli*, potatoes have been modified to vaccinate against the Norwalk virus (one cause of the symptoms often called the stomach flu, but not related to influenza), and, as you read earlier, lettuce has been modified to vaccinate against hepatitis B. Other scientists are working on methods to grow the modified plants, and then turn them into vaccine pills, which would help make them easier to distribute and make the doses even. These methods, however, have not yet been fully developed. Currently, there are no edible vaccines approved for use in the United States.

Analysis

1. What are the steps involved in genetically modifying an organism?

2. Compare the genetic modification of "vaccine lettuce" to the process of selectively breeding rice with desirable traits, which you learned about in Activity 7, "Breeding Better Rice." In what ways are the processes similar? Different?

3. What are the benefits and trade-offs of using genetic modification to produce an organism with a specific phenotype?

KEY VOCABULARY

DNA construct   vaccine

genetic modification

20 Are GMOs the Solution?

YOUR COUNTRY IS *facing the possibility of an economic and social crisis. Over the last 40 years, the country has grown more soybeans and fewer other crops. Now, the primary crop grown in your country is soybeans. Only a small percentage of the soybeans are sold within your country for human and animal consumption. Most of the soybeans are exported to other countries, which contributes significantly to your country's economic and social well-being.*

For several years soybean production has been low due to an ongoing drought. Last year a virus, soybean mottling virus (SMV), wiped out two-thirds of the already small soybean crop. SMV is transmitted by aphids and causes plants to grow fewer leaves, smaller pods, and fewer, if any, soybeans. Genomics Unlimited, Inc., has offered to fund the growing of soybeans genetically modified to protect against SMV. The GM soybean, called Soy*, has had a gene inserted from another plant which produces a substance that deters aphids. As a scientific advisor to your government's Panel on Genetic Modification, your job is to recommend what action the government should take.

Some viruses infect up to 94% of a healthy soybean field. The soybeans above are healthy, while the soybeans at left have contracted a virus.

Challenge

▶ Should the government Panel on Genetic Modification approve the planting of genetically modified soybeans?

MATERIALS

FOR EACH STUDENT
Student Sheet 20.1, "GM Soybean Study Comparison"

Procedure

1. With your partner, examine the graphs below. Discuss together what the graphs indicate about the sustainability of your country's agriculture. Write your answers in your science notebook.

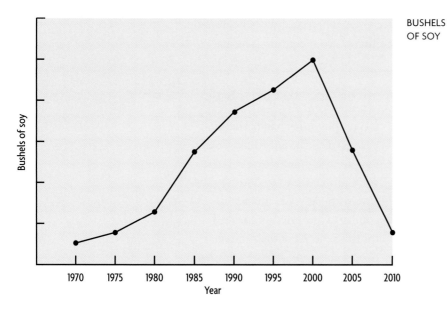

BUSHELS OF SOY

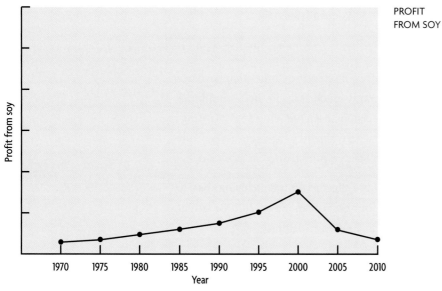

PROFIT FROM SOY

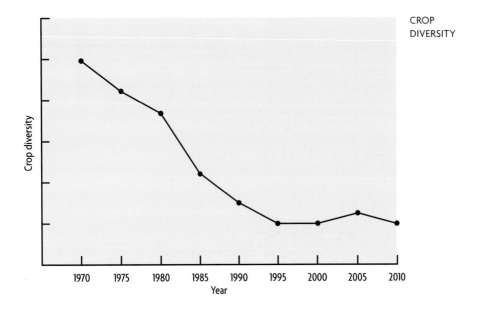

2. Read the proposal below. In your science notebook, record the benefits and trade-offs of the proposal based on the situation your country is facing.

Proposal by Genomics Unlimited, Inc. to Grow Soy*

Genomics Unlimited, Inc. (GU) has developed a genetically modified strain of soybean called Soy*. Their studies have shown that Soy* resists infection by SMV. They believe that if your farmers raise Soy*, it will restore soybean production in your country to profitable levels.

GU proposes that half of the soybean farmers in your country plant Soy* for this year's crops. Because your farmers have faced such problems with SMV, GU offers your country a low price on the seed for this year. All of their initial effectiveness and safety testing has shown positive results, and they are confident that this GM seed will be a great help in solving your SMV problems.

3. Now your group will read four summaries of scientific studies that have been done on Soy*. You will analyze the data and conclusions in these summaries to help you make an evidence-based decision about allowing Soy* planting in your country. With your group, decide who will read which summary. Complete Student Sheet 20.1, "GM Soybean Study Comparison," as you read.

Study conclusions are provided for Study 1. Record your conclusions based on the results for Studies two through four on Student Sheet 20.1. Be sure to consider all study results when you form your conclusions.

Study 1: Genetically Modified Soybeans—A Laboratory Study

Study Time Frame: 12 months (January 2008–December 2008)

Research Group: Genomics Unlimited, Inc.

Study Objectives: Test susceptibility of Soy* genetically modified soybeans to SMV transmitted by aphids (common carrier of SMV).

Study Procedures: Twenty test greenhouses were set up, 10 to grow unmodified soybeans and 10 to grow Soy* genetically modified soybeans. Once a week the numbers of leaves and soybean pods were counted on each plant. Half the greenhouses for each type of crop were exposed for two months to aphids carrying SMV. All plants were checked once a week to determine if they had contracted SMV. All crops were watered and fertilized regularly. Trials were repeated three times, for 120 days each. Results were averaged.

Study Results are shown at right.

Study Conclusions: Soy* plants are more resistant to SMV than unmodified soy and have a higher yield than unmodified soy when exposed to SMV. No significant differences in growth and yield result when the plants are not exposed to SMV.

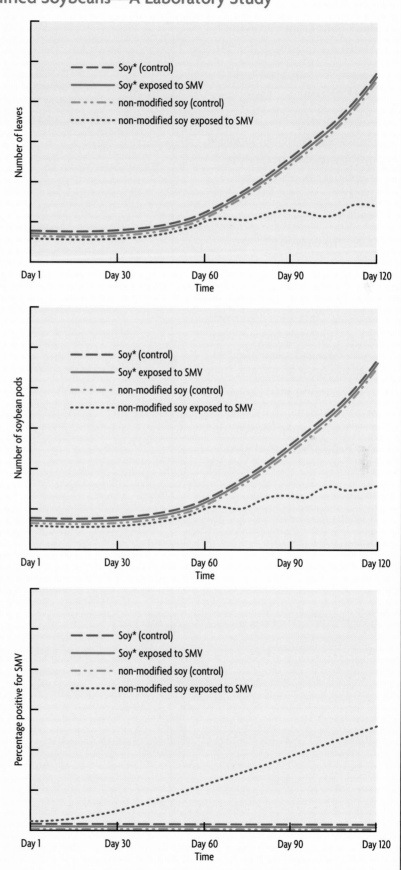

Study 2: Genetically Modified Soybeans—A Field Study

Study Time Frame: 9 months (March 2009–November 2009)

Research Group: State Agricultural University

Study Objectives: Test susceptibility of Soy* genetically modified soybeans to SMV transmitted by aphids (common carrier of SMV) in typical growing conditions.

Study Procedures: Four test fields were set up, two to grow unmodified soybeans and two to grow Soy* genetically modified soybeans. Once a week numbers of leaves and soybean pods were counted for each plant. Half of each type of crop was exposed to aphids carrying SMV. Crops were watered and fertilized regularly. Trials were repeated twice, for 120 days each. Results were averaged.

Study Results are shown at right.

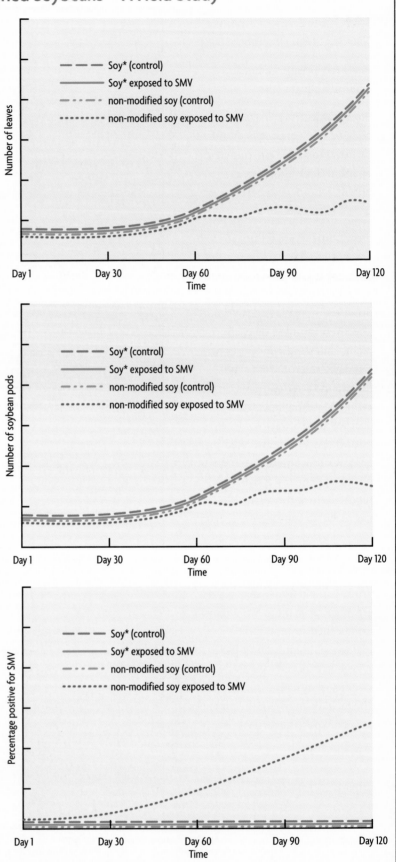

Study 3: Genetically Modified Soybeans—A Field Study

Study Time Frame: 3 years (October 2006–October 2009)

Research Group: International Scientific Review Board

Study Objectives: Test susceptibility of Soy* genetically modified soybeans and unmodified beans to SMV transmitted by aphids (common carrier of SMV) in difficult growing conditions.

Study Procedures: Four test fields were set up, two to grow unmodified soybeans and two to grow Soy* genetically modified soybeans. Once a week numbers of leaves and number of soybean pods were counted for each plant. Half of each type of crop was exposed for two months a year to aphids carrying SMV. Crops were given limited water to mimic drought conditions. Crops were grown in minimally fertilized soil to mimic poor soil conditions. Trials were repeated nine times, for 120 days each. Results were averaged.

Study Results are shown at right.

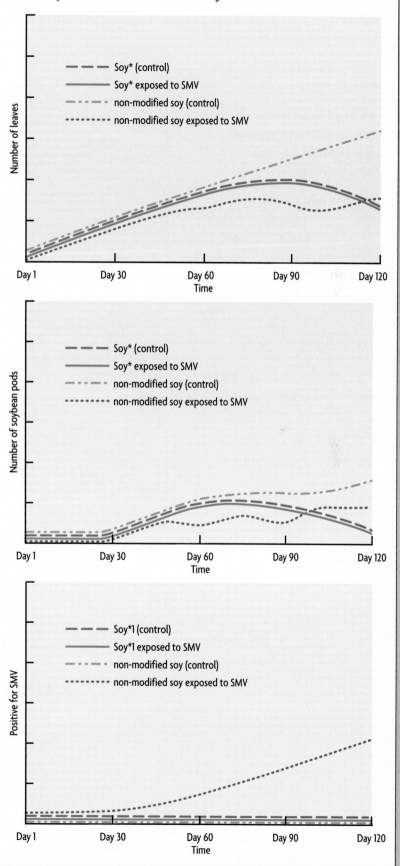

Study 4: Genetically Modified Soybeans—Effects on Insects, a Laboratory Study

Study Time Frame: 18 months (June 2007—December 2009)

Research Group: International Society of Entomologists

Study Objectives: Test potential effects of Soy* on genera of insects commonly found living in or near soybean crops.

Study Procedures: Eight insect habitats, each populated with one group of insects and one type of soybean, were set up, as shown in the graphs at right.

Habitats were monitored, and insect populations were counted weekly. Plants were watered and fertilized regularly to mimic ideal growing conditions. Trials were repeated four times, for 120 days each. Results were averaged.

Study Results are shown at right.

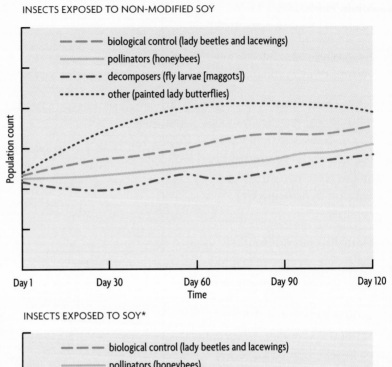

INSECTS EXPOSED TO NON-MODIFIED SOY

biological control (lady beetles and lacewings)
pollinators (honeybees)
decomposers (fly larvae [maggots])
other (painted lady butterflies)

Population count

Day 1   Day 30   Day 60   Day 90   Day 120
Time

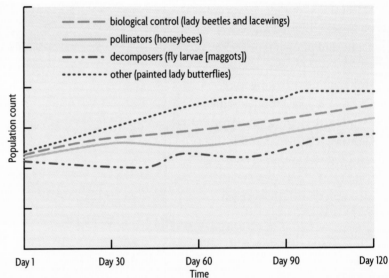

INSECTS EXPOSED TO SOY*

biological control (lady beetles and lacewings)
pollinators (honeybees)
decomposers (fly larvae [maggots])
other (painted lady butterflies)

Population count

Day 1   Day 30   Day 60   Day 90   Day 120
Time

4. Share your notes with your group, and complete Student Sheet 20.1, "GM Soybean Study Comparison," for the other three studies. Discuss any questions or thoughts you had while reading the summaries, and write them in your science notebook.

5. Discuss the original proposal with the class, following your teacher's instructions.

6. Based on the ideas you recorded on Student Sheet 20.1, "GM Soybean Study Comparison," and on the information from your class discussion, decide if you support growing Soy*. In your science notebook write a memorandum to the government Panel on Genetic Modification, in which you state your recommendation, explain the benefits and trade-offs of the proposal, and cite evidence from the summaries that supports your recommendation.

Analysis

1. Explain the similarities and differences in experimental design of the four studies on Soy*.

2. How might the differences in experimental design of the four studies on Soy* affect the outcomes and conclusions of the studies?

3. Describe how your recommendation will affect the social, economic, and environmental sustainability of your country.

4. What information should policymakers evaluate when making decisions about genetically modified organisms?

KEY VOCABULARY

genetic engineering   trade-offs

Unit Review: Genetics

Genetic Modification

Understanding the relationship between the structure and function of DNA, chromosomes, and genes makes it possible for scientists to manipulate genes and thereby create new combinations of traits and new varieties of organisms. Genetically modified organisms are those into which a gene or genes from another organism have been inserted, or organisms which have had one or more of their genes deleted. Through genetic modification scientists have developed organisms with a specific desirable trait, such as pest or disease resistance, drought tolerance, and enhanced nutritional qualities. Potential applications for genetically modified organisms include improving agricultural crops, creating alternative fuels, and treating human diseases. The production and use of a genetically modified organism might have unintended consequences for humans and ecosystems. The farming of genetically modified plants or animals poses risks and benefits, and making decisions about them involves trade-offs.

The sequence of steps involved in creating a genetically modified organism is: identification of a desirable gene; isolation of the gene; preparation of a DNA construct that contains the desired gene and a selectable marker; delivery of the desired gene into the target organism; and raising the transformed organisms using a selective medium to verify that insertion of the gene into the organism was successful. DNA constructs are inserted into organisms in several ways, including shooting them in with a gene gun, bacterial transformation, and delivering them via a virus. Scientists alter small pieces of DNA called plasmids to transfer desired genes into bacteria.

KEY VOCABULARY	
biofuel	genetically modified organism
DNA construct	trade-off
genetic engineering	vaccine
genetic modification	

History of the Study of Genetics

Gregor Mendel (1822-1884) was a monk, teacher, and scientist, who studied the relationship between heredity and traits, mainly by experimenting with pea plants. He is credited with much of the early understanding of genetics and heredity.

Much has been learned since Mendel, and a large part of the research focus now is on genomics. Genomics is the study of the entire genetic makeup of an organism. This field has expanded rapidly over the past four decades. In 2003, the Human Genome Project completed its mission to catalog the human genome. The information generated by the project has allowed scientists to explore the role of genes in human diseases and health and new approaches to finding cures. Genomics has the potential to contribute to solving sustainability problems related to biodiversity, alternative energy, and human and animal health.

KEY VOCABULARY

genome   genomics

DNA and Basic Genetics

In all organisms, genes carry the instructions for specifying the characteristics of the organism. Genes are sequences of deoxyribonucleic acid (DNA) that code for a particular trait. Genes are organized into larger structures called chromosomes. Most of the cells in most eukaryotic organisms are diploid: they contain two copies (a pair) of each kind of chromosome. Cells contain two copies of each gene—one on each chromosome. These copies may code for different versions of the gene, and are called alleles. In organisms that reproduce sexually, one allele of each type of gene is inherited from each parent.

The DNA stored in cells guides the cells' functions. DNA is a macromolecule composed of two complementary strands, each made of a sequence of nucleotide subunits. Each strand of DNA has a sugar-phosphate backbone and a sequence of nitrogenous bases. The nucleotide subunits found in DNA are adenine, guanine, cytosine and thymine, represented as A, G, C, and T. Two strands of DNA together form a double helix. The chemical and structural properties of DNA are the basis for how the genetic information that determines heredity is both encoded in genes (as a string of molecular "bases") and replicated by means of a template. The genetic information stored in DNA directs the synthesis of the thousands of proteins the cell needs. Changes in DNA (mutations) occur spontaneously at low rates. Some of these changes make no difference to the organism, but others have a variety of effects.

Understanding DNA makes it possible for scientists to manipulate genes to create new combinations of traits and new varieties of organisms. DNA is isolated from cells by breaking the cells and adding chemicals that precipitate the DNA. DNA electrophoresis, a method for working with known samples and markers to match DNA, separates DNA fragments based on size.

KEY VOCABULARY	
amino acid	gel electrophoresis
base pair	gene
cell	hydrogen bond
chromosome	isolation
deoxyribonucleic acid (DNA)	nucleotide
DNA	replication
double helix	sugar–phosphate backbone

Reproduction

Heredity is the passing of genetic traits from one generation to the next. Through selective breeding and genetic modification of organisms, people have significantly transformed the genetic makeup of all sorts of populations. Selective breeding develops organisms with desirable traits by influencing the phenotypes and genotypes of offspring. Studying the results of sexual reproduction of a model organism, such as corn, provides information about the behavior of genes and the relationship between genotype and phenotype.

Asexual reproduction produces genetically identical offspring from a single parent through mitosis. Mitosis is the process by which replicated chromosomes divide and, following cytokinesis, form two identical daughter cells.

Sexual reproduction produces offspring with genes from both parents. Fertilization occurs when a sperm and an egg unite in sexual reproduction. This produces an offspring with two copies of each chromosome, one from the paternal parent and one from the maternal parent. Gametes—sperm in males and eggs in females—contain half the number of chromosomes found in the somatic cells of the same organism. Gametes are formed through meiosis, which creates four haploid sex cells, each containing only one copy of each kind of chromosome. The independent segregation of chromosomes during meiosis is the basis for traits that exhibit independent assortment. As a result of independent segregation and crossing over during meiosis, one individual produces an almost limitless variety of gametes. Abnormalities in chromosome number from errors occurring in gamete production often result in loss of viability or abnormal development of affected offspring. A karyotype is a graphic tool that allows geneticists to visualize the chromosomes of a cell and to check for certain abnormalities.

KEY VOCABULARY

asexual reproduction	heredity
centrioles	karyotype
centromere	law of independent assortment
chromatid	meiosis
crossing over	mitosis
cytokinesis	nondisjunction
daughter cell	parent cell
diploid	selective breeding
gamete	sexual reproduction
haploid	somatic cell

Phenotype/Genotype (Gene Expression)

According to the laws of simple dominance, dominant traits will appear in the phenotype of an organism, while recessive traits are masked by the presence of a dominant trait. Dominance is not always complete. Incomplete dominance refers to the blending of two traits, while codominance refers to the expression of both traits in a heterozygote. From pedigrees scientists infer the genetic mechanism of inheritance of single-gene traits.

Punnett squares are models of the transmission of alleles from one generation to the next. They predict the phenotypes and genotypes of a cross between two parents for one or more traits that are not linked. A Punnett square demonstrates the possible phenotypic and genotypic results of a cross and how likely it is that each genotype and phenotype will occur from that cross.

Some traits are determined by one gene, while many others are determined by multiple genes. Environmental factors also affect many traits. The expression of specific genes regulates cell differentiation and cell functions. Somatic cells in an individual organism have the same genome, but selectively express the genes for characteristic proteins. The proteins a cell produces determine that cell's phenotype.

KEY VOCABULARY

allele	protein
carrier	protein synthesis
codominant	Punnett square
dihybrid cross	recessive
dominant	replication
expressed (gene)	repressed (gene)
gene expression	RNA
genotype	sex-linked
heterozygous	sex-linked recessive
homozygous	trait
incomplete dominance	transcription
mRNA	transcription factor
mutation	translation
pedigree	tRNA
phenotype	

Inquiry and the Nature of Science

Individuals and societies must decide on proposals involving new research and the introduction of new technologies into the environment. Decisions require assessment of alternatives, risks, costs and benefits, and consideration of who benefits and who does not, who pays and who gains, and what the risks are and who or what bears them. Basic concepts and principles of science and technology contribute to evidence-based debate about the economics, policies, politics, and ethics of various science- and technology-related innovations.

Evolution: Maintaining Diversity

THERE IS GREAT VARIETY within and between the earth's ecosystems. Each ecosystem differs from others in its varieties of species, genetic makeup of its species, and the evolutionary relationships of species. All of these levels of variation comprise the earth's biodiversity.

This biodiversity is the product of billions of years of evolution. Ecologists and evolutionary biologists study the evolutionary processes that produce biodiversity, what caused the subtle and dramatic shifts that occurred in the past, and how biodiversity might change in the future. Conservationists often focus on understanding the biodiversity of an area in order to establish priorities for conservation of species. They and other scientists are also concerned with how human activities affect biodiversity.

In this unit you will investigate the levels of biodiversity, and the evolutionary processes that increase, decrease, or maintain biodiversity. You will also examine humans' social, environmental, and economic influences on biodiversity, and make recommendations for which forest area on a fictitious island should receive funds for conservation.

1 Biodiversity and Sustainability

IN THE WORLD'S many ecosystems—whether desert valleys, coral reefs, river-banks, or backyard gardens—are unique assortments of species. The species vary in numbers and in how closely or distantly related they are to one another. Also within each species are variations in the genetic compositions of individuals. The combination of these levels of variability is referred to as **biological diversity** or more commonly, **biodiversity.**

Biodiversity is a characteristic of many ecosystems on Earth.

Ecologists and evolutionary biologists study the biodiversity in ecosystems and how it changed in the past and might change in the future. They examine how environmental factors, including human activities, influence biodiversity and how the sustainability and biodiversity of an area are linked. **Sustainability** is the ability to meet a community's present needs without compromising the ability of future generations to meet their own needs. Some conservationists track the levels of biodiversity in ecosystems in an effort to establish priorities for saving threatened species. One of their approaches is to identify and focus on hotspots, which are areas with a large number of endemic species that are experiencing an extraordinary loss of habitat. **Endemic** species are those that are found exclusively in one area.

In this activity you will examine the biodiversity on the fictitious island of Kapikua and explore some of the factors affecting biodiversity. You will be responsible for managing one ecosystem on the island. Your decisions and responses to events will have consequences for the many species and people in and around your ecosystem.

Challenge

▶ How are the biodiversity of an ecosystem and the sustainability of human communities related?

MATERIALS

FOR EACH GROUP OF FOUR STUDENTS

4 sets of 26 Species Cards—one for each ecosystem

 set of 18 Event Cards

4 Protected Area Cards

 set of 50 transparent, colored plastic Money Chips

 set of 50 opaque, colored plastic Social Chips

 number cube

FOR EACH STUDENT

 Student Sheet 1.1, "Biodiversity Challenge Rules"

 Student Sheet 1.2, "Species Card Record"

 Student Sheet 1.3, "Sustainability Scores"

 Student Sheet 1.4, "Biodiversity Challenge Reflection"

Procedure

1. The map below shows the island of Kapikua, which is located near the equator. There are four major ecosystems on the island. After reading the information about the four ecosystems, have each group member choose one to manage. The ecosystems are:

Tropical Montane Cloud Forest

This ecosystem is in the higher altitudes of the mountain range running through the island. It is densely forested but the trees are generally much smaller than those found in the lowland rainforest. The air is always damp from the clouds and fog that envelop the area.

Lowland Tropical Rainforest

This area is a mix of primary and secondary forest. The primary forest is mainly undisturbed and consists of well-spaced tall trees that let little light through to the forest floor. The secondary forest has grown where sections of the primary forest were previously cleared. It has smaller trees that create a dense and tangled jungle environment.

THE ISLAND OF KAPIKUA

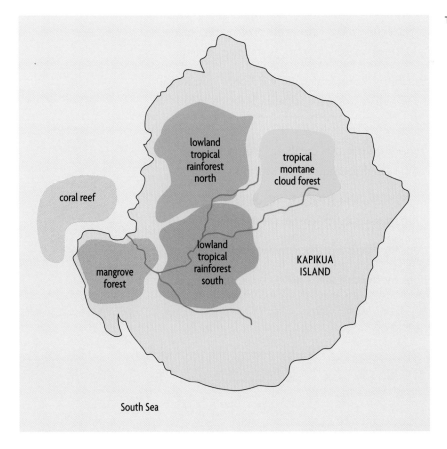

Mangrove Forest

This is an area of mangrove trees and shrubs along the coast where the forest floor is muddy and often covered by brackish water. There exist in this forest varied living conditions for the organisms that inhabit the ecosystem.

Coral Reef

This region lies just offshore from the mangrove forest and close to where the island's largest river flows into the sea. Here the ocean is shallow and much of the reef is easily accessible to swimmers and divers.

2. Once you have determined which ecosystem you will manage, read Student Sheet 1.1, "Biodiversity Challenge Rules." If you did not draw at least two forest or two coral Species Cards, exchange a different Species Card for either a forest or a coral Species Card. If you have questions, discuss them as a group before asking your teacher.

3. Before you begin playing the game, make a list of your eight species on Student Sheet 1.2, "Species Card Record." You will also record your species cards at the end of each round on this sheet.

4. Look at the information on your cards, and note on Student Sheet 1.2, "Species Card Record," any relationships you see between the species on the cards. For example, an organism of one species may rely on an organism of another species for food or shelter. These relationships will be important as you play the game.

5. On Student Sheet 1.3, "Sustainability Scores," calculate and record your initial sustainability score. You will recalculate this score at the end of each round and at the end of the game.

6. Play the game for the three rounds indicated in the Biodiversity Challenge Rules. Your goal is to finish with as high a sustainability score as possible.

7. Follow the instructions at the end of Student Sheet 1.1, "Biodiversity Challenge Rules," to adjust your third-round sustainability score to produce a final score.

8. Follow your teacher's directions for discussing this activity with the class.

9. Follow your teacher's directions for discussing the hotspots on the map at the end of this activity.

Analysis

1. What levels of biodiversity did you investigate in this activity?

2. Describe how the levels of biodiversity you investigated changed within your ecosystem on Kapikua.

3. **Ecosystem services** can be broadly defined as the benefits received from ecosystems, including natural resources and processes that humans and other species rely on for survival. What types of ecosystem services did your group encounter in the game?

4. Give examples of relationships you observed between ecosystems. Cite one of those examples to explain why what happened in one ecosystem affected others.

5. How is the sustainability of a region tied to its biodiversity?

6. **a.** Describe how the biodiversity of the ecosystems in your group changed during the game.

   b. How might the biodiversity of various regions of the earth have changed in the past?

   c. How might the biodiversity of various regions of the earth change in the future?

KEY VOCABULARY	
biodiversity	hotspot
biological diversity	**sustainability**
ecosystem services	**trade-off**
endemic	

Biodiversity Hotspots

California Floristic Province

Area in unchanged condition: 25%. Protected area: 37%
(Percentages are approximate.)

SPECIES	NUMBER OF SPECIES	NUMBER OF ENDEMIC SPECIES
Plants	3,488	2,124
Mammals	157	18
Birds	340	8
Reptiles	69	5
Amphibians	46	25
Freshwater fishes	73	15
Extinct species*	2	

*Recorded since 1500

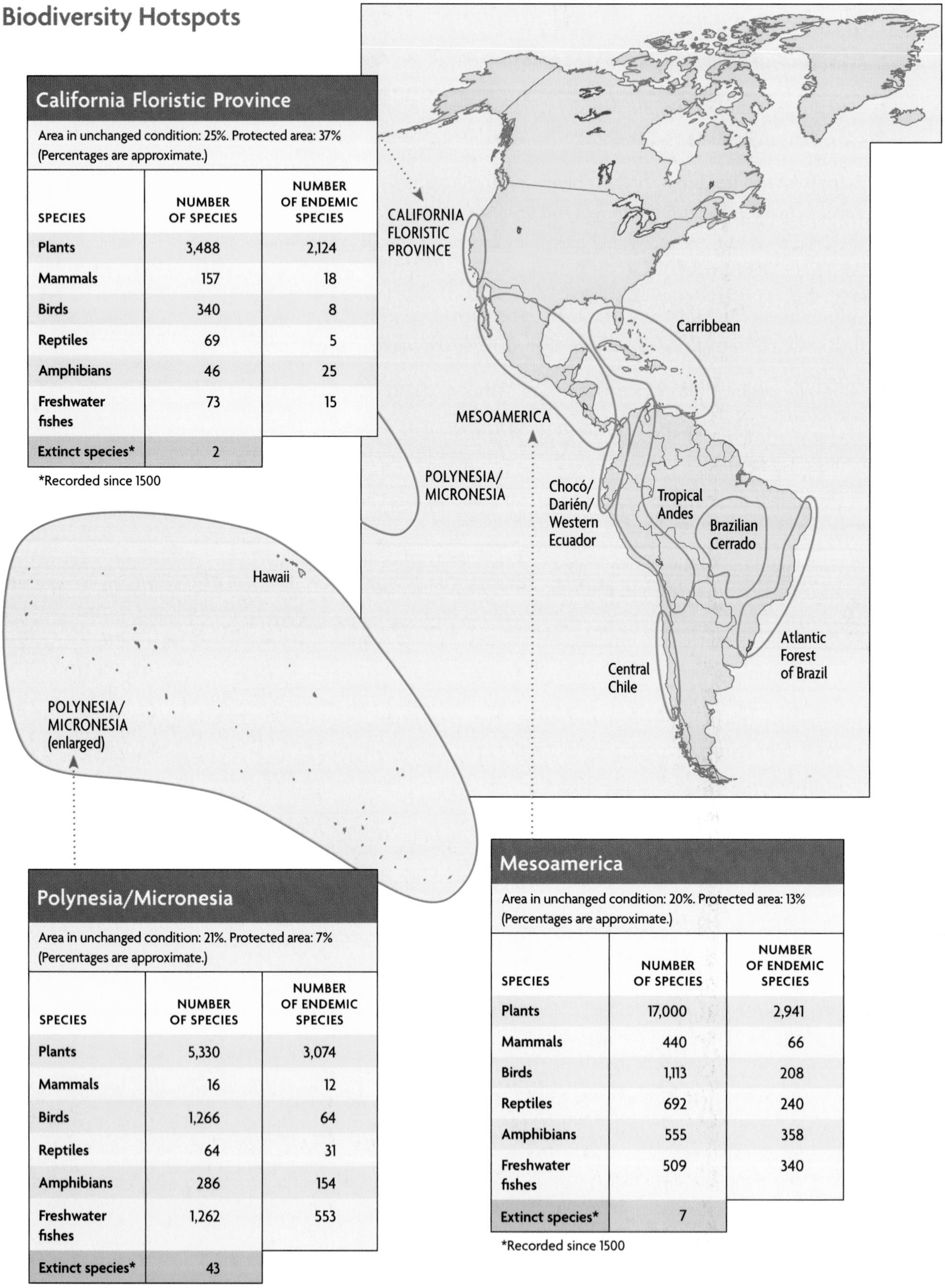

Polynesia/Micronesia

Area in unchanged condition: 21%. Protected area: 7%
(Percentages are approximate.)

SPECIES	NUMBER OF SPECIES	NUMBER OF ENDEMIC SPECIES
Plants	5,330	3,074
Mammals	16	12
Birds	1,266	64
Reptiles	64	31
Amphibians	286	154
Freshwater fishes	1,262	553
Extinct species*	43	

*Recorded since 1500

Mesoamerica

Area in unchanged condition: 20%. Protected area: 13%
(Percentages are approximate.)

SPECIES	NUMBER OF SPECIES	NUMBER OF ENDEMIC SPECIES
Plants	17,000	2,941
Mammals	440	66
Birds	1,113	208
Reptiles	692	240
Amphibians	555	358
Freshwater fishes	509	340
Extinct species*	7	

*Recorded since 1500

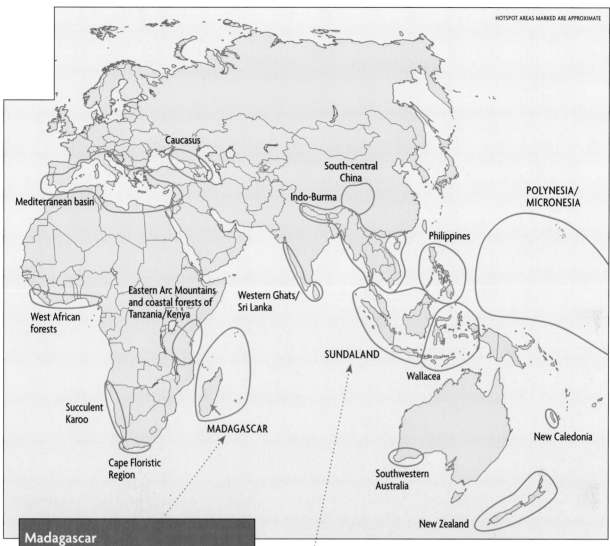

HOTSPOT AREAS MARKED ARE APPROXIMATE

Caucasus

South-central China

Indo-Burma

Mediterranean basin

POLYNESIA/ MICRONESIA

Philippines

Eastern Arc Mountains and coastal forests of Tanzania/Kenya

Western Ghats/ Sri Lanka

West African forests

SUNDALAND

Wallacea

Succulent Karoo

MADAGASCAR

New Caledonia

Cape Floristic Region

Southwestern Australia

New Zealand

Madagascar

Area in unchanged condition: 50%. Protected area: 3%
(Percentages are approximate.)

SPECIES	NUMBER OF SPECIES	NUMBER OF ENDEMIC SPECIES
Plants	13,000	11,600
Mammals	150	135
Birds	310	181
Reptiles	384	367
Amphibians	230	229
Freshwater fishes	164	97
Extinct species*	45	

*Recorded since 1500

Sundaland

Area in unchanged condition: 5%. Protected area: 10%
(Percentages are approximate.)

SPECIES	NUMBER OF SPECIES	NUMBER OF ENDEMIC SPECIES
Plants	25,000	15,000
Mammals	380	172
Birds	769	142
Reptiles	452	243
Amphibians	244	196
Freshwater fishes	950	350
Extinct species*	4	

*Recorded since 1500

Human Activities and Biodiversity

THERE ARE THREE general levels of biodiversity on earth. **Ecosystem diversity** is the variation within and between ecosystems. **Species diversity** is the number of species that exist in an area. **Genetic diversity** is the variation in the genes within a population of organisms.

In this activity, you will look at some examples of how human activities have altered the biodiversity of groups of taxa. **Taxa** (singular **taxon**) are levels of classification, for example species or genus.

Challenge

▶ How do humans alter the biodiversity of groups of taxa?

Human Activities that Affect Biodiversity

HABITAT DESTRUCTION

Humans change natural habitats through such activities as agriculture, building, mining, forestry, and pollution.

INTRODUCED SPECIES

Humans intentionally or accidentally move species from their native locations to new areas. When an introduced species causes or is likely to cause harm to the environment, the economy, or human health, the species is considered an invasive species.

OVEREXPLOITATION

Humans harvest animals or plants for ecosystem services, such as for food, medicine, lumber, collecting, and trading. The harvesting is considered overexploitation when the rate of harvest exceeds the ability of the population to recover.

Clearcutting of the Zambian rainforest.

Japanese beetles were accidentally introduced into the United States in 1916, and have since been severely destructive to turfgrass and ornamental plants.

So many striped narrow-headed softshell turtles have been taken from the wild for food and the international pet trade that natural populations are at risk.

Procedure

1. In your science notebook, copy the following chart. Give it an appropriate title.

Scenario	Type(s) of human impact	Type(s) of biodiversity altered

2. Follow your teacher's directions for which scenario(s) to read.

3. Work by yourself to read your assigned scenario(s). As you read, fill in the columns on the chart.

4. In your group, take turns summarizing your assigned scenario(s). As you listen, fill in the columns on the chart for each scenario that you did not read.

DISRUPTION OF NETWORKS

Ecosystems encompass a network of interdependent interactions. If the population of one species declines or goes extinct, that affects others in the network. An example of a network that could be disrupted is a food web.

A harmful algal bloom causes illness or death in fish, seabirds, marine mammals, and humans who eat seafood contaminated with a neurotoxin from the algae. Algal blooms also reduce the oxygen levels in bodies of water.

BREEDING AND CLONING

People breed and clone populations of other organisms for various purposes. In doing so they might, for example, decrease genetic diversity in species of edible plants to create uniformly desirable crops.

A geneticist checks an ear of experimental corn for genetic changes.

Vast amounts of rainforest in Borneo were cleared to plant oil palm trees.

The Rainforests of Borneo

From an airplane above the island of Borneo, you can see the sudden divide between the rainforest and the straight rows of oil palm trees that have displaced the forest.

Borneo is a large island of more than 427,000 sq km (165,000 sq mi) between the South China and Java seas. On it are more than 15,000 known species of plants and some of the tallest tropical rainforests in the world. The rainforests are filled with an array of animals, including some that glide as they leap from tall trees, such as flying lizards, flying frogs, and flying snakes. Two species of gibbons and eight species of monkeys inhabit and climb in the trees. Sun bears, clouded leopards, elephants, orangutans, and rhinoceroses also live in and roam the rainforest. Even today scientists continue to discover species on the island that were never seen by other scientists before.

The greatest threat to the biodiversity of Borneo is forest destruction. Over the past two decades, approximately 40 million acres of forest have been cleared. Parts of the forests were cleared to plant palm trees, the fruits of which produce oil for cooking, body lotions, and fuel. The forests have also been extensively logged for timber to use for building and making paper. At the rate at which the forests of Borneo are being cut, the risk of current and future loss of biodiversity on the island is high.

The Potato in Ireland

After the potato was brought to Ireland from Spain in the 17th century, the Irish found they could grow more food in a smaller area with less labor when they planted just one variety: the lumper potato. That potato turned out to be a good source of nutrition and became a staple crop for Irish peasants. Like other living organisms, however, the potato is susceptible to microbes that cause disease, and lumpers are particularly susceptible to the fungus *Phytophthora infestans,* which causes potato blight. Making the Irish food supply more vulnerable, the lumper

In Ireland in the 1800s, potato blight killed whole crops of genetically identical lumper potatoes, causing widespread famine.

potatoes were all genetically identical to each other. In 1845, spores of the potato blight fungus were carried by the wind from England. A putrid stench hit the air as entire fields of potatoes died in just a few days.

While the potato blight reached all of Europe, only Ireland experienced devastating famine and suffering. One in eight Irish people died in three years.

Cichlids and Nile Perch

Within the last 200,000 years in Africa's huge Lake Victoria, more than 300 species of cichlid fish evolved to live in the various habitats in the lake. Some cichlids, such as tilapia, are edible, and some larger species are popular sport fishing prey. Genetic evidence suggests that the cichlids evolved from a common ancestor.

In the 1950s, the British government introduced the large Nile perch into the lake with the idea that the perch would provide the local people with a new protein source and a new commercial fishery.

Unfortunately, the perch ate the cichlids and other fish. Because cichlids were also fished along with the perch, introducing the perch appears to be the reason for the extinction of as many as 200 species of cichlids and the decline of other fish, such as catfish and lungfish.

a

b

When the Nile perch (a) was introduced into Lake Victoria, they ate the cichlids (b) and other fish that lived there.

In a further threat to the lake's biodiversity, the loss of the cichlid species that ate algae allowed the amount of algae in the lake to rise. Because algae consume oxygen, their abundance made it difficult for other small plants and animals in the lake to get enough oxygen for themselves. The Lake Victoria ecosystem is adjusting to these changes, but will not likely reach the level of biodiversity that existed before the introduction of Nile perch.

The Dodo Bird

The small Indian Ocean island of Mauritius was once home to populations of the large, flightless dodo bird, which had evolved over several million years on the island. Mauritius is isolated, and because they had little competition from other organisms the dodos had freely fed on fruit that had fallen to the ground. Those dodos with the ability to store large amounts of fat in times when food was scarce were better able to survive and reproduce. Eventually, over generations, the dodos increased in size. Flightlessness also evolved. As plant eaters in an environment with no predators, the inability to fly would have had no effect on the dodo's ability to survive. In the 16th and 17th centuries, Portuguese and Dutch explorers sailed to the island. The flightless dodos could not flee from humans who hunted them for food and for their eggs. The sailors also brought with them pigs, monkeys, and rats that fed on the dodos' eggs and chicks, and perhaps even adult dodos. On a small island, the relatively small dodo population could not survive under these changed conditions. In a small population, the genetic diversity of the population is relatively low. When genetic diversity is low, there is a low probability that any individual in the population will have the trait(s) required for survival and reproduction if the environment changes. Eighty years after humans arrived, dodos became extinct.

Dodo fossil bones confirm that the bird was flightless.

Florida Panther

By the 1950s, the once-large panther population of the south-eastern United States had been hunted to near extinction because of the threat people thought they posed to humans, livestock, and other animals. Today, urban and agricultural development and resulting habitat loss have decreased the panthers' range to only 5% of what it originally was. In 2009, a record number of 16 Florida panthers were killed by cars. With fewer than 100 panthers total remaining in southern Florida, this is a significant loss to the endangered panther population. Florida panthers are found in forested areas, including the mixed swamp, pine, and hardwood forests of the Everglades.

The Florida panther originally inhabited Florida, Louisiana, Arkansas, Mississippi, Alabama, Georgia, and parts of Tennessee and South Carolina. Between 1991 and 2003, more than 728,000 hectares (1.8 million acres) of forest in southern Florida were destroyed, and approximately 17,700 km (11,000 mi) of public roads were developed.

As people took over more and more land the panther population in Florida became isolated by habitat loss. Their isolation prevented them from breeding and exchanging genes with other panther populations. The inbreeding has led to reduced fertility, heart abnormalities, and infectious diseases in the population. In 1995, eight female panthers from Texas were introduced into the Florida population in an effort to help it recover. However, evidence suggests that so far this strategy has had limited success.

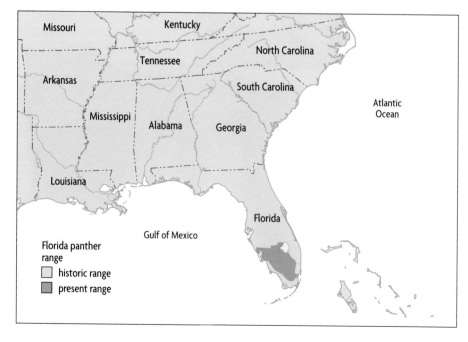

This depiction of the historic and current ranges of the Florida panther population shows how severely their habitat has been reduced.

Domestic Dogs

Domestic dogs are members of the subspecies *Canis lupus familiaris*. They are the result of thousands of years of dog breeding that began about 14,000 years ago when humans first domesticated the gray wolf, *Canis lupus*. The wolf populations in various parts of the world were made up of genetically different individual wolves. As wolves that interacted socially with humans became part of human communities, people took notice of their natural variations and the behavioral traits in their offspring that appeared to be inherited. Soon people were breeding wolves for particular desired traits, such as abilities for hunting, herding, hauling, or protecting their masters. Over centuries of such artificial selection, the descendants of the wolves became what we recognize as dogs.

Today there are hundreds of breeds of *Canis lupus familiaris*, from golden retrievers and poodles to chihuahuas and Pekingese lap dogs to pit bulls and rottweilers. Each breed has specific characteristics selected by the human breeders. For example, golden retrievers were bred to assist hunters by retrieving game. Because they are intelligent and sociable, they have also become popular as family pets. For

a

b

After gray wolves (a) were domesticated by humans, they were bred over centuries to produce hundreds of kinds of modern dogs (b–d).

c

d

decades the art of dog breeding has been big business, with mating of dogs of the same breed to produce dogs for show or superior performance in certain tasks. Now there is a trend to mate one breed with desirable traits to another with other desirable traits. The media has labeled the newly created mixed breeds "designer dogs," and some people are willing to pay thousands of dollars for such a puppy. The labradoodle, for example, is a mix of labrador retriever and poodle. While not all of the offspring in a litter have the exact same mix of traits, labradoodles' desired traits include a friendly, loyal disposition and a nonshedding coat.

Labradoodle

Flying Foxes

Some of the most important pollinators and seed dispersers of plants in the South Pacific islands are flying foxes, which are actually bats with ears, eyes, and snout comprising what looks like the face of a fox. Flying foxes are mammals that can weigh up to 1 kg (2.2 lbs).

Flying foxes feed on nectar, blossoms, pollen, and fruit. Reproduction of more than 79% of the plants of the Samoan islands is dependent on the flying fox for seed dispersal or pollination. In turn, the plants support much of the animal

The endangered flying fox bat is an important pollinator.

diversity on the island and provide ecosystem services for humans. The wild banana is an example of a tree that largely depends on flying foxes to spread the pollen from one tree or one banana flower to another. Because of their important role in pollination and seed dispersal, the flying fox population is crucial for the maintenance of the Pacific island ecosystem. Local people depend on the wild banana for food and as a source of fiber to make textiles, rope, and paper.

A great threat to flying foxes, however, is people's taste for exotic foods. Each year from 1975 to 1990, between 8,000 and 29,000 flying foxes were hunted to supply the luxury food market. The bats are also hunted for their medicinal properties and sport.

Populations of flying foxes are especially vulnerable to destruction by hunters and other pressures because most females do not begin reproducing until they are one-to-two-years old. Once they start reproducing, they give birth to only one off-spring per year. The flying fox is classified as endangered under the United States Endangered Species Act, and cannot be imported into this country.

Northern Elephant Seals

Hundreds of thousands of northern elephant seals once lived in the Pacific Ocean with a range that spanned from the north in Alaska and British Columbia to the south in California. They are so named for their large size and the large nose that suggests an elephant's trunk. Male elephant seals grow to a weight of approximately 2,300 kg (5,000 lbs), and a length up to 4 m (14 ft), while mature females grow to weigh around 635 kg (1,400 lbs), and to be up to 3 m (11 ft) long.

Northern elephant seal

Elephant seals spend most of their time in the ocean but come ashore regularly to molt, breed, and give birth on land, making them a much easier target for hunters than whales. From 1820 to 1880, whale and seal hunters slaughtered whole colonies of elephant seals to make oil from their blubber. The blubber harvesting was so extensive that the species was nearly wiped out. In fact, estimates of their remaining population numbered from 20 to 100 individuals from the late 1880s to 1900. Scientists describe such a severe but temporary reduction in population size as a bottleneck.

Beginning in the early 1900s, the Mexican and United States governments protected the elephant seals with a ban on their hunting, and their numbers gradually increased. Today, astonishingly, there are more than 100,000 northern elephant seals. Of some concern to conservationists, however, is that the current seal population has been traced through genetic testing back to just one male who survived to reproduce with females. This means the genetic diversity is very low. But so far, at least, the low genetic diversity has not hindered the growth of the elephant seal population.

Analysis

1. For which scenario(s) did humans alter

   a. ecosystem diversity?

   b. species diversity?

   c. genetic diversity?

2. Explain how humans changed the ecosystem, species, and genetic diversity of the groups you identified in question 1.

3. What is the relationship between extinction and

   a. species diversity?

   b. genetic diversity?

4. Do you think it is important for humans to be aware of how we alter the genetic and species diversity of groups of organisms? Explain.

KEY VOCABULARY	
biodiversity	**species diversity**
ecosystem diversity	**taxa**
genetic diversity	**taxon**

3 Geologic Time

T HE EARTH'S HISTORY spans 4.5 billion years. Scientists use the terms **deep time** and **geologic time** interchangeably when describing this vast time scale. They have distinguished historical eras, or ages, in geologic time, such as the Archaean era and Proterozoic era. The eras are further divided into periods, such as the Cambrian period or Silurian period, and epochs based on when major changes in plants and animals occurred. Scientists learned about these changes by observing fossils. All of the periods of the earth's history together make up the geologic timeline.

It may be difficult to visualize just how long a billion years is, yet knowing about this immense span of time has been central to understanding the origins and evolution of life on the earth. In this activity, you will develop a scaled model to help you visualize geologic time and the history of life during that time.

Challenge

▶ What are the key events of geologic time?

The Burgess Shale in the Canadian Rockies in British Columbia is a rock formation that accumulated during the Middle Cambrian period approximately 500–550 million years ago. The fossils found there are some of the most diverse and well preserved in the world. Many of the fossils are from organisms that lived on the sea floor.

MATERIALS

FOR EACH PAIR OF STUDENTS

set of 6 Geologic Event paper strips

scissors

calculator

FOR EACH STUDENT

Student Sheet 3.1, "Ideas about Evolution"

Student Sheet 3.2, "Geologic Time and Major Events"

Procedure

1. Review the statements on Student Sheet 3.1, "Ideas about Evolution."

2. Follow your teacher's instructions for responding to and discussing the statements on Student Sheet 3.1.

3. With your partner, examine the information on Student Sheet 3.2, "Geologic Time and Major Events," and the chart below. Convert each geologic time period from millions of years ago (mya) into yards on a football field, and record both the time in mya and the era/event, period, or epoch on the Student Sheet.

The Geologic Time Scale

GEOLOGIC ERA OR EVENT	GEOLOGIC PERIOD	GEOLOGIC EPOCH	TIME (MYA)
Earth is formed	—	—	4,500
Archean	—	—	4,300
Proterozoic	—	—	2,500
Paleozoic	Cambrian	—	542
Paleozoic	Ordovician	—	488
Paleozoic	Silurian	—	444
Paleozoic	Devonian	—	416
Paleozoic	Carboniferous	—	359
Paleozoic	Permian	—	299
Mesozoic	Triassic	—	251
Mesozoic	Jurassic	—	200
Mesozoic	Cretaceous	—	145
Cenozoic	Tertiary	Paleocene	65
Cenozoic	Tertiary	Eocene	55.8
Cenozoic	Tertiary	Oligocene	33.9
Cenozoic	Tertiary	Miocene	23
Cenozoic	Tertiary	Pliocene	5.3
Cenozoic	Quaternary	Pleistocene	1.8
Cenozoic	Quaternary	Recent (Holocene)	0.01

4. Collect the sheet showing six Geologic Events, and with your partner, cut it into six Geologic Event strips. Read the information on the strips, and on Student Sheet 3.2, "Geologic Time and Major Events," arrange them where you think each occurred in geologic time. Once you have decided on an order, use a pencil to record the placement on the Student Sheet.

5. Follow your teacher's instructions for observing on an actual football field the events in geologic time that you recorded in Step 4.

6. Observe your Geologic Event paper strips again. Using your experience on the football field, record on Student Sheet 3.2, "Geologic Time and Major Events," the correct time placement of the six geologic events you were given. In your science notebook, record any changes you made to your original order.

7. Now record the following events on the timeline on Student Sheet 3.2, "Geologic Time and Major Events":

   • Starting 500 mya: first vertebrates in fossil record

   • Starting 416 mya: first insects in fossil record

   • Starting 230 mya: first dinosaurs in fossil record

   • Starting 144 mya: mass extinction, including dinosaurs

8. Look at the following diagrams, which are evolutionary trees showing relationships between taxa. Based on the trees, add the following events to the timeline on Student Sheet 3.2, "Geologic Time and Major Events":

   • First seed plants in fossil record

   • First reptiles in fossil record

   • The extinction of pterosaurs

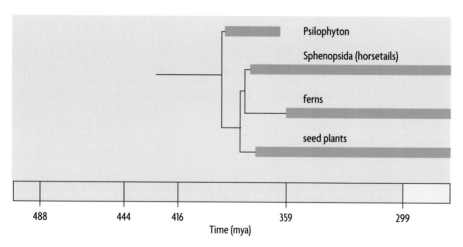

EVOLUTIONARY TREE FOR SOME GROUPS OF PLANTS

EVOLUTIONARY TREE FOR
SOME GROUPS OF VERTEBRATES

Analysis

1. In four to six sentences summarize the geologic timeline and major evolutionary events.

2. How did the conversions to a football-field scale help you understand geologic time and earth's events?

3. How have your ideas about geologic time and major events within it changed after doing this activity?

4. What impact would it have had on biodiversity across geologic time if no species had ever become extinct? Explain.

KEY VOCABULARY

biodiversity	extinction
deep time	**geologic time**
extinct	geologic time scale

4 Darwin and the Development of a Theory

STARTING IN THE 1830s, British naturalist Charles Darwin suggested and
developed some ideas about evolution that revolutionized the field of biology. **Biological evolution,** or **evolution,** is a change in the genetic composition of
a population that gives rise to new life forms from common ancestors. Darwin's
thinking was influenced by the ideas of several other people who worked before
and during his time.

Challenge

► How did Darwin build on his and others' work to develop his ideas about natural selection
and evolution?

MATERIALS

FOR EACH STUDENT

3 sticky notes

Student Sheet 4.1, "Scientists, Ideas, and Events that Influenced Darwin"

Procedure

1. As you read, follow the "Read, Think, and Take Note" strategy. To do this:

   • Stop at least three times during the reading to mark on
   a sticky note your thoughts or questions about the reading. Use the list of guidelines on the next page to start
   your thinking.

   • After writing a thought or question on a sticky note,
   place it next to the passage in the reading that prompted
   your note.

   • Discuss with your partner the thoughts and questions
   you had while reading.

Charles Darwin

Read, Think, and Take Note: Guidelines

As you read, from time to time, write one of the following on a sticky note :

- Explain a thought or reaction to something you read

- Note something in the reading that is confusing or unfamiliar

- List a word that you do not know

- Describe a connection to something you learned or read previously

- Make a statement about the reading

- Pose a question about the reading

- Draw a diagram or picture of an idea or connection

2. After finishing the reading, complete the diagram on Student Sheet 4.1, "Scientists, Ideas, and Events that Influenced Darwin."

Reading

Before Darwin

In the early 1800s, naturalists had begun to consider the idea that species of living things are not fixed, a revolutionary idea at the time. Instead, they suspected, species have undergone changes ever since they first evolved on earth.

In France, Jean-Baptiste Lamarck was one of the naturalists considering changes in species. In 1809 (the year Charles Darwin was born), Lamarck published *Zoological Philosophy,* a book that presented one of the first theories of evolution. He suggested that when the environment changes, organisms must also change in response if they are to survive. He favored a mechanism for evolution proposed by earlier scientists that was based on use and disuse of organs. He stated that, for example, if giraffes continually stretched their necks to reach high treetops for food, their necks could lengthen over their lifetime, and their offspring could inherit these changes. If an animal did not use a particular organ, the organ would become smaller from one generation to the next or disappear entirely. Lamarck's theory would say, for example, that because snakes could slither through the grass, the legs of snake species gradually became smaller and smaller.

Lamarck was ignored or attacked by most of his colleagues for his theory of use and disuse because he had no evidence for his mechanism, and many of his ideas were pure speculation. Today, his theory is not accepted because scientists' investigations of heredity have shown that acquired characteristics (characteristics that develop during life, that are not inherited), such as strong muscles due to exercise, are not passed through from the body to the genes, and are not, therefore, passed on from parents to offspring.

Darwin's Observations on the Galapagos Islands

In 1831, one of Darwin's college professors recommended him to Captain Robert Fitzroy to join the voyage of the HMS Beagle, a survey ship that would travel all over the world. Appreciating Darwin's education and impressed by his wealthy background, Fitzroy accepted the 22-year-old Darwin on board.

While at sea Darwin read the first volume of Charles Lyell's recently published *Principles of Geology.* The main point of Lyell's book was that the geology of the earth in its present form helps explain the geologic past. Lyell proposed that large-scale geologic change results from small changes over extremely long periods of time. For example, the slow erosion of rock over many years can lead to the formation of a canyon. In addition, he, as had others, thought that the earth was much older than several thousand years.

Over the five years of the voyage, Darwin observed and collected a variety of animals, plants, and fossils to bring back to England. His work on the voyage included explorations on land in South America where he noted geological formations, and several weeks studying the organisms on the Galapagos Islands, about 970 km off the coast of Ecuador. Those 10 islands, as Darwin observed, were all formed from volcanic rocks and all had similar soil, climates, elevation, and size. He also noticed that the plants and animals on the islands had adapted to all kinds of environments.

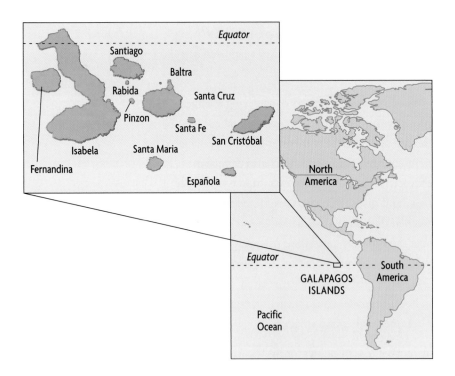

Darwin's observations of plants and animals on the Galapagos Islands made him wonder about the origins of their similarities and differences.

Darwin made extensive observations of the Galapagos plants and animals. He wondered why the species on each island differed from each other but were much more like each other than species elsewhere.

Among the organisms Darwin brought back to England were the now-famous Galapagos finches. Darwin had collected a number of birds that he assumed were blackbirds, grosbeaks, and woodpeckers because they varied so much in beak structure, tails, and body form. Showing his collection to England's bird experts, he was surprised to learn that his birds were all members of 13 closely related species of finches. He had seen one group of finches often climbing around the flowers of cactus trees, while another group tended to flock together and feed on seeds on the ground. For each species of finch the birds' beaks were suited to the food sources available on the island they lived on. Although Darwin examined many other groups of organisms, including mockingbirds and tortoises, the finches became best known because they showed how a diverse group of species could evolve through natural selection from a common ancestor that originated on the mainlands.

Darwin observed biodiversity in many groups of organisms as he developed his ideas about natural selection, including the Galapagos finch (a), Galapagos mockingbird (b), and the Galapagos tortoise (c).

a

b

c

Variety and Artificial Selection through Breeding

Back in England as he thought about the patterns of organisms on the islands—different from and yet similar to those on the mainland—Darwin began to develop his ideas about biodiversity. From pigeon breeders he learned that selective breeding could be used to produce a great variety of pigeons in a relatively short period of time. A breeder would cage two individual pigeons with a desirable trait together to mate in order to obtain offspring that inherited and reinforced that trait. These improved offspring were then selected for further breeding, and the breeder would continue the process for generations. Meanwhile, another breeder would be mating his pigeons for another desirable trait. People had applied such artificial selection for thousands of years in breeding better crops and animals. Dogs, cows, corn, and tulips are just some of the organisms modified by humans through selective breeding.

Darwin became so fascinated with this that he began to breed pigeons at his home. In observing characteristics of tails, heads, beaks, and necks, he was once again astonished by the variety he could bring out among the pigeons, an astonishment similar to when he understood the variations among finches on the Galapagos. He also learned that if he crossbred varieties of pigeons, some offspring would resemble the birds he first started with when he began breeding. Darwin considered how this great variety might arise in nature. He wrote in his autobiography:

> After my return to England, it appeared to me that by following the example of Lyell in *Geology*, and by collecting all facts which bore in any way on the variation of animals and plants under domestication and nature, some light might be thrown on the whole subject. I soon perceived that selection was the keystone of man's success in making useful races of animals and plants. But how selection could be applied to organisms living in a state of nature remained for some time a mystery to me.

Darwin learned from pigeon breeders how selective breeding can produce a variety of pigeons.

Thomas Malthus

A BRITISH ECONOMIST who proposed in an essay in 1798 that human population growth will always exceed the amount of food available to feed the population, Malthus argued that the geometric growth of the human population would lead to starvation and suffering by the poorer members of society. He suggested that individuals in the population compete with each other for limited resources. Those successful in competing would survive, while those who failed were doomed to starvation. ∎

Darwin's breakthrough came in reasoning that the selection produced artificially by humans might occur in all sorts of species, as a result of changes in the environment. Also in his autobiography he wrote:

> In October 1838, that is, fifteen months after I had begun my systematic inquiry, I happened to read for amusement Malthus on Population, and being well prepared to appreciate the struggle for existence which everywhere goes on from long-continued observation of the habits of animals and plants, it at once struck me that under these circumstances favorable variations would tend to be preserved, and unfavorable ones to be destroyed. The result of this would be the formation of new species. Here, then, I had at last got a theory by which to work.

The Origin of Species

Darwin spent the next 20 years gathering more facts for the theory of natural selection. While he planned to write a large work on the theory, he spent time on many other projects as well. In 1858, however, another world-traveling naturalist, Alfred Russel Wallace, sent Darwin a summary of his own theory of evolution in which he drew conclusions similar to Darwin's. Wallace requested that Darwin, who was a respected naturalist, send the paper to the Linnaean Society, a group of influential naturalists of the day. Through Lyell and others, a meeting of the Linnaean Society was organized to present both men's work together. Soon after, in 1859, Darwin published his thorough and detailed explanation of natural selection in his book *On the Origin of Species.*

In *On the Origin of Species,* Darwin laid out his evidence that all living species change through a series of steps, as characteristics slightly more favorable to surviving in a particular environment are preserved successively over time. An accumulation of enough of these changes would give rise to a new species. In addition to recognizing that all species diverge and change through evolution, Darwin proposed that these changes take place through what he called **natural selection.** He reasoned that if breeders could use artificial selection to create dramatic changes in species over short periods of time, natural processes could lead to change over very long periods. As Darwin saw it, natural selection explained the differences in closely related species. The Galapagos finches provided an example of how an original small population could evolve into a number of different species. Because they are most closely related to South American finches, it appears that these finches first arrived on the islands from the mainland, perhaps as a result of storms that blew them off course.

Likely scattered among the 10 islands, individuals in the population encountered new food sources and habitats, which differed from island to island. The beaks of individual finches from the mainland would have had a certain amount of variation in their shapes and sizes. Those individuals with beaks that could feed easily on available food sources survived longer, reproducing more offspring that inherited the genes for similar traits. Over an unknown number of generations, this resulted in finches with different beaks in different habitats, depending on whether the type of food available was seeds, insects, or fruit. Long, pointed beaks, for example, were well suited for digging seeds out of cactus fruits. Short, wide beaks were best for eating seeds from the ground. Thin, sharp beaks were suited to catching insects. At the same time, other changes in characteristics, such as body size, tail shape, and behavior were also accumulating in the populations. Gradual accumulations of these changes through natural selection eventually led to the separation of a population into different species.

Alfred Russel Wallace

CONSIDERED THE CO-DISCOVERER of natural selection, Alfred Russel Wallace is also known for his accomplishments in the field of biogeography. One of his key contributions was to divide the world into seven major biogeographical areas. The name "Wallace's Line" was given to the divide between Southeast Asia and the Australia and New Zealand region because the plants and animals in the two areas were very different even though they were geographically close to one another. ∎

In *The Descent of Man,* published in 1871, Darwin identified another mechanism for evolution, which he called sexual selection. **Sexual selection** refers to differential reproduction resulting from variation in the ability to obtain mates. For example, female peacocks tend to preferentially mate with males that have showy tail feathers. Darwin distinguished this type of selection from natural selection because these features are not necessarily adaptive for the conditions of life; they promote reproductive success in a very different way that in some cases may even conflict with natural selection. For example, the showy tail display of a male peacock attracts potential female mates leading to increased reproduction, but may also attract predators, reducing survival.

Darwin's famous work drastically changed the field of biology. His story reflects how science progresses and theories are developed. Theories are complex and require support from a large body of evidence from many independent sources. **Evidence** is information used to support or refute a claim. Darwin made careful observations and thought about the patterns he saw while also thinking about ideas he learned by reading and talking to other scientists. His breakthrough came in putting these ideas together and providing a detailed description for how natural selection and sexual selection could give rise to diverse life forms from common ancestors. Since its development, a large body of evidence has been gathered to support the theory of natural selection, which provides a logical, scientifically tested explanation for the evolution of life.

Analysis

1. Look carefully back at the reading and write a five-to-eight sentence summary about who influenced Darwin's thinking and how they did so.

2. What did you learn from Darwin about how a scientific theory is developed?

3. **a.** What kinds of traits evolve through natural selection? Give a few examples.

   b. What kinds of traits do not evolve through natural selection? Give a few examples.

KEY VOCABULARY	
biological evolution	**natural selection**
evidence	**sexual selection**
evolution	theory

5 Using Fossil Evidence to Investigate Whale Evolution

LIVING ORGANISMS SOMETIMES leave behind physical evidence of themselves in rock, ice, tar, amber, or volcanic ash when they die. When this evidence is preserved over geologic time, it creates a **fossil.** In this activity you will use fossil evidence to investigate the evolution of whales.

Challenge

▶ How does fossil evidence determine the relationships of whale ancestors and their descendants?

Modern whales include the toothed whales, and the baleen whales. The sperm whale (a) is a toothed whale, and the humpback (b) is a baleen. This whale fossil (c), found in the northern Caucasus, Russia, dates from approximately 10 million years ago.

MATERIALS

FOR EACH PAIR OF STUDENTS

    set of 5 Fossil Skeleton cards, B, K, M, O, and T

2 additional Fossil Skeleton cards, A and D

FOR EACH STUDENT

    Student Sheet 5.1, "Whale Fossil Chart"

    Student Sheet 5.2, "Whale Evolutionary Tree"

    Student Sheet 3.2, "Geologic Time and Major Events," from Activity 3

Procedure

1. Compare the first set of five skeleton cards B, K, M, O, and T. With your partner, based on similarities you observe, group the skeletons into two sets, one
   with two cards and one with three. Name the set of skeletons containing
   skeleton M Group 1, and name the other set Group 2.

2. Create a data table in your science notebook for recording the following
   information:

   • Which skeletons you put into Groups 1 and 2

   • Five similarities and five differences within each group

3. In your science notebook, copy the Venn diagram shown below.

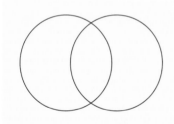

4. Discuss the similarities within each group. Record them on the Venn diagram
   in the areas where the circles do not overlap.

5. Write down as many similarities as you can between Group 1 and Group 2.
   Record the similarities between the groups on the Venn diagram in the space
   where the two circles overlap.

6. From the similarities and differences you noticed among all of the skeletons,
   arrange the cards vertically in the order you think each first appeared in
   geologic time, assuming M was found in the deepest rock layers of the earth.
   Place skeletons either in a single line or in a branched pattern from a common ancestor, depending on your observations.

   Hint: If there is a skeleton that doesn't seem to fit into a single-line arrangement, place it off to the side, next to the line.

7. Record your arrangement of the skeletons in your science notebook. Write a brief description of the reasoning behind your placement.

8. Obtain Student Sheet 5.1, "Whale Fossil Chart," which has more information. With that information rearrange your skeleton cards if necessary. Record any changes in your science notebook.

9. Obtain Student Sheet 5.2, "Whale Evolutionary Tree." Copy that tree into your science notebook below your arrangement of the skeletons. Record any similarities and differences you notice between the tree you copied and the arrangement you described in Step 7.

10. Obtain the two other cards A and D. With your partner, observe the cards and discuss where to place them on your arrangement. Record your placement of A and D on the tree you drew in your science notebook. Enter the following:

    • A claim: your conclusion about the most logical placement of A and D on the tree

    • Evidence: the evidence you gathered that supports the claim

    • Reasoning: how the evidence you gathered supports the claim

11. Go back to the geologic timeline you constructed in Activity 3, "Geologic Time." On Student Sheet 3.2, "Geologic Time and Major Events,"

    • record whale evolution at the appropriate time it began.

    • mark the time span in which whale evolution occurred.

Analysis

1. What types of skeletal changes occurred during whale evolution?

2. What change (or transition) in habitat did whales' ancestors make?

3. Which fossil organism in whale evolution do you think was the first to live mostly in water? Explain your claim with evidence and reasoning.

4. Explain the changes in the skeletons during the transition in habitat, according to the theory of natural selection.

5. a. Explain what is happening at the region of the tree where remingtonocetids are observed.

   b. What can you infer remingtonocetids looked like based on the other information you have on the tree?

KEY VOCABULARY	
evidence	evolutionary tree
evolution	**fossil**

6 Evidence from the Fossil Record

THE **FOSSIL RECORD** includes all of the fossils that have existed in the 4.5 billion years of earth's history—whether they have been discovered or not. Fossils may be bones, teeth, shells, footprints, or prints of other structures. Fossils form in several ways. An organism might have been preserved in ice, tar, amber, or volcanic ash. An organism's footprints or parts, such as leaves and feathers, might be preserved in rocks if the environmental conditions did not destroy them first. Paleontologists, the scientists who study the fossil record, use several methods to figure out when a fossil formed. The structures and ages of fossils provide evidence for macroevolution—the formation of major new groups of organisms. Fossil evidence has helped scientists figure out how such groups as dinosaurs, birds, and mammals evolved.

Challenge

▶ How do scientists interpret evidence in the fossil record?

MATERIALS

FOR EACH STUDENT

Student Sheet 3.1, "Ideas about Evolution," from Activity 3

Student Sheet 3.2, "Geologic Time and Major Events," from Activity 3

This fossil worm from the Burgess Shale lived in the Middle Cambrian era, approximately 500 million years ago. The worm lived in burrows in sediment on the seabed.

Procedure

1. When reading, answer the Stopping to Think questions in your mind.

2. Go back to the geologic timeline you constructed in Activity 3, "Geologic Time." On Student Sheet 3.2, "Geologic Time and Major Events," label the origin of tetrapods at the appropriate time it occurred.

3. Go back to the statements on Student Sheet 3.1, "Ideas about Evolution," from Activity 3. Add information from this activity or a previous activity to support whether any of the statements are correct or incorrect.

Reading

Determining the Age of a Fossil

Paleontologists rely mainly on two methods to determine the age of the earth and the ages of rock layers and the fossils they contain. With stratigraphy, they determine the sequence of events, such as the formation of particular rock layers. With radiometric dating, they determine how many years ago rock layers and fossils formed.

Stratigraphy is the study of rock layers. Rock layers form from lava flows or from sediments. As hot lava spills over an area and cools, it becomes a layer of hard rock. Sediment layers form from small particles of rock and soil that settle and build up over millions of years. Most sediment forms from ash or small particles of rock that have been worn away by ice, water, or wind. Sediment layers are softer than hardened lava and often contain many fossils. As sediment layers build up, their weight creates pressure that squeezes them into solid rock. Layers of lava and of compressed sediments are called **strata.** Stratigraphy is based on the logical reasoning that deeper strata and the fossils found in them are older, while upper strata and the fossils they contain formed more recently.

Some of the sediments that make up the layers of the Grand Canyon in Arizona were transported by wind and water from the Appalachian Mountains in eastern North America.

About 200 years ago, scientists observed that certain layers of rock in different geographic areas contained similar characteristic fossils. This observation led scientists to the idea that these layers of rock and the fossils preserved in them formed at the same time. The geologic timeline you studied in Activity 3, "Geologic Time," divides geologic time into periods based on the presence or absence of various kinds of fossils in rock strata.

STOPPING TO THINK 1

How do strata form?

What is the relationship between strata and the fossils that formed in them?

Stratigraphic dating provides the relative ages of rock layers and the fossils within them. Interpreting evidence from stratigraphy requires an understanding of geology. For example, wind and water might erode strata and uncover deeper layers. The movement of the earth's surface from an earthquake might tilt or uplift the strata, which breaks the sequence of the layers. Paleontologists consider these factors when interpreting stratigraphic evidence.

With **radiometric dating** scientists estimate not only the order of rock layer and fossil formation, but how many years ago rock layers and fossils formed. It is based on the decay of radioactive atoms of certain elements. For example, radioactive carbon is trapped in fossils in sedimentary rock layers. Organisms take up radioactive carbon-14 when they are alive. After they die, the radioactive carbon decays. Carbon-14 has a half-life of 5,730 years, which means that half of the carbon-14 present in an organism when it dies will have decayed in 5,730 years. The graph below shows how the fraction of carbon-14 remaining indicates the age of the fossil. Measuring carbon-14 is accurate in determining dates up to 50,000–60,000 years ago. For fossils older than that, the amount of carbon-14 remaining can no longer be measured accurately.

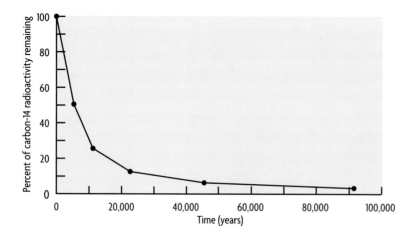

DATING FOSSILS USING CARBON-14

To figure out the dates of older samples, scientists work with other radioactive isotopes, such as potassium and uranium. These radioactive elements are trapped in igneous rock layers that formed as molten lava cooled, and they have longer half-lives. The table below shows how these radioactive elements provide a clock that tells the ages of rock layers.

Atomic Half-lives and Radiometric Dating

RADIOACTIVE ELEMENT	HALF-LIFE (YEARS)	USEFUL RANGE (YEARS)
Carbon-14	5,730	< 60,000
Potassium-40	1.26 billion	100,000–4.5 billion
Uranium-238	4.5 billion	2 million–4.5 billion

STOPPING TO THINK 2

How does information from radioactive data help to determine the age of a fossil?

Studying Fossils to Determine the Origin of Tetrapods

Paleontologists primarily study fossils. They learn a lot about extinct species by directly observing the fossils and determining how old they are. From fossils they also infer the habitats and behavior of previous organisms.

One of the most fascinating evolutionary puzzles paleontologists have studied is the macroevolution of terrestrial tetrapods from marine fish. **Terrestrial tetrapods** are the four-limbed mammals, reptiles, amphibians, and birds that live on land. In the late 19th century, paleontologist Edward Cope proposed that tetrapods evolved from aquatic vertebrates that had fleshy fins with structural similarities to limbs. These fleshy-finned organisms were similar to the coelacanth and lungfish alive today. But the details of the evolution of tetrapods remained mostly unknown, including the timeframe of the events. Until 1987, the fossil evidence was based on two forms, *Eusthenopteron* and *Ichthyostega*. They were not "fishes" as we think of them today; they were distinct from the true ray-finned fishes such as tuna and trout. Rather, they were fleshy-finned forms, whose limbs and fins were covered with fleshy muscle, like our hands and the hands of all tetrapods. *Eusthenopteron* and *Ichthyostega* are not tetrapods, but they are on the line to tetrapods, as shown in the tree on the next page.

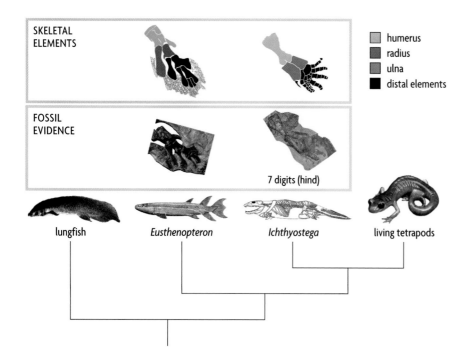

Edward Cope's hypothesis, shown as an evolutionary tree

You have probably seen a drawing of an organism, such as a lungfish, crawling out of water onto land. Scientists were curious about whether this was how tetrapods evolved. Did a fish propel itself onto land with its fins and then evolve limbs? Or did tetrapods evolve in an aquatic environment? *Eusthenopteron* and *Ichthyostega* did not provide evidence to answer these questions.

Since the late 1980s, scientists have found fossils that have helped them figure out the sequence of events leading to the divergence of the tetrapods. They have sequenced the fossils by a process similar to the one you used in Activity 5, "Using Fossil Evidence to Investigate Whale Evolution." Stratigraphy and radiometric dating helped them determine the age of fossils they discovered. A particularly important fossil is the skeleton of *Acanthostega*, discovered in East Greenland in 1987. This organism had legs and feet, but it lacked other body parts associated with life on land. Its legs did not have ankles strong enough to support its weight on land; instead, they were like paddles. And while it had both lungs and gills, its rib cage was too short to prevent the chest cavity from collapsing when on land.

Acanthostega changed the thinking about events leading to life on land. It suggested that aquatic organisms evolved such features as lungs and legs with feet in the shallow-water environments along coastal margins during the Devonian period. Scientists hypothesized that these features allowed hunting, mating, and perhaps laying eggs in low-water areas of tangled vegetation. According to this hypothesis, the lungs and legs were later co-opted in new evolving species for life on land. **Co-opted features** are those that evolved to serve one function, and later evolved through natural selection to perform a new function.

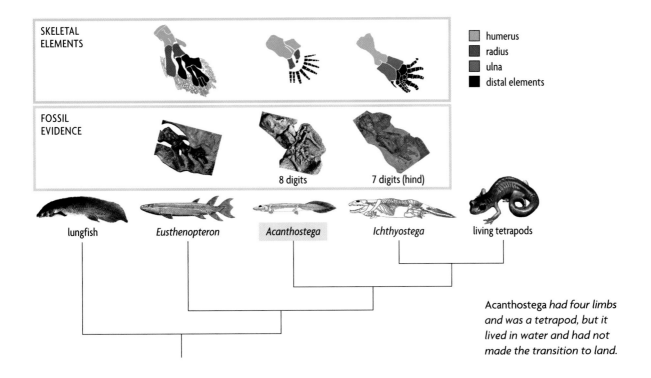

Acanthostega *had four limbs and was a tetrapod, but it lived in water and had not made the transition to land.*

STOPPING TO THINK 3

How did Acanthostega *change scientists' thinking about the evolution of tetrapods?*

As scientists continued hunting for fossils all over the world, they discovered more fish-like tetrapods and tetrapod-like fishes. These examples began to fill in branches of the evolutionary tree between *Eusthenopteron* and *Acanthostega*. They also suggested that tetrapods originated 380–363 million years ago, in the Middle Devonian time period. In 1999, a team of scientists set out to hunt for fossils in rock layers they knew had formed between 380 and 363 million years ago. They chose an area of the Canadian Arctic that paleontologists had not searched before. This was an ideal place to search because no buildings, roads, or trees covered the rock layers. After seven years, in 2006, the team announced their headline-making discovery of *Tiktaalik*, a 375-million-year-old fleshy-finned fossil. *Tiktaalik* had the scales and gills of other aquatic vertebrates, but it had lungs too, like other fleshy fins including the lungfish and coelacanth. It had a tetrapod-like head and the beginnings of a neck. Its fleshy fins had thin ray bones for paddling in water, but stronger interior bones for support, much like those in tetrapods. Because of its clear transitional features, *Tiktaalik* is humorously nicknamed "the fishapod," but in fact it is only one in a series of forms in the transition to land.

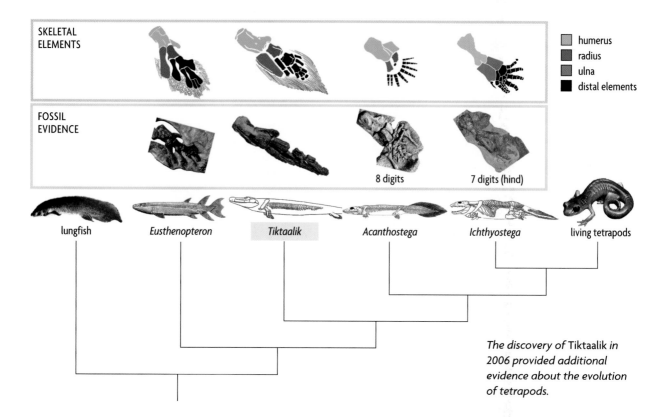

The discovery of Tiktaalik *in 2006 provided additional evidence about the evolution of tetrapods.*

Transitional Fossils

Such fossils as *Tiktaalik, Acanthostega,* and *Ichthyostega,* have helped scientists understand and explain the evolutionary stages that led to the origin of tetrapods and life on land. Fossils that show the intermediate state between an ancestor and its descendants are sometimes called transitional fossils. Transitional fossils that have not been discovered have been referred to as "missing links." This term is misleading, because scientists do not expect that a given fossil will be the direct ancestor of another. At best it may be a distant cousin, but it will have many of the features that the undiscovered direct ancestors did have. Thus, the fact that a perfectly transitional fossil has not been discovered does not mean that the taxon did not exist.

Scientists expect that many direct and distantly related transitional fossils will never be found for several reasons. First, some organisms or body parts of organisms do not form fossils well. Second, the environmental conditions or natural geologic processes may have prevented fossil formation or destroyed fossils before they could be found. Third, only a tiny fraction of existing fossils will ever be found because many are buried under ice caps or are so far underground that they are impossible to reach. And finally, finding fossils is difficult, slow, and costly in areas that have harsh weather conditions. Despite these obstacles, many transitional fossils have been found since the 1800s. These include fossils in lines of descent that led to reptiles, birds, and mammals.

STOPPING TO THINK 4

What makes a fossil a transitional fossil?

What are the reasons scientists expect there to be gaps in the fossil record?

Transitional Features

Because many transitional fossils are unlikely to be found, many evolutionary biologists focus on **transitional features,** those specific features of fossils that show the intermediate state between an ancestor and its descendants. This approach is based on the idea that, even though nobody finds the single direct ancestor leading to a group of organisms, someone may find other organisms that have branched from the same line of descent. By studying the features of these organisms, scientists can put together a picture of the evolution of features that led to major new groups of organisms.

Although not all fossils are likely to be found, there is abundant fossil evidence to show that evolution occurs. And, as shown by the origin of tetrapods, the work of scientists has reconstructed the steps by which major transitions occurred. This has led to a better understanding of the process of evolution.

Analysis

1. Based on what you know about the geologic timeline and the formation of the earth, explain which fossils would be newer and older in the various layers of rock in the Grand Canyon.

2. Explain why Cope's ideas about the evolution of tetrapods were considered a hypothesis and not a theory.

3. **a.** What new hypothesis was suggested for the evolution of tetrapods following Cope's original hypothesis?

   b. Explain the evidence that led to the hypothesis you described in (a).

KEY VOCABULARY	
co-opted features	**stratigraphic dating**
evolution	**stratigraphy**
fossil record	**terrestrial tetrapods**
macroevolution	**transitional features**
radiometric dating	transitional fossils
strata	

7 The Phylogeny of Vertebrates

KNOWLEDGE OF THE evolutionary history and relationships of groups of species helps scientists and conservationists understand the biodiversity of an area. Such information helps conservationists decide where and how to focus their efforts.

To understand the relationships of groups of species, scientists have devised various systems for classifying species. Some classification systems compare the observable characteristics of organisms, such as their physical structures, reproduction capabilities, and embryological development, and then assign the organism to a taxon. The higher-level taxa are those above the species level. Above species, starting at the highest, taxon classifications descend in this order: kingdom, phylum, class, order, family, and genus.

There are limitations, however, to classifying taxa based on their physical characteristics alone. That system raises several questions. For example, which similarities and differences are the most important to consider? Should whales be classified as fishes because they have flippers and live in the water? Or are whales mammals because they maintain a constant body temperature and produce milk?

In the taxon classification system, the domestic cat's classification levels are:

Kingdom: Animalia
Phylum: Chordata
Class: Mammalia
Order: Carnivora
Family: Felidae
Genus: Felis
Species: F. domesticus.

Modern classification, therefore, is based on phylogenetics, which is the study of the evolutionary relationships among taxa. In a phylogenetic study, scientists work with specific characteristics, often called characters. A **character** is a recognizable structure, function, or behavior of an organism. A **homologous character,** or **homology,** is shared by taxa and their common ancestor. For example, all vertebrates and their common ancestor have a vertebral column. Homologous characters provide information about common ancestry, which is more reliable evidence for classifying organisms than their physical similarities and differences or ecological roles.

Homologies are shared by the common ancestor and some or all of its descendants. Those homologies shared by all populations of a single species or group of species descended from a common ancestor are called **shared derived characters.** Therefore, they are very important in determining relationships. To find shared derived characters, scientists examine large amounts of evidence, such as fossil, physical, and molecular (proteins, chromosomes, DNA) data. Scientists then construct an **evolutionary tree,** or tree, which is a branched diagram for classifying taxa. A tree represents a hypothesis about the evolutionary relationships of taxa.

In this activity you will examine the forelimbs of some vertebrates. You will then look at additional shared derived characters to determine which tree hypothesis best supports the evolution of vertebrates.

Challenge

▶ How do you test a tree hypothesis for a group of taxa?

MATERIALS

FOR EACH PAIR OF STUDENTS
set of seven Vertebrate Cards
set of seven Forelimb Skeleton Cards
colored pencils

FOR EACH STUDENT
Student Sheet 7.1, "Evidence in Anklebones"
Student Sheet 3.1, "Ideas about Evolution," from Activity 3

Procedure

Part A: Comparing Vertebrate Forelimbs

It is often difficult to determine if shared characters are also derived characters. One way scientists approach this is to compare the position and structures of the characters.

1. With your partner, observe the forelimbs of the animals shown on the Vertebrate Cards. A forelimb is a front limb of an organism, such as the front leg of a horse, the arm of a human, or the wing of a bird. In your science notebook, record the similarities and differences you observe in the forelimbs of the seven organisms. For example, observe the function, such as walking or flying, the shape, and the number of digits (toes, fingers), if any.

2. With your partner, look at the Forelimb Skeleton Cards, showing all of the bones in the forelimbs of the organisms. In your science notebook, record the similarities and differences you observe between the skeletal structures of the forelimbs of the organisms. For example, note the types, positions, and structures of the bones and joints.

3. In your group, discuss and explain how the forelimb evidence supports the following statement:

   All of the taxa share a common ancestor that had forelimbs with similar structures. The taxa gradually evolved as certain features enabled them to take advantage of opportunities in their environment.

Part B: Creating Trees with Evidence

4. With your partner, examine the table below, which shows a matrix of characters for a set of species, including the forelimbs for some of the vertebrates you investigated in Part A (0 = absent, 1 = present). Follow your teacher's instructions to construct an evolutionary tree in your science notebook for the six taxa in the matrix. Be sure to label the characters from the matrix and the names of the organisms on your tree.

Character Matrix for Six Vertebrates

CHARACTER	LAMPREY	FROG	BIRD	WHALE	PIG	HUMAN
Pelvic remnants (small portion of what was once a whole pelvis)	0	0	0	1	0	0
Body hair	0	0	0	1	1	1
Amniotic egg	0	0	1	1	1	1
Forelimbs	0	1	1	1	1	1
Vertebral column (backbone)	1	1	1	1	1	1

5. Were any of the taxa difficult to place on the tree? List them, and explain why they were difficult to place.

6. When scientists construct evolutionary trees, they sometimes need to gather more evidence to determine the most likely placement of each organism they are studying. Obtain Student Sheet 7.1, "Evidence in Anklebones." This is one of many examples of evidence used to determine the evolutionary relationships of mammals. Record your observations of the positions, shapes, and parts of the bones.

7. Work by yourself to examine the three evolutionary tree hypotheses shown below. Decide which tree is consistent with the characters in the matrix and the anklebone evidence. In your science notebook, copy the tree you decided on. Then, write a four-to-six sentence explanation for which tree hypothesis you chose.

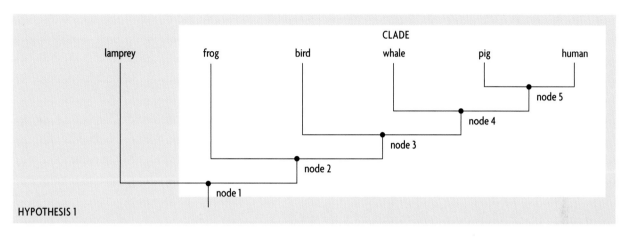

HYPOTHESIS 1

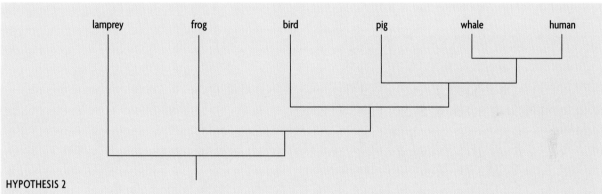

HYPOTHESIS 2

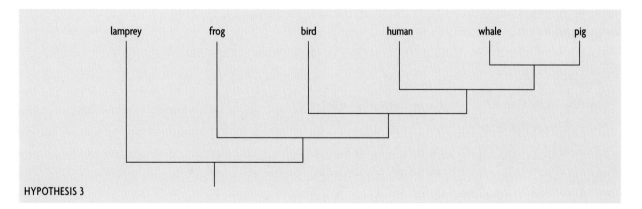

HYPOTHESIS 3

8. Go back to the statements on Student Sheet 3.1, "Ideas about Evolution," from Activity 3. Record information from this activity to support whether any of the statements is correct or incorrect.

Analysis

1. How would fossil evidence provide additional support for the statement in Step 3?

2. A **clade** is a group on an evolutionary tree that includes a common ancestor and all of its descendants. Draw a box around one clade in the tree from Step 7.

3. Based on the tree you chose:

   a. Which are more closely related to humans: birds or frogs? Support your answer with evidence.

   b. Which are more distantly related to birds: humans or lampreys? Support your answer with evidence.

   c. Which group shares a more recent common ancestor with whales: pigs or humans? Support your answer with evidence.

4. Based on the portion of a tree shown below, what can you say about the relationship of taxa X to horses and humans?

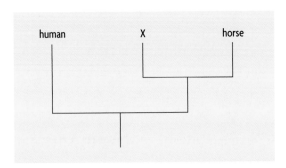

KEY VOCABULARY	
character	hypothesis
clade	node
evidence	phylogenetics
evolutionary tree	**shared derived character**
homologous character	taxa
homology	taxon

8

Studying Hominids

IN ACTIVITY 5, "Using Fossil Evidence to Investigate Whale Evolution," you were working with evidence for the evolution of the whale lineage. A **lineage** is a series of populations of a single species or several species descended from a common ancestor. On an evolutionary tree a branch represents a lineage.

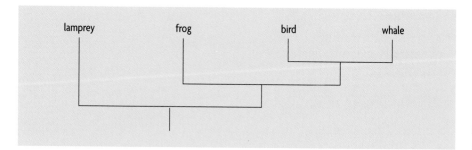

Each line shown on this tree for vertebrates is a lineage.

The evolution of another lineage supported by a growing body of evidence is the one that led to humans. In this activity, you will examine some of the evidence about the species that make up hominids, which include humans and apes.

A Neanderthal fossil skeleton.

Challenge

▶ How do biologists study the evolutionary relationships of hominids?

MATERIALS

FOR EACH GROUP OF FOUR STUDENTS
set of six Cranium Diagrams

FOR EACH PAIR OF STUDENTS
metric ruler
protractor
sticky notes

FOR EACH STUDENT
Student Sheet 8.1, "Cranium Comparisons"
Student Sheet 3.1, "Ideas about Evolution," from Activity 3
Student Sheet 3.2, "Geologic Time and Major Events," from Activity 3

Procedure

Part A: Physical Evidence for Human Ancestry

1. With your group, compare the six cranium diagrams. Record in your science notebook similarities and differences you observe.

2. Group the six organisms according to how closely related you think they are based on the similarities and differences you recorded in Step 1. Write your groupings in your science notebook.

3. Obtain Student Sheet 8.1, "Cranium Comparisons." Observe the characteristics shown on the chart, and record the information in the appropriate column. Measure lengths with a ruler, and measure angles with a protractor.

   Note: Diagrams 1, 2, and 3 already show the lines you will measure. For diagrams 4, 5, and 6 you will need to draw the lines that you will then measure.

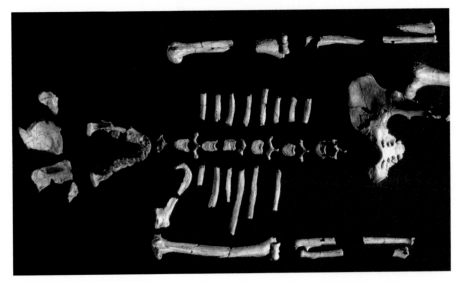

The skeleton of "Lucy" provides evidence about the evolution of the human lineage.

4. Examine your observations from Step 3. Record any patterns in the data that suggest changes over time.

5. Complete the reading, "Natural Selection in the Human Lineage," on the following pages to learn more about the ape and human lineages. As you read, follow the " and Take Note" strategy, using the sticky notes as you did in previous activities.

6. Based on your data and the information in the reading, what conclusions can you draw about the relationships between the six species?

Part B: Molecular Evidence for Human Ancestry

7. The box below shows a portion of the amino acid sequence for hemoglobin in humans, chimpanzees, and gorillas. Sketch a tree hypothesis suggested by the amino acid data and the information you gathered in Part A. Label the root of the tree "common ancestor."

Amino Acid Sequence Data

HUMAN

MVHLTPEEKSAVTALWGKVNVDEVGGEALGRLLVVYPWTQRFFESFGDLSTPDAVMGNPKVKAHGKKVLGAFSD
GLAHLDNLKGTFATLSELHCDKLHVDPEN **F** RLLGNVLVCVLAHHFGKEFTPPVQAAYQKVVAGVANALAHKYH

CHIMPANZEE

MVHLTPEEKSAVTALWGKVNVDEVGGEALGRLLVVYPWTQRFFESFGDLSTPDAVMGNPKVKAHGKKVLGAFSD
GLAHLDNLKGTFATLSELHCDKLHVDPEN **F** RLLGNVLVCVLAHHFGKEFTPPVQAAYQKVVAGVANALAHKYH

GORILLA

MVHLTPEEKSAVTALWGKVNVDEVGGEALGRLLVVYPWTQRFFESFGDLSTPDAVMGNPKVKAHGKKVLGAFSD
GLAHLDNLKGTFATLSELHCDKLHVDPEN **K** RLLGNVLVCVLAHHFGKEFTPPVQAAYQKVVAGVANALAHKYH

---

8. Go back to the statements on Student Sheet 3.1, "Ideas about Evolution," from Activity 3. Record on it information from this activity to support whether any of the statements is correct or incorrect.

9. Go back to the geologic timeline you constructed in Activity 3, "Geologic Time." On Student Sheet 3.2, "Geologic Time and Major Events," record the origin of hominins (humans and their extinct bipedal ancestors).

Analysis

1. Suppose you analyzed the DNA sequences for a number of DNA segments in humans, chimpanzees, and gorillas, and you collected the data in the table below:

DNA Sequences in Humans, Chimpanzees, and Gorillas	
DNA COMPARISON	SEQUENCE DIFFERENCE (%)
Human–chimpanzee	1.24
Human–gorilla	1.62
Chimpanzee–gorilla	1.63

Explain how these data are related to the amino acid data from Part B and how they explain the evolutionary relationship between humans, chimps, and gorillas.

2. Based on the portion of the hominid tree from Procedure Step 7, how would you respond to someone who claims that

   a. scientific evidence suggests that humans descended from chimps and gorillas?

   b. scientific evidence suggests that humans, gorillas, and chimpanzees share an evolutionary ancestor?

3. How does the scientific process you followed in this activity reflect the way that scientists ask and answer questions about the natural world?

KEY VOCABULARY	
evidence	hominid
evolutionary tree	**lineage**

READING

Natural Selection in the Human Lineage

MODERN HUMANS (*Homo sapiens*) are classified as members of the family Hominidae, as are gorillas and chimpanzees. Evidence suggests that the human and chimpanzee lineages split approximately 5 million years ago as shown in the tree below.

Scientists are still gathering evidence that would allow them to reconstruct the early history of the hominids. The fossil and DNA data they have collected, however, suggest that the adaptation for walking upright on two legs (bipedalism) defines the divergence of the human lineage. The chart above summarizes the locomotion methods for the six hominid species that you are investigating in this activity.

Locomotion Methods for Six Hominid Species

SPECIES	LOCOMOTION
Gorilla gorilla (gorilla)	Knuckle walking most of the time and bipedal walking for short distances
Pan troglodytes (chimpanzee)	Knuckle walking most of the time and bipedal walking for short distances
Australopithecines boisei ("Lucy," extinct)	fully bipedal
Homo erectus (extinct)	fully bipedal
Homo neanderthalensis ("Neanderthal," extinct)	fully bipedal
Homo sapiens (modern humans)	fully bipedal

There are several physical characters that allow for full-time upright walking in humans:

- Humans have larger vertebrae to carry the weight of the upper body.
- The point at which the spinal cord enters the skull is near the center of the cranium, which allows the head to balance on top of the spine.
- The human pelvis is positioned for greater balance while walking. The structure of the human foot includes a weight-bearing platform and a shock-absorbing arch.

(Continued on next page)

TREE HYPOTHESIS FOR PRIMATES

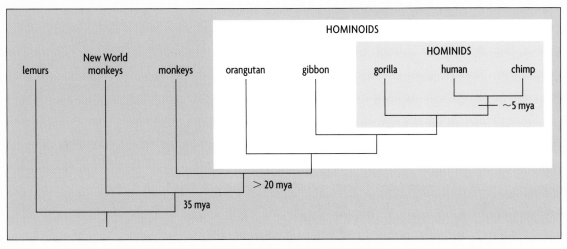

463

(Continued from previous page)

As new fossil and DNA evidence is discovered, scientists evaluate hypotheses for the evolution of bipedalism by natural selection. There is evidence to suggest that early hominins (living humans and extinct bipedal ancestors) had both the character for bipedal motion and the character in quadrupeds (taxa with four-legged locomotion) for grasping when moving in trees. A 4.4 million-year-old fossil, called "Ardi," had features for walking on two legs on the ground and grasping when moving in the trees. Ardi's pelvis was structured to support large hind limb muscles for climbing, resulting in a walk without the side-to-side gait of a chimpanzee. Ardi had big toes spread out from the rest for climbing, like those of an ape. She had an additional bone inside a tendon in the big toes that made them more rigid, and suitable for walking. These characters, which indicate Ardi was capable of foraging in the grasslands and climbing trees, provide clues about the evolution of bipedalism and the environment in which the human lineage might have evolved. Additional evidence will help scientists understand more clearly the factors that led to the divergence of the human lineage from its ancestors. ■

9 Studying Lineages for Conservation

IN PREVIOUS ACTIVITIES you examined the evidence for the evolution by natural selection of the whale and human lineages. You also learned how evolutionary trees show the pattern of the relationships of lineages to one another through time. This variation between taxa on a tree is called **phylogenetic diversity.** Of great value to conservationists when they consider sustainable conservation measures, trees show which lineages are either rich or limited in species diversity. Trees also illustrate which lineages are ancient or unusual.

The island of Madagascar, off the east coast of Africa, is a biodiversity hotspot where conservationists are focusing on phylogenetic diversity. As you have learned, biodiversity hotspots have both a high number of endemic species and extraordinary habitat loss. Of immediate concern is the welfare of lemurs, which are found only in Madagascar and the Comoro Islands nearby.

Suppose you are a member of a team of conservationists that must prioritize conservation efforts on Madagascar. The map on the next page shows the areas on the island that are being considered for protection, the lemur species that live in those areas, and the parks and reserves already established on the island.

Challenge

▶ How does evidence about phylogenetic relationships assist evolutionary biologists and conservationists in making sustainable conservation decisions?

MATERIALS

FOR EACH STUDENT
sticky notes

The ring-tailed lemur is one of the best-known lemurs, because of its long tail with black and white rings.

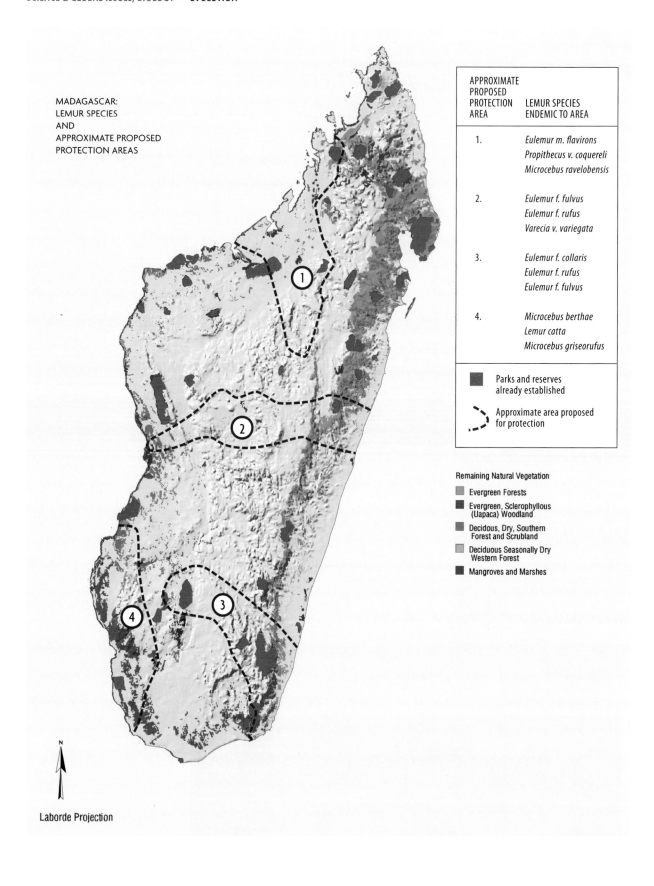

MADAGASCAR:
LEMUR SPECIES
AND
APPROXIMATE PROPOSED
PROTECTION AREAS

APPROXIMATE PROPOSED PROTECTION AREA	LEMUR SPECIES ENDEMIC TO AREA
1.	*Eulemur m. flavirons*
	Propithecus v. coquereli
	Microcebus ravelobensis
2.	*Eulemur f. fulvus*
	Eulemur f. rufus
	Varecia v. variegata
3.	*Eulemur f. collaris*
	Eulemur f. rufus
	Eulemur f. fulvus
4.	*Microcebus berthae*
	Lemur catta
	Microcebus griseorufus

▪ Parks and reserves already established

⌐ Approximate area proposed for protection

Remaining Natural Vegetation

▪ Evergreen Forests
▪ Evergreen, Sclerophyllous (Uapaca) Woodland
▪ Decidous, Dry, Southern Forest and Scrubland
▪ Deciduous Seasonally Dry Western Forest
▪ Mangroves and Marshes

N

Laborde Projection

Procedure

1. Read the case study about Madagascar on the following pages to learn more about the island.

2. Discuss with your partner the thoughts and questions you had while reading.

3. The tree shown below was assembled with genetic evidence for the lemur taxa of Madagascar. In your science notebook, describe the phylogenetic diversity of the lemurs in each area that is being considered for wildlife protection.

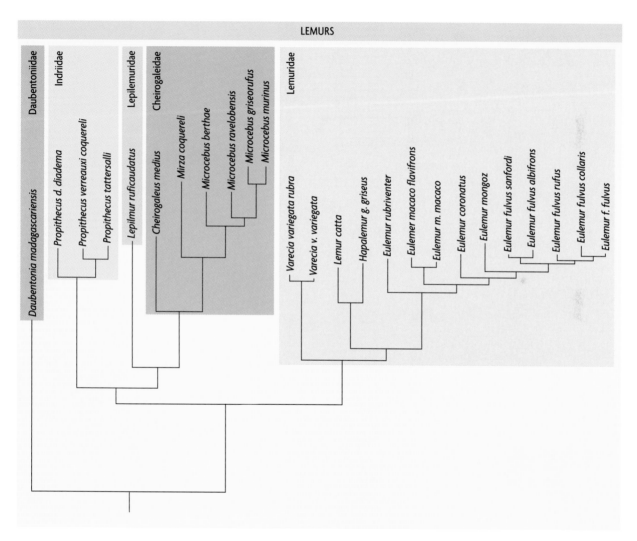

SOURCE: Modified from Julie Horvath et al., (2008) "Development and application of a phylo-genomic toolkit: Resolving the evolutionary history of Madagascar's lemurs."

Analysis

1. Why is phylogenetic diversity important when making conservation decisions?

2. **a.** How would you prioritize the four areas suggested for conservation on Madagascar? Consider evidence from the activity to rank them, and explain your reasoning.

   b. Suppose you have enough funds to protect the area that you assigned the highest priority in your ranking. What are the trade-offs of your decision?

3. What other information would you need for making the most informed and sustainable conservation decision?

KEY VOCABULARY	
endemic	**phylogenetic diversity**
evidence	species diversity
evolutionary tree	trade-off
hotspot	tree
lineage	

CASE STUDY

Madagascar

SINCE 1953, the island of Madagascar has lost approximately half of its forest cover. The lemurs, which live primarily in forests and depend on trees for shelter and food, are severely affected by forest loss.

Deforestation in Madagascar

GEOGRAPHIC LOCATION AND ECOSYSTEMS

Madagascar is the largest of a series of islands in the Indian Ocean off the southeast coast of Africa. Madagascar became an island approximately 160 million years ago when it broke away from the African continent. Over many millions of years, and through the movement of the earth's plates, it drifted about 400 km to the southeast of Africa.

Madagascar has a variety of ecosystems. Hills and rice-growing valleys occupy a central plateau region. There are several montane forest areas ranging from an altitude of approximately 2.4 km to 2.9 km (8,000–9,000 ft). The highest mountain on Madagascar is in the northern area and rises 2,876 km (9,436 ft) above sea level. In the west are dry forests, swamps, and grassy plains, and the eastern coast and lowlands on the island are mostly wet evergreen rainforest. Along the eastern coastline is a reef that is rich with marine life. The southern areas of the island are mostly dry desert forests.

UNIQUE AND THREATENED BIODIVERSITY

Thousands of species of organisms have evolved on the island that are not present on the nearby African continent or anywhere else in the world. Some of these endemic species were living on the land that became the island when it broke away from the African continent. Others, such as the ancestors of lemurs, migrated to the island after it split away. Isolated over many generations, the thousands of species evolved into different species from those living on the continent. Madagascar's species diversity is shown in the table at left.

(Continued on next page)

Species Diversity on Madagascar

SPECIES	TOTAL NUMBER OF SPECIES	NUMBER OF ENDEMIC SPECIES
Plants	13,000	11,600
Mammals	150	135 (51 are threatened)
Birds	310	181
Reptiles	384	367
Amphibians	230	229
Freshwater fishes	164	97
Extinct species*	45	

*Recorded since 1500

(Continued from previous page)

LEMURS

Lemurs living on the island today are of various sizes and colors and are classified into five families. One of their ecological roles is dispersing the seeds from the fruits they eat, which ensures steady growth of new plants. The five lemur families and their genera are described in the table at right.

HUMAN IMPACTS

Approximately 2,000 years ago, humans made their way on boats to Madagascar. Today Madagascar is inhabited by approximately 21 million people, and the population is growing by 3% annually. The source of livelihood for more than 90% of Madagascar's residents is the resources from the forests, such as the wood from cutting down the trees. As of today most of Madagascar's forests have been cut down or burned to make space for dwellings, crops, and livestock, leaving only 15% of the island forested. Because lemurs live almost exclusively in the forests, they are threatened by the forest destruction. Other human impacts on lemur populations are hunting and collecting. From their arrival on the island until the early 1960s, when it became illegal to keep or kill lemurs, people hunted them for food. All of the largest lemur species eventually became extinct.

Five Lemur Families

FAMILY	GENUS	DESCRIPTION
Daubentoniidae	*Daubentonia*	Only one species of it exists. It is the aye-aye, the largest nocturnal primate in the world. The aye-aye is a tree-dwelling omnivore that eats grubs, fruits, nectar, seeds, and fungi.
Indriidae	*Avahi* *Indri* *Propithecus*	Among these medium and large lemurs, sizes range widely from 30 to 74 cm (1.0–2.4 ft), and from 0.6 to 9 kg (1.3–19.8 lb). Members of the Indriidae family are tree-dwelling herbivores that eat leaves, fruits, and flowers. They are diurnal.
Lepilemuridae	*Lepilemur*	These medium-sized lemurs grow to 30–35 cm (1.0–1.1 ft) and weigh up to 0.9 kg (2.0 lb). Members of the Lepilemuridae family are tree-dwelling herbivores that eat mostly leaves. They are nocturnal.
Cheirogaleidae	*Allocebus* *Cheirogaleus* *Microcebus* *Mirza* *Phaner*	These are the smallest primates in the world, ranging in size from 13 to 28 cm (0.4–0.9 ft) and weighing from 60 to 500 g (0.1–1.1 lb). Members of the Cheirogaleidae family are tree-dwelling omnivores that eat fruit, flowers, leaves, insects, spiders, and small vertebrates, such as birds. Some also eat nectar. They are nocturnal.
Lemuridae	*Eulemur* *Hapalemur* *Lemur* *Prolemur* *Varecia*	Depending on the genus, these medium-sized lemurs grow to 32–56 cm (1.0–1.8 ft) in length and weigh from 0.7 to 5 kg (1.5–11.0 lb). Members of the Lemuridae family are tree-dwelling herbivores that eat fruit and leaves. Some eat nectar. Many species are nocturnal, and some are diurnal.

CONSERVATION ACTIONS

In 2003, to the delight of conservationists and evolutionary biologists around the world, Madagascar tripled the area it had designated for conservation. Today 46 areas protected from human activities make up approximately 2.7% of the land on Madagascar. These areas include national parks, nature reserves to conserve ecosystems, and special reserves to conserve particular species. In some areas, ecotourism has provided valuable income to the people of Madagascar. Ecotourism is a term for travel to natural areas to view animals and plants in their habitats. In many regions this has created jobs for local people, whether in transporting, feeding, housing, or guiding tourists, or guarding the protected areas.

Sustainability Factors Related to Madagascar's Forests		
SOCIAL	**ECONOMIC**	**ENVIRONMENTAL**
Cutting down trees provides jobs and wood for building, furniture-making, and other endeavors. People work as tour guides, and in hotels and restaurants in areas where there is ecotourism.	Forests provide coffee, vanilla, cocoa, and other economic resources. Ecotourism in conserved areas provides income to people who live on the island.	Forests are destroyed to clear land for planting crops, such as sugar cane and sweet potatoes, for raising livestock, and to make space for building. Forest destruction affects species that live on the island.

SUSTAINABILITY

The table above summarizes the factors that affect the sustainability of the island of Madagascar. ∎

10 What Is a Species?

THINK ABOUT THE many different types of organisms you see in a typical day. In addition to humans, you might see mammals such as dogs and cats; birds such as robins and pigeons; insects such as ants and flies; and plants ranging from dandelions to oak trees. On a farm or at the zoo or aquarium, you would see even more examples.

The original idea of different types, or species, of organisms was based on the observable differences in their appearances. A species was defined as a group of organisms with similar physical characteristics. Beginning in the late 1700s, species became the basic unit of classification.

As scientists learned more about evolution and the causes of differences among groups of organisms, their ideas about species changed. Scientists now know that some populations of organisms that appear identical are in fact different species, and others that appear different are the same species. The original species concept was replaced by concepts that focus on evolutionary relationships.

There are now several alternative definitions for species. In this activity, you will explore the **biological species concept.** This method of defining a species is based on whether the organisms actually or can potentially breed with each other to produce fertile offspring. If they can, they are of the same species. This approach gives evolutionary biologists and conservationists a snapshot of where species are in the process of separation from one another. The classification of populations into the same or separate biological species may affect their conservation status. For example, if two populations are determined to be in separate species, it is more likely that both will be considered for protection.

The pickerel frog (a) and moor frog (b) are two species of frogs in the Rana *genus.*

a

b

Other species concepts are applied in other fields of biology. For example, evolutionary biologists use a phylogenetic species concept, which defines a species as a distinct lineage and reflects the evolutionary relationships among taxa.

Challenge

▶ How do new species separate from existing species?

MATERIALS

FOR EACH GROUP OF FOUR STUDENTS

set of 14 Species Pair Cards

set of eight Reproductive Barrier Cards

BACKGROUND INFORMATION

The Biological Species Concept

ACCORDING TO THE biological species concept, a **biological species** is all of the populations of individuals that actually or can potentially breed with each other in nature to produce fertile offspring. The result of this interbreeding is movement of genes, called **gene flow,** throughout the species. Members of the same species share a common group of genes—a **gene pool**—and a common evolutionary history. Should members of different populations mate but produce no or no fertile offspring or very rarely breed with each other even when present in the same location, they are considered different biological species.

OTHER WAYS TO CATEGORIZE SPECIES

The biological species concept is straightforward, but it turns out that there are a number of areas where it is not helpful. For example, many species, such as bacterial species, do not reproduce

sexually. The concept also does not fit many plant species that cross-breed under natural or artificial conditions. Also, the concept cannot be applied to fossil organisms because their breeding cannot be observed.

Nevertheless, the biological species concept gives scientists a snapshot of the evolution of new species in many groups of plants and animals. As you review the examples on the following pages, keep in mind that the populations that share a common gene pool are most likely in the early stages of separation from one another. This is likely to be the case if individuals in the two populations meet the following two conditions:

- They usually breed together if they meet in the wild.

- Their breeding produces offspring able to produce their own offspring. ∎

Procedure

Part A: Species Separation

1. Read the information on the biological species concept in the box on the previous page.

2. In your science notebook, prepare an entry like the one below. It should take up about one-fourth of a notebook page.

Species Separation	
Example number/ organism name	
Claim	
Evidence to support the claim	
Reasoning	

3. On another page in your science notebook, across the entire page, draw and label an arrow like the one shown below. The arrow shows a continuum from early to late for the process of separation of new species from existing species.

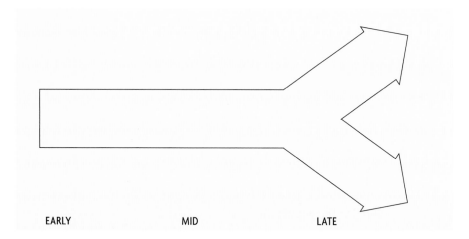

EARLY   MID   LATE

4. Work as a class with your teacher to complete some of the examples on the following pages.

5. Following your teacher's instructions, complete some of the following examples with your group and some on your own.

6. In your science notebook, record each of the following:

   • The example number and the name of the organisms

   • Your claim: a statement about what stage of separation the species are in

   • Place the names of the organisms at the appropriate stage of separation (early, mid, late) along the arrow you drew in Step 3.

   • Your evidence: the information available about the mechanism of the separation between species

   • Your reasoning: an explanation of the mechanism of separation that supports your claim. Refer to the biological species concept to explain each species' stage in the separation process.

7. Repeat Step 6 for all of your assigned examples.

The Separation of Species

EXAMPLE 1

Red and Purple Sea Urchins

Red and purple sea urchins live in shallow ocean waters along the eastern Pacific coast from Alaska to Mexico. The sperm of one of these organisms fertilizes the eggs of the other only in the laboratory, where scientists mix the eggs with much higher concentrations of sperm than are likely in the wild. The embryos produced, however, do not survive beyond the very early stages of development. ■

Red sea urchins

Purple sea urchins

EXAMPLE 2

Eastern and Great Plains Narrowmouth Frogs

The eastern narrowmouth frog's range extends along the east coast of the United States from the Carolinas to Florida and west into parts of Oklahoma and Texas, where it lives in moist areas. The Great Plains narrowmouth frog's range is from Baja California in Mexico to eastern Texas, eastern Oklahoma, and northern Missouri, where it lives in drier regions. These two types of frogs occasionally breed naturally in the areas where they overlap, but the fertility of their offspring is not known. Most of the time the frogs select mates of their own type, perhaps because of differences in their mating calls. The two groups of frogs are distinguished by their colors. ■

Great Plains narrow mouth frog (top),
Eastern narrow mouth frog (bottom)

EXAMPLE 3

Northern and California Spotted Owls

Northern spotted owls range from northwestern California to western Oregon, Washington, and Canada. California spotted owls are found in the Sierra Nevada from northern to southern California. The two owl populations overlap in parts of northern California. Field observations and genetic evidence suggest that when birds of each type come into contact they have bred and produced fertile offspring. These offspring have a hybrid (mixed) genetic makeup. However, this cross-breeding is rare. Northern and California spotted owls show some differences in appearance and genetics. ■

EXAMPLE 4

Horses and Donkeys

A female horse and a male donkey can mate to produce a mule. Horses have 64 chromosomes, while donkeys have 62. The mule is born with 63 chromosomes that cannot divide evenly, and this makes mules sterile. Although there are some cases of female mules breeding successfully with male horses or donkeys to produce live but infertile offspring, there are no known cases of male mules breeding successfully with female mules, donkeys, or horses. ■

The mule is the sterile offspring of a horse and a donkey.

EXAMPLE 5

Dogs and Wolves

There is great variety among domesticated dogs, which were bred from wolves approximately 10,000 years ago. Most dogs can breed with one another and have puppies that show a mix of the traits of the parent dogs. For example, a breeder of designer dogs can mate a boxer and a poodle to produce a boxerdoodle. Dogs from different breeds often mate to produce a mixed breed dog, commonly called a mutt. Dogs can also breed with wolves to produce fertile offspring. These mixed offspring can reproduce with similar dogs, other dog breeds, or wolves. Genetic analysis reveals very little difference between dogs and wolves. Wolves are much more similar genetically to dogs than to coyotes. ■

EXAMPLE 6

Midas Cichlid and Arrow Cichlid Fish

Scientists are studying two types of cichlid fish in a volcanic lake in Nicaragua. The Midas cichlid is a bottom-feeder, has a wide body, and eats algae. The arrow cichlid has a slender body for swimming and eats winged insects. The two types of fish select mates of their own kind, and fail to reproduce live offspring when people try to breed them. ■

*Arrow cichlid (top),
Midas cichlid (bottom)*

EXAMPLE 7

Blue and Red Cichlid Fish

Two very similar types of cichlid fish live in Lake Victoria in Africa. One is blue, and the other is red. Females of these two types prefer mates of the same color, and in nature these two types of fish do not breed. However, in a lab, when they are put in lighting conditions where they cannot see the color of the other fish, they will freely mate with fish of the other color. In these lab conditions, the females would now mate with either color male, and produce fully fertile offspring. ■

EXAMPLE 8

Green Lacewings

Two populations of lacewings that look identical and live in the same locations do not mate in the wild because they have different mating signals. Female lacewings exhibit a strong preference in the wild for males with a similar mating signal. Genetic analysis suggests that the changes in mating signal result from changes in just a small number of genes, but that these changes prevent the mating of males and females with different mating signals. When mated in the laboratory, offspring of these two types of lacewings are fertile. ■

EXAMPLE 9

Copper-resistant and Copper-tolerant Yellow Monkey Flower

Copper is toxic to most plants. However, scientists have observed a few plants that have developed a tolerance for copper. One of those is the yellow monkey flower. When scientists crossed copper-tolerant plants with plants sensitive to copper, many of the hybrid plants did not survive. In early growth stages, their leaves turned yellow and they died soon after. ■

EXAMPLE 10

Orchids

Three populations of orchids each flower at different times of the year for just a single day. Therefore, even though these orchids grow in the same tropical forest area, there is no chance that members of one population will fertilize the other in the wild. ■

Part B: The Formation of New Species

Evolutionary biologists focus on the question of how new species and other taxa evolve. As you have learned, two populations that have different physical characteristics might still belong to the same species if they can interbreed to produce fertile offspring and do so in nature. This interbreeding allows gene flow, with the two populations sharing a common gene pool.

How do new species evolve? According to the biological species concept, two populations must be reproductively isolated. Reproductive isolation is caused by several kinds of barriers. Once they become reproductively isolated, the two populations will no longer share a common gene pool. Each population will change independently of the other as a result of selection by the different environments. Eventually the two populations could evolve into two separate species.

8. With your group, spread the Species Pair Cards out on a table.

9. Examine the information on each card carefully, noting the barriers to reproduction between the two species described on the card.

10. Sort the cards into groups based on the barriers to reproduction. Work with your group to agree on a name that describes each kind of barrier. While doing so,

    - listen to and consider the explanations of your group members.

    - if you disagree, explain how and why you disagree.

11. In your science notebook, write the title: Our Groupings. Beneath this title, list the groups that you created and the names you picked to describe each group. Be sure to record which species pairs belong to each group.

12. Following your teacher's instructions, your team will present your groupings to the class. As you look at other students' groupings, observe the similarities and differences between their systems and yours. Discuss your observations with your team members.

13. Your group will receive eight Reproductive Barrier Cards from your teacher. Each card represents a barrier that leads to reproductive isolation of related species. Based on the information on the Reproductive Barrier Cards place each Species Pair Card under a Reproductive Barrier Card.

14. Record this new set of groupings in your science notebook under the title Scientific Groupings.

15. List the isolating mechanisms you examined in this activity. Write a definition for each mechanism in your own words.

16. List the two types of reproductive isolation in this section, and describe them in your own words.

Analysis

1. Why is appearance alone no longer considered sufficient evidence for classifying organisms?

2. Explain how geographic isolation can lead to speciation.

3. Lions and tigers do not overlap in range and do not breed in nature. In captivity, a male lion may mate with a female tiger and produce offspring. Although more rare, a male tiger may also mate with a female lion to produce offspring. In both cases, the male offspring are sterile, while the females might or might not be fertile. Explain where lions and tigers are on the speciation continuum, according to the biological species concept. Support your answer with evidence and reasoning.

4. How did your groupings of the reproductive barriers in Part B resemble or differ from those used by scientists as shown by the cards in Procedure Step 13?

5. Why do you think you came up with a different set of groups in Part B than scientists do in their groupings?

6. Did any of the species pairs in Part B show more than one barrier to reproduction? List examples, and describe the barriers they display.

7. Describe the barriers that are causing reproductive isolation for each of the following from Part A:

   a. Red and purple sea urchins

   b. Eastern and Great Plains narrowmouth frogs

   c. Northern and California spotted owls

8. Two related species of frogs appear to be very similar, but they have different mating calls. In addition, one species breeds in the fall, and the other breeds in the spring. What mechanisms contribute to reproductive isolation of these species?

9. Two related species of birds appear to be similar, but when they breed, their offspring rarely survive past a few days old. What mechanism leads to reproductive isolation of these species?

10. A genetic change occurs in the gene pool of a population of a single flower species with large white tubular flowers. This species is normally pollinated by a species of large bee that is attracted to large white tubular flowers. Pollination is essential for these flowers to produce seeds. In some individuals, one genetic change leads to the production of much smaller flowers. Explain how this could lead to speciation in the population.

KEY VOCABULARY	
biological species	**gene flow**
biological species concept	**gene pool**
evidence	species

11 Natural Selection

EVERY ENVIRONMENT ON earth changes. These changes might be gradual or fairly sudden results of geologic events, changes in climate, or human activities. When environmental changes occur, natural selection of populations living in the affected areas is likely to follow. Organisms also encounter new environments when they migrate. Both environmental changes and newly available environments can lead to the evolution of new species.

In a new environment a species splits into two lineages, and speciation continues in repeated cycles. Sometimes the evolutionary change is relatively rapid, and other times it is slower. An **adaptive radiation** is the relatively rapid evolution from a common ancestor of multiple species that occupy newly available environments. Adaptive radiation contributes to the biodiversity of an area as new species evolve over relatively short periods of time.

The evolution of honeycreepers on the Hawaiian Islands is a striking example of adaptive radiation. It occurred over 200,000–300,000 years after the arrival of the first ancestors.

Challenge

▶ How does natural selection lead to speciation?

MATERIALS

FOR EACH PAIR OF STUDENTS
computer with Internet access

FOR EACH STUDENT
Student Sheet 11.1, "Natural Selection"
Student Sheet 3.1, "Ideas about Evolution," from Activity 3

Procedure

1. Visit the *Science and Global Issues* page of the SEPUP website at *sepuplhs.org/sgi*. With your partner, go to "Natural Selection," and follow the simulation.

2. Go back to the statements on Student Sheet 3.1, "Ideas about Evolution." Record information from this activity to support whether any of the statements are correct or incorrect.

Analysis

1. A few of the individuals in the population that first inhabited each area on the island started out with variations in beak shape and size, body size, color, and breeding season. What biological processes caused some individuals to have these variations?

2. Describe the three conditions that are required for natural selection to take place in a population.

3. **a.** What conditions can lead to extinction?

   b. How does extinction lead to the evolution of new taxa?

4. Explain in evolutionary terms why a high level of biodiversity increases the likelihood that a species or ecosystem would be sustainable.

KEY VOCABULARY

adaptive radiation	mutation
evolution	natural selection
extinct	species
extinction	taxa

12 The Genetic Basis of Adaptation

THROUGHOUT THIS UNIT you have studied environmental and evolutionary influences on biodiversity. In the previous activity, you observed how some species evolve in a relatively short period of time, adapting to newly available environments and contributing to the biodiversity of an ecosystem. A **biological adaptation,** or **adaptation,** is an inherited characteristic that favors the survival or reproduction of an organism, and is the result of natural selection.

Some evolutionary biologists study how environmental and evolutionary changes affect populations at the genetic level. Scientists studying the rock pocket mouse, *Chaetodipus intermedius,* have found that changes in the coat colors of mouse populations illustrate the genetic mechanism of natural selection. The coat color of a rock pocket mouse is an example of an adaptation.

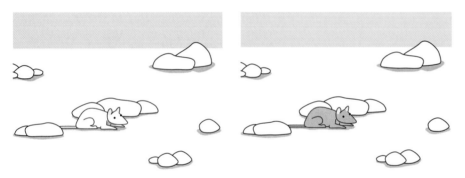

Light and dark-colored rock pocket mice on light granite.

In this activity you will model genetic changes in a population of rock pocket mice as a result of natural selection.

Challenge

▶ How did a change in the environment lead to genetic changes in populations of the rock pocket mouse?

MATERIALS

FOR EACH GROUP OF FOUR STUDENTS
8-sided number cube
cup containing 8 <u>D</u> cards and 8 d cards

FOR EACH PAIR OF STUDENTS
colored pencils

FOR EACH STUDENT
Student Sheet 12.1, "Changes in the Gene Pool of a Mouse Population"
Student Sheet 3.1, "Ideas about Evolution," from Activity 3
graph paper

Procedure

1. With your partner, read the information below about the rock pocket mouse.

2. In your science notebook, use your understanding of natural selection to write a prediction of what is likely to happen to the frequency of light and dark mice if the environment changes from a light desert background to a dark volcanic background. Explain your reasoning.

BACKGROUND INFORMATION

The Rock Pocket Mouse

Rock pocket mice live in the deserts of the southwestern United States. They are nocturnal rodents that spend their nights gathering food while trying to hide from owls, their primary predators. Because the owls must be able to see their prey from above, coat color is an important factor in the survival of the mice.

Most rock pocket mouse populations are light colored and live in a dry desert environment where light-colored granite rock is common. However, several dark-colored populations live on the dark-colored basalt lava beds that formed in Arizona 1.7 million years ago after a volcano erupted.

Light-colored mice have two copies of the recessive allele for light coat color. Their genotype is represented as dd. Dark-colored mice have either one or two copies of the dominant allele for dark coat color. Their genotype is either <u>DD</u> or <u>D</u>d. ■

---

3. Assign each student in your group to take one of the following sets of cards from the cup. Each of you represents one desert-dwelling parent mouse living in a light-colored granite environment:

   • Student 1: <u>D</u>, d

   • Student 2: d, d

   • Student 3: d, d

   • Student 4: d, d

   Shuffle the two cards for the parent mouse you were assigned, and place them face down on the table in front of you. These two cards represent the possible alleles of one parent mouse in Generation 1.

4. Without looking, you and your partner will each randomly pick one of the two cards in front of each of you to turn face up. These two cards represent the genotype for the first offspring of the parents in Generation 1. On Student Sheet 12.1, "Changes in the Gene Pool of a Mouse Population," record the genotype (<u>D</u>d, or dd) and phenotype (use a pencil to shade the dark mice) for the first offspring in the box labeled Generation 2. The example below shows how this would be recorded for <u>D</u>d and dd Generation 2 offspring.

5. Repeat Step 4 until you have recorded on the Student Sheet the genotypes and phenotypes for a litter of eight offspring mice in Generation 2.

6. Light mice with the genotype dd are more likely to be caught and eaten by owls in the dark environment. Draw an "X" through all but one of the mice with dd genotypes in the litter.

7. There are other influences besides coat color that determine whether a mouse will survive and successfully reproduce offspring. Roll the number cube to determine which one of the surviving mice will reproduce the third generation of offspring, and circle it on the Student Sheet. If you roll a number for a mouse that has died, roll the number cube until you roll the number for a living mouse.

8. Obtain the appropriate cards from the cup to represent the genotype of the offspring that was successful in Step 7.

9. Now assume the class represents a population of mice. Randomly choose another student from the class to work with in this round. Follow Steps 3–7 for your surviving mouse and the surviving mouse of your partner to determine the genes for a litter of eight offspring in Generation 3. When you need a number cube, use one at a nearby table. Record on Student Sheet 12.1, "Changes in the Gene Pool of a Mouse Population," the genotype and phenotype of each offspring.

10. Repeat Steps 3–9 with another randomly chosen student from the class until you have completed five generations on the Student Sheet.

11. Work with your group of four to add up the following for each generation. Your teacher will collect each group's totals to compile the class data for the following:

   • The number of each allele present in only the mice that reproduced (the mice that were circled).

   • The number of light- and dark-colored mice present in each generation, including living, dead, and reproducing.

12. In your science notebook, make a chart like the one below. Follow your teacher's directions to record the information for the class for all of the generations.

Generation	Number of D alleles in parent mouse population	Number of d alleles in parent mouse population	Total number of light-colored offspring mice	Total number of dark-colored offspring mice

13. On one side of a sheet of graph paper, draw a line graph with a colored pencil showing the number of D alleles present in each of the mouse generations you modeled. Be sure to label the axes. With a different-colored pencil draw a line graph on the same set of axes to show the number of d alleles present in each generation.

14. In colored pencil draw a second line graph to show the number of light-colored mice present in each of the generations you modeled. Be sure to label the axes. With a different-colored pencil draw a line graph on the same set of axes to show the number of dark-colored mice present in each generation.

15. Go back to the statements on Student Sheet 3.1, "Ideas about Evolution," from Activity 3. Record information from this activity and any previous activity to support whether any of the statements are correct or incorrect.

Analysis

1. Explain how a change in the environment led to selection for:

    a. genetic changes in the population of mice over several generations.

    b. phenotypic changes in the population of mice over several generations.

2. Did the evidence provided by your model match your prediction? Explain.

3. What aspects of natural selection were modeled in this activity?

4. What eventually would have happened in the mouse population if all of the mice had the genotype dd when the volcanic eruption occurred in their area?

KEY VOCABULARY	
adaptation	evolve
allele	gene
biological adaptation	genetic diversity
evolution	

The Processes and Outcomes of Evolution

SOME OF THE most intriguing questions in biology have to do with biodiversity. Why is there such a variety of life on earth? How did the variety develop? Why is there more biodiversity in tropical areas than in temperate areas? Many evolutionary biologists and conservationists study how evolution explains biodiversity.

Evolutionary processes increase, decrease, or maintain biodiversity. **Microevolution** is evolution on a small scale, and it results in changes in the proportion of genes in a population. As you have seen, small changes or differences can lead to the formation of new species. **Speciation** is the formation of species as a result of barriers to gene flow that split the gene pool, followed by an accumulation of differences between the gene pools. **Macroevolution** is the larger changes and patterns in evolution. It includes evolutionary changes at or above the species level. Processes of macroevolution include speciation, the evolution of taxa, such as flowering plants or insects, and extinction. When the last member of a species dies, **extinction** is complete, and the species is said to be **extinct.**

Challenge

▶ How do evolutionary processes lead to changes in biodiversity?

Through the Cretaceous and later, flowering plants and the insects that pollinate them have affected one another's evolution.

MATERIALS

FOR EACH STUDENT

Student Sheet 13.1, "Anticipation Guide: The Processes and Outcomes of Evolution"

Student Sheet 3.1, "Ideas about Evolution," from Activity 3

Procedure

1. Fill in only the Before column of Student Sheet 13.1, "Anticipation Guide: The Processes and Outcomes of Evolution."

2. Complete the Reading.

3. Fill in the After column on Student Sheet 13.1, "Anticipation Guide: The Processes and Outcomes of Evolution."

4. Go back to the statements on Student Sheet 3.1, "Ideas about Evolution." Record information from this activity to support whether any of the statements are correct or incorrect.

Reading

Microevolution

In Activity 12, "The Genetic Basis of Adaptation," you investigated changes in the proportion of genes for coat color in a population of rock pocket mice. This was an example of a microevolutionary change. Four main factors lead to microevolutionary change: mutation, natural selection, genetic drift, and gene flow.

The process of natural selection requires variation in heritable genetic traits that determine the fitness of individuals in a population competing for environmental resources. In other words, variation provides the raw material for evolution. This variation in heritable traits arises through either mutation or recombination of the genetic material. The **fitness** of an organism has two components: 1) the probability of the organism's survival to reproductive age, and 2) the number of offspring the organism produces. The most **fit** individuals have an advantage in the competition for resources. Without competition, there would be no differential survival or reproduction and no evolutionary change would take place.

Genetic drift is the term for unpredictable changes in the proportion of genes in a population. These changes result from alterations in the environment that remove a significant number of individuals in a population, such as those caused by storms, volcanoes, hunting, or logging. In the reduced gene pool, the alleles of some genes in the remaining population might be overrepresented, underrepresented, or completely absent.

Genetic drift caused by events such as the net fishing shown in this model can reduce the size of a population and its gene pool.

Gene flow is the sharing of genes that results from sexual reproduction. In Activity 10, "What Is a Species?" you learned that as long as gene flow occurs between populations, the populations share a common gene pool, and their individuals can mate to produce offspring. Migration of individuals into or out of a population results in gene flow between populations and can lead to changes in the gene pool. If there is a barrier to gene flow, there is no longer a free exchange of genes in a common gene pool, and successful reproduction stops. This can lead to speciation.

Adaptation

Natural selection leads to an increase in biological traits that enhance an organism's ability to survive. Traits that result from natural selection and that enhance fitness are called adaptive characters, or adaptations. An **adaptive character** is a physical trait, such as body shape or structure of limbs; a behavior, such as a mating call or caring for offspring; a biochemical process, such as making venom or the ability to perform photosynthesis; or other inherited trait that enhances fitness. Examples of each of three types of adaptations are shown on the following page.

It is important to note the difference between everyday usage of the word adaptation, the scientific meaning of adaptation used by evolutionary biologists, and other applications of the word. In evolutionary terms species do not have control over or choice in the adaptive characters that evolve as a result of natural selection. Also, adaptive traits that evolve through natural selection do not develop over the lifetime of an individual organism. This is different from physical adaptations, such as producing more red blood cells after a few days or weeks at high altitude. It is also different from the everyday use of the term in which you might say, for example, that you adapted to a new school after a certain amount of time.

Sometimes, an existing trait that evolved to serve a certain function is modified through natural selection to serve a new function. This trait is called a co-opted feature. In Activity 6, "Evidence from the Fossil Record," you read about how the lungs and legs of tetrapod ancestors evolved in shallow-water environments and were later co-opted for life on land. Another example of a co-opted trait is feathers. Based on the fossil record, scientists hypothesize that feathers first evolved for insulation or perhaps for mate recognition, and were later co-opted for flight.

Evidence suggests that birds inherited feathers from a flightless ancestor.

Examples of Adaptation

A PHYSICAL ADAPTATION IN VENOMOUS SNAKES

Venomous snakes have a set of skull bones that are adaptations for delivering venom for immobilizing prey and for self-defense. For example, in vipers, there is a short skull bone attached to a single hollow fang. The fang leads to a gland that releases venom. When the snake opens its mouth, the skull bones move so that the skull bone attached to the fang rotates 90°. The rotation of the bone causes the fang to swing down from the roof of the mouth so that venom can be delivered through the fang.

A BEHAVIORAL ADAPTATION IN HONEYBEES

Honeybees that forage for food communicate the location of new food sources to other honeybees in the nest or hive with dance language. The dancing is an adaptive behavior. Three distinct types of dance communicate the distance to and quality of the food. Honeybees with this behavior have an advantage in finding food sources and are, therefore, more fit than honeybees that do not exhibit the behavior.

A BIOCHEMICAL ADAPTATION IN INSECT-POLLINATED ORCHIDS

Numerous species of orchids have evolved the ability to produce a scent. The scent of the orchids mimics the scent of the insects that pollinate them. The mirror orchid *(Ophrys speculum)* produces a chemical similar to the mating pheromone of a particular female wasp in order to attract the wasps that pollinate it with pollen from an orchid of the same species. Increased pollination increases the reproductive success of the orchid.

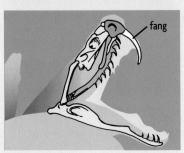

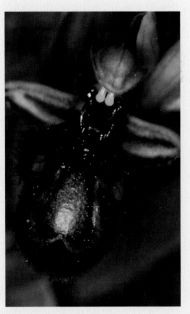

As the bones shown in blue move forward, the bone shown in purple rotates 90° outward, and the fang swings down from the roof of the mouth.

The bee shown in the center is dancing to communicate a food source to the other bees in the hive.

The wasp shown here was attracted to the scent of the orchid it is pollinating.

Speciation

Microevolution in a population can eventually lead to speciation and larger changes of macroevolution. In many cases, geographic isolation is the first step in the evolution of a new species. The many closely related cichlid fish in African lakes provide an example. Evidence suggests that these species diverged through adaptive radiation from a much smaller number of species when a large lake dried up. As separate, smaller lakes developed, populations were isolated and gene flow was restricted. The isolated populations evolved in very different ways as natural selection acted on a variety of traits. Even when these small lakes merged, the many environments in the large lakes allowed ecological specialization and mating differences that promoted further speciation.

The Galapagos finches are another example of a group of species that evolved and branched from one or more ancestral populations through adaptive radiation. The closest relatives of the Galapagos finches live on the west coast of South America. This relationship led Darwin to hypothesize that the Galapagos finches evolved from finches that were blown off course from mainland South America. The descendants of these original finches evolved new genetic and phenotypic features from those on the mainland when they encountered new conditions and food sources in various island habitats. For example, the beaks of the finches would have had a certain amount of variation in their shape and size. These variations determined which finches in the population could feed on available food sources, survive, and reproduce more successfully. Long, pointed beaks were well suited for digging seeds out of cactus fruits. Short and wide beaks were best for eating seeds from the ground. Thin, sharp beaks were suited for catching insects. The offspring of the more fit finches inherited their favorable beaks, to the extent that the variation was heritable. Over time, this resulted in differential survival of birds with beaks suited

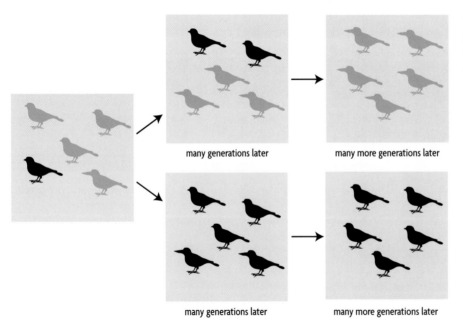

many generations later

many more generations later

many generations later

many more generations later

Through adaptive radiation, a population of birds might look very different after many generations.

to each habitat, depending on whether the type of food available was seeds, insects, or fruit. As a result of geographic isolation or other isolating mechanisms, such as differences in behavior or habitat, changes accumulated through natural selection. Reproductive isolation led to the separation of the populations into different species. Modern researchers have provided evidence for selection of larger beaks during periods of drought, when the food sources change even over short periods of time.

Macroevolution and Extinction

Macroevolution leads to the large-scale patterns of biodiversity observed on earth. One of the most striking patterns is that some areas on earth, including tropical rain forests and coral reefs, have great biodiversity, while other areas, such as deserts and polar regions, have little biodiversity.

Macroevolution is shaped by both speciation and extinction, including mass extinction. To study macroevolutionary processes, scientists observe the fossil record, the geographic areas, and the ecosystems where speciations and extinctions occurred. Charles Darwin was one of the first to understand that the extinction of lineages was the main factor that shaped the gaps in the fossil record between groups of organisms observed today.

The majority of species that have lived on the earth are now extinct. Some scientists estimate the percentage to be 99.99%. Extinction can result when any environmental change leads to the reduced fitness of a species. For example, a species in competition with another closely related species that has evolved or migrated into its environment might be out-competed. Or the habitat of a species may be destroyed by human impact, processes such as erosion, natural disasters, or disease. On some evolutionary trees, branches that end before the present show extinction events.

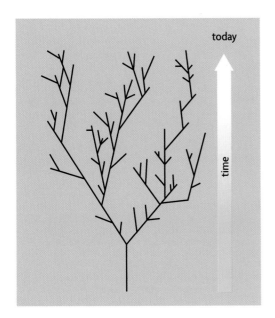

Wherever a lineage ends on this tree (before the present day), an extinction occurred.

While species extinctions are common, there have also been several **mass extinction** events in which many major taxa died out. Approximately 250 million years ago at the end of the Permian period, during the time when the continents were united, the largest known mass extinction occurred. This was caused by massive volcanic activity, changes in ocean oxygen levels, sea level, and climate, and other environmental events.

The most well-known mass extinction, 65 million years ago, included the last of the dinosaurs and the dominant land vertebrates. Partly due to limited current knowledge of the fossil record of the dinosaurs, there are multiple theories about the exact cause of the mass extinction. Three of the theories are testable and best explained by the known fossil evidence. They are based on evidence that three events—an asteroid strike, volcanic activity, and sea-level regression—led to major environmental changes. One or more of these events may have contributed to the mass extinction 65 million years ago.

As taxa have gone extinct, especially during mass extinctions, new taxa fit for survival in the changed environment have evolved. For example, when the dominant vertebrates went extinct 65 million years ago, new habitats opened up, and mammals evolved.

Analysis

1. Explain how adaptive radiation led to the evolution of more than 13 species of finches from a common ancestor.

2. Many Hawaiian honeycreeper birds evolved a musk-like odor that is distasteful to predators. Explain how this adaptation might have evolved through natural selection.

3. How does each of the following lead to extinction?

   a. Environmental changes

   b. Lack of population diversity

4. In what ways do humans affect speciation, extinction, and biodiversity?

5. Why would a conservationist want to know the rates of speciation compared to the rates of extinction in two areas being considered for conservation?

KEY VOCABULARY

adaptation	genetic drift
adaptive character	geographic isolation
adaptive radiation	**macroevolution**
co-opted feature	**mass extinction**
extinct	**microevolution**
extinction	natural selection
fit	reproductive isolation
fitness	**speciation**
gene flow	

14 Ideas about Evolution

THROUGHOUT THIS UNIT you have learned about the evolutionary processes that result in the earth's biodiversity. In this activity you will reexamine the scientific evidence you have evaluated and review the statements of evolutionary ideas that you were introduced to in Activity 3, "Geologic Time."

Challenge

▶ What scientific evidence and reasoning supports ideas about evolution?

MATERIALS

FOR EACH GROUP OF FOUR STUDENTS
> poster paper or chart paper
> colored pencils
> markers

FOR EACH STUDENT
> Student Sheet 3.1, "Ideas about Evolution," from Activity 3

Procedure

1. With your partner, discuss your responses to the five statements on Student Sheet 3.1, "Ideas about Evolution." Are there patterns in the similarities and differences in your answers? Are there common explanations for why you agreed or disagreed with any of the statements?

2. Your teacher will assign your group some of the statements to present to the class. Go back to all of the activities in the unit, and, with your group, compile the scientific evidence and reasoning for or against the statements you have been assigned. Record any additional information on Student Sheet 3.1, "Ideas about Evolution."

3. Obtain a piece of chart paper for presenting your group's evaluation of your assigned statements. Decide on a format for clearly recording each statement, whether it is scientifically correct or incorrect, and the evidence and reasoning from the unit to support your evaluation.

4. Follow your teacher's instructions for presenting your statements to the class.

Analysis

1. Choose one of the five statements from Student Sheet 3.1, "Ideas about Evolution." Write a short evaluation of the statement. Include in it

   • the statement you are evaluating and whether the statement is scientifically correct or incorrect.

   • an explanation of the evidence and reasoning from the unit that supports whether the statement is correct or incorrect.

KEY VOCABULARY	
adaptation	evolution
evidence	natural selection

Conservation of an Island Biodiversity Hotspot

THE GOVERNMENT OF *Kapikua wants to expand biodiversity conservation efforts
on the island. The government has two goals: 1) to protect the overall biodiversity
and sustainability of the island ecosystem, and 2) to protect the endemic primates that
live in the forests on the island. The endangered primates are unique and very sensitive to habitat changes. This puts them at a higher risk of extinction. The primates
have also become a well-known attraction for ecotourists from around the world. The
government has enough funds to fully support conservation at only one of four forest
areas being considered for conservation. You are a member of the conservation team
that will advise on which area should get full conservation support.*

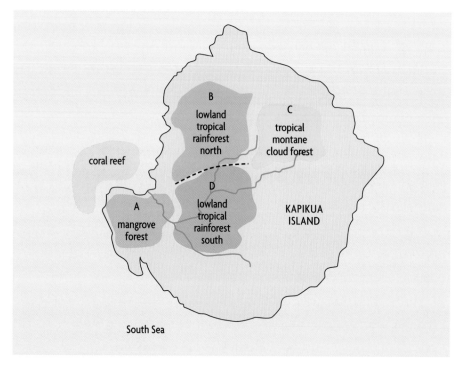

THE ISLAND OF KAPIKUA

In this activity you will learn more about each of the four areas and select one for
conservation. You will use additional evidence from an evolutionary tree for the
primates to decide which area should be conserved.

Challenge

▶ Which of four areas should receive priority for conservation?

Procedure

Part A: Four Possible Conservation Areas

1. With your group, assign to each student one of the four forest areas under consideration for conservation. Work by yourself to read below and on the next pages the summary of your assigned area.

2. In your science notebook, make a chart like the one shown below. Fill in the chart for your assigned forest area.

Forest area	Economic outcomes if conserved	Social outcomes if conserved	Environmental outcomes if conserved	Benefits of conserving the area	Trade-offs of conserving the area

3. Present a summary of your forest area to the members of your group. As your group members present the information about their forest areas, complete the chart.

Area A: Mangrove Forest

UNIQUE CHARACTERISTICS

The mangrove forest on the island is dense with stilt mangrove trees and shrubs that grow in brackish coastal swamps. The roots of the mangrove trees filter the salts out of seawater. They also filter silt and nutrients from river water, allowing clear water to flow to the nearby coral reef. The vegetation serves an important role in the coastal area as a buffer to protect the nearby shoreline villages from hurricanes and other storms. The vegetation also prevents erosion along the riverbanks. Mangroves provide food and shelter to a variety of organisms.

CONSERVATION CONSIDERATIONS

In recent years, partly because of mangrove forest degradation, the inland areas of the island have been damaged by flooding from severe storms that have blown in. Almost all of the buildings and houses in one village were lost to the flooding. The villagers lost their crops and homes, and had to move to other areas.

Mangrove Forest	
LAND AREA TO BE CONSERVED (%)	3
NUMBER OF ENDEMIC SPECIES IN THE AREA	14
NUMBER OF ENDEMIC SPECIES THREATENED	7

If the area is conserved, the island government plans to offer limited permits at a reasonable cost for sustainable ecotourism to the area. For those who live on the island, ecotourism would provide jobs ranging from researchers and tour guides to restaurant waiters, cooks, hotel workers, drivers, and boat crewmen. People who make handicrafts and other goods also would earn money by selling their wares to tourists. Park fees would bring in revenue that would also contribute to the island's economy.

Currently, island residents have unlimited access to the mangrove forest for fishing and shrimping. Some fishermen have small businesses in which they sell their catch at local markets. Others fish for recreation or to feed their families. If the mangrove is conserved, a strict catch limit will be enforced in order to protect the food sources for a variety of organisms in the ecosystem. The new limits could force the local fishermen to downsize their businesses and reduce their income.

Area B: Lowland Tropical Rainforest North

UNIQUE CHARACTERISTICS

The lowland tropical rainforest is the most bio-diverse area on the island, although the northern region of the rainforest is less diverse than the southern region. The earliest settlers in the northern area introduced new plants and animals to provide sources of food, medicine, building materials, and decoration. They cleared land to plant agricultural crops, and hunted lizards and birds for additional food. Since the first settlers came to the area, log-ging, development, and agriculture have destroyed 95% of the northern region's forest.

Lowland Tropical Rainforest North

LAND AREA TO BE CONSERVED (%)	3
NUMBER OF ENDEMIC SPECIES IN THE AREA	135
NUMBER OF ENDEMIC SPECIES THREATENED	10

CONSERVATION CONSIDERATIONS

A small family-run business harvests coffee from the plants they have grown in this forest area. The exported coffee is a desirable commodity for people in other countries, and it is marketed as some of the best quality and most sustainable in the world. It benefits the family and a small number of workers hired to help with the harvest. If the forest is desig-nated for conservation, the family will no longer have access to the forest for their coffee. This would mean lost income, with family members and the small number of people employed by the business losing their jobs. However, the species that live in the remaining 3% of undeveloped area will be protected.

Area C: Lowland Tropical Rainforest South

UNIQUE CHARACTERISTICS

The southern region of the lowland tropical rain-forest is the most biodiverse on the island. It is larger than the northern region of the rainforest, and because the earliest settlers remained mostly in the northern region of the forest, this area was not as severely deforested as the north. Medical research scientists search for unique species in this area that may provide substances for new medicines. A number of tree-dwelling species depend on the kapok trees as a highway that allows them to move around the forest without having to travel on the ground.

Lowland Tropical Rainforest South	
LAND AREA TO BE CONSERVED (%)	7
NUMBER OF ENDEMIC SPECIES IN THE AREA	254
NUMBER OF ENDEMIC SPECIES THREATENED	75

CONSERVATION CONSIDERATIONS

If this area were conserved, the vast biodiversity of the area would be protected, including the plant species central to pharmaceutical research and product development. Research scientists would be assigned permits to collect specimens in a sustain-able manner from the area. Recently, a team of sci-entists was sent to the island to research a plant found nowhere else that shows potential as a new malaria treatment. If the treatment is successful, it could save millions of lives. The research institute signed an agreement with the Kapikua government that a percentage of the profit made from products con-taining substances from Kapikua plants will go back into the island economy.

If this area is conserved, the government plans to build a primate center to research and protect the endemic primates that live in the island forests. This center will also be the focus of a program to educate the public. Permits will be available for ecotourists to visit the center to observe the primates and learn more about them through tours and exhibits. However, the cost of the permits will be much higher for this remote area than the cost to tour the mangrove forest. The primate center and access for ecotourists will require the construction of roads and facilities, which will be done in the most sustainable manner possible. For island residents it will provide such jobs as tour guides, drivers, lab technicians, and instructors.

Area D: Tropical Montane Cloud Forest

UNIQUE CHARACTERISTICS

The tropical montane cloud forest ecosystem plays an important role in the water cycle and climate on the island. Experiments have shown that cloud forests prevent the evaporation of precipitation far better than non-cloud forests do. The precipitation in the cloud forest is mostly in the form of fog, which condenses on the trees and drips onto the ground. The water soaks into the soil, where it is stored. Any excess runoff drains into stagnant water pools in the forest. The large water supply in the soil and the pools supports a wide variety of organisms.

CONSERVATION CONSIDERATIONS

Such human activities as logging and clearing the land to plant crops have degraded the cloud forest on Kapikua. This is a concern because during the dry season it is important that water from the cloud forest reaches the lower elevations where it is needed for irrigation, power generation, and drinking water. Recently, there have been reports of pollution problems with the water supply in another area of the island. Because of these reports, the government is concerned that in the future there will not be an adequate supply of clean water for the island. If conserved, the cloud forest would supply one source of clean drinking water.

Tropical Montane Cloud Forest	
LAND AREA TO BE CONSERVED (%)	4
NUMBER OF ENDEMIC SPECIES IN THE AREA	11
NUMBER OF ENDEMIC SPECIES THREATENED	5

Two decades ago, a corporation bought a portion of the cloud forest to develop a large tea plantation. The tea is highly desirable worldwide because the unique growing conditions give it a flavor that people love. Currently, there is a plan underway to expand the plantation to meet the growing demand for the tea. If the cloud forest is conserved, the tea plantation would not be permitted to expand, the company would not increase its profits, and no additional jobs for islanders would be created.

However, if the area were conserved, the risk of further adverse effects on the water cycle, climate, and organisms that depend on these resources would be reduced. For example, the fastigo whipping frog is a rare species that inhabits only the cloud forest. It lives in bushes close to shallow pools of standing water and breeds in the standing water. If the forest area is not conserved, the frog might be further endangered.

4. In your science notebook, write a brief summary for which forest area you would select for conservation based on the information you have so far. Explain your reasoning.

Part B: Evolutionary Tree Analysis

5. In your science notebook, add to the chart you created in Step 2 a column labeled "Phylogenetic diversity of primates."

6. With your group, compare the evolutionary tree below for each of the four forest areas. The tree shows evolutionary data for primate taxa that are endemic to the island. In the column you created in Step 5, record the number of the node that represents the most recent common ancestor for all of the primates collectively living in each of the four areas.

7. In the column you created in Step 5, describe the phylogenetic diversity of the primate species living in each forest area.

8. Conduct a Walking Debate as a way to share your ideas with the class about which forest area should have conservation priority. Your teacher will explain how to run the debate.

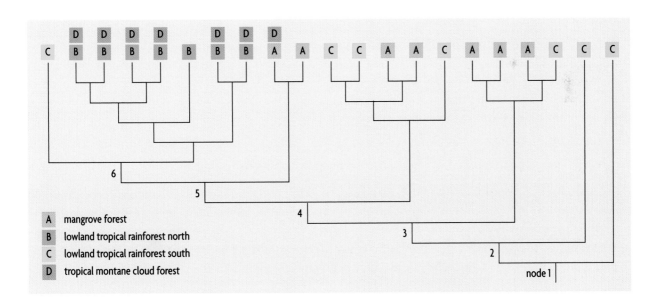

A   mangrove forest
B   lowland tropical rainforest north
C   lowland tropical rainforest south
D   tropical montane cloud forest

Analysis

1. Which forest did you decide should be conserved? Cite at least three pieces of evidence to explain your reasoning, and state the trade-offs of your decision.

2. Describe three indicators you would recommend using to monitor the success of the conservation over the next 10 years if your recommendation from Question 1 were implemented. These indicators can be any observations that will help determine if the recommendation is successful.

3. What social, economic, and environmental elements of sustainability were involved in your considerations about which area should be conserved?

4. What scientific evidence influenced your considerations about which area to conserve?

KEY VOCABULARY	
biodiversity	lineage
ecosystem services	phylogenetic diversity
endemic	sustainability
evidence	taxa
evolution	taxon
evolutionary tree	trade-off
indicator	

Unit Review: Evolution

Biodiversity and Sustainability

Biodiversity encompasses variability between and within ecosystems, between species, and within a species' gene pool as evidenced by genetic diversity. Biodiversity is closely linked to sustainability.

Human activities often cause biodiversity to increase or decrease. Such activities as acquisition of resources, urban growth, and waste disposal accelerate rates of natural change, and may lead to habitat loss, ecosystem destruction, or species extinctions.

Human activities may also diminish ecosystems services—the benefits that people and non-human species obtain from ecosystems. These include natural resources and processes that humans rely on for survival. Some examples of ecosystem services are materials derived for food, medicine, and shelter, water purification, carbon dioxide removal, and pollution control.

Protected areas are sections of land and sea especially dedicated to the maintenance of biological diversity and of natural and associated cultural resources. They are usually managed by governmental agencies or nonprofit organizations.

KEY VOCABULARY

biodiversity	hotspot
biological diversity	indicator
ecosystem diversity	species diversity
ecosystem services	sustainability
endemic	trade-off
genetic diversity	

Geologic Time and the Fossil Record

Earth formed approximately 4.5 billion years ago. The geologic timeline reflects the vast time scale since Earth originated. It shows that life began on Earth approximately 4.3 billion years ago, and multicellular life originated relatively recently in geologic time, approximately 640 million years ago. Most key events in the evolution of life occurred in very recent geologic time.

From fossils scientists have developed and tested hypotheses for how major groups of organisms, such as tetrapods, evolved. Scientists use stratigraphy and radiometric dating to determine the ages of rock layers (strata) and the fossils within them. Stratigraphy is based on the idea that older rock strata are found beneath strata that were formed more recently. Fossils in lower strata are generally older than fossils found in upper strata. In the absence of transitional fossils, scientists focus on transitional features in fossils—key features that demonstrate the evolutionary changes that resulted in macroevolution.

KEY VOCABULARY	
co-opted features	geologic timeline
deep time	radiometric dating
extinct	strata
extinction	stratigraphic dating
fossil	stratigraphy
fossil record	terrestrial tetrapods
geologic time	transitional features
geologic time scale	transitional fossils

Darwin and the Theory of Natural Selection

The millions of species of plants, animals, and microorganisms that live on earth today evolved over many generations and are related by descent from common ancestors. Natural selection is the primary means by which diverse organisms evolve from common ancestors. Charles Darwin (1809–1882) developed the theory of evolution by natural selection by putting together his own observations and ideas with the findings and ideas of other naturalists, geologists, and an economist.

The theory of natural selection and its evolutionary results provide a scientific explanation for the fossil record of ancient life forms and the striking molecular similarities found among diverse species of living organisms. Natural selection acts on any trait—including physical, biochemical, or behavioral traits—that increases the probability of survival and reproduction. The broad patterns of behavior exhibited by animals have evolved by natural selection to ensure reproductive success.

Natural selection is not random. For natural selection to occur in a population there must be heritable variation among individuals, competition for resources needed for survival, and differential survival and reproduction. Natural genetic variation is the result of mutation and recombination in the individuals that make up a population. Based on environmental conditions, favorable traits that enhance survival are passed on during reproduction. As more individuals inherit the favorable trait(s), the population changes. Environmental changes can lead to natural selection of traits that were previously rare but now enhance fitness in the new environment. Adaptive radiation is the relatively rapid evolution from a common ancestor of multiple species that occupy newly available environments.

There is a large body of physical, molecular, and fossil evidence to support the natural selection theory of evolution.

KEY VOCABULARY

adaptive radiation	natural selection
mutation	sexual selection

Phylogeny

Modern biological classifications show how organisms are related in a hierarchy of groups and subgroups based on similarities that reflect their genealogical relationships. Phylogenetic diversity results from the relationships of lineages to one another, and helps people make sustainable conservation decisions.

Evolutionary trees represent hypotheses for evolutionary ancestry. Shared derived characters determine where to place taxa on a tree. Evidence about structure, function, biochemistry, and behavior of taxa leads scientists to hypothesize the evolutionary relationships of taxa.

Scientists apply fossil and molecular data to develop hypotheses for how major groups of organisms, such as the hominids (African apes and humans), evolved. For example, fossil and genetic data suggest that humans and apes share a common ancestor. Chimpanzees and humans share a more recent ancestor than either does with gorillas. Evolutionary biologists and paleontologists focus on transitional features in fossils—those key features that demonstrate the evolutionary changes that resulted in macroevolution.

KEY VOCABULARY

character	node
clade	phylogenetic diversity
evolutionary tree	phylogeny
hominid	shared derived character
homologous character	taxa
homology	taxon
lineage	

Processes and Outcomes of Evolution

Evolutionary processes led to the biodiversity of life, all of which is related by descent from a common ancestor. Evolution is the ongoing process by which traits favorable to living in a particular environment are selected for and passed on to offspring.

Microevolution is evolution on a small scale and results in changes in the proportion of genes in a population. Genes store genetic information that interacts with environmental factors to determine the traits, or phenotypes, of organisms. Natural selection acts on existing genetic variability in a population. Over many generations the gene for a selected trait becomes increasingly common in the population.

Species is the basic unit of classification. Scientists have found that the original definition of species as groups of organisms with similar structure, function, biochemistry, and behavior does not reflect underlying evolutionary processes. The biological species concept defines a species as a population of individuals that actually does or can potentially interbreed in nature to produce fertile offspring. Natural selection and reproductive isolation lead to speciation in new environments.

Adaptations are inherited characteristics that improve the survival and reproduction of an organism and are the results of natural selection. Adaptive characters include physical traits, behaviors, biochemical processes, or any other traits that enhance fitness and evolve through natural selection. Adaptations are the result of natural selection and do not occur over the lifetime of individuals.

Macroevolution is any change that occurs at or above the species level and is shaped by both speciation and extinction. Macroevolution leads to the large-scale patterns of biodiversity on earth.

Extinction occurs when the environment changes and a species is no longer fit for the new environment. Less diverse populations have fewer variations that might enhance survival in new environments and are at greater risk of extinction. The biodiversity at any time in earth's history depends on both the evolution of new taxa and the extinction of existing taxa.

KEY VOCABULARY

adaptation	fitness
adaptive character	gene
allele	gene flow
biological adaptation	gene pool
biological evolution	geographic isolation
biological species	macroevolution
biological species concept	mass extinction
evolution	microevolution
evolve	reproductive isolation
extinct	speciation
extinction	species
fit	

Inquiry and the Nature of Science

Scientific explanations must adhere to such criteria as application of appropriate evidence, consistently logical reasoning, and basis in accepted historical and current scientific knowledge. Scientific theories are based on natural and physical phenomena. Scientific theories are well-established and highly reliable explanations. Scientific hypotheses are tentative-and-testable statements that are either supported or not supported by observational evidence.

Science is a social enterprise, but alone it only indicates what can happen, not what should happen. The latter involves human decisions about the application of knowledge. Scientists usually build on earlier knowledge and are influenced by other experts and their society and culture. Occasionally, a scientific advance has important long-lasting effects on science and society because of its explanation of natural phenomena. The theory of biological evolution by natural selection is an example of such an advance.

KEY VOCABULARY

evidence

hypothesis

theory

A Literacy Strategies

On the following pages are templates or instructions for the literacy strategies that are used throughout this book. Use them for reference or to copy into your science notebook.

Writing a Formal Investigation Report

Writing Frame (EVIDENCE AND TRADE-OFFS)

Writing Review

Discussion Web

Instructions for Constructing a Concept Map

KWL

Venn Diagram Template

"Read, Think, Take Note" Reading Strategy

Writing a Formal Investigation Report

Use the information from your science notebook to write a formal report on the investigation you performed.

Title:
Choose a title that describes the investigation.

Abstract: What were you looking for in this investigation, and what did you find?
Write a paragraph that summarizes what you already knew about the topic, your purpose, your hypothesis, and your results and conclusions.

Experimental Design:
Describe the materials and investigational methods you used to answer the question.

State what variables you worked with and any controls.

Data: What did you find?
Report observations and measurements. Include an organized data table if appropriate to help someone reviewing your report to easily see the results.

Don't forget to use proper units of measurement and write clear labels for your table columns.

Data Analysis: Represent the data in a way that can be easily interpreted.
Use graphs, diagrams, or charts where appropriate to help a reviewer interpret your data.

Conclusion: What do the data mean?
Summarize the data.

Discuss your conclusion based on the accuracy of your hypothesis and the data you collected.

Discuss any errors that occurred that may have interfered with the results.

Describe any changes that need to be made the next time the investigation is performed.

Describe any new questions to be investigated based on the results of this investigation.

Writing Frame—Evidence and Trade-offs

There is a lot of discussion about the issue of _____

_____

_____

_____

My decision is that _____

_____

_____

_____

My decision is based on the following evidence: _____

_____

First, _____

_____

_____

_____

Second, _____

_____

_____

_____

Third, _____

_____

_____

_____

The trade-off(s) of my decision is (are): _____

_____

_____

_____

_____

Writing Review

Use these questions to review someone else's writing. Answer the following questions after you have read or heard this person's answer at least twice.

Name of person whose writing you reviewed _____

1. State the topic of the writing. _____

_____

_____

_____

2. a. Are all of the facts clear and accurate? _____

  b. If you answered "no," which facts need to be clearer or need correction? _____

_____

_____

_____

3. a. Do all of the facts support the writer's position? _____

  b. If you answered "no," which facts do not support the writer's position? _____

_____

_____

_____

4. List any statements or ideas that the writer did not support with facts. _____

_____

_____

_____

5. Do you agree with the writer's conclusion? Explain why or why not. _____

_____

_____

_____

_____

_____

_____

Discussion Web

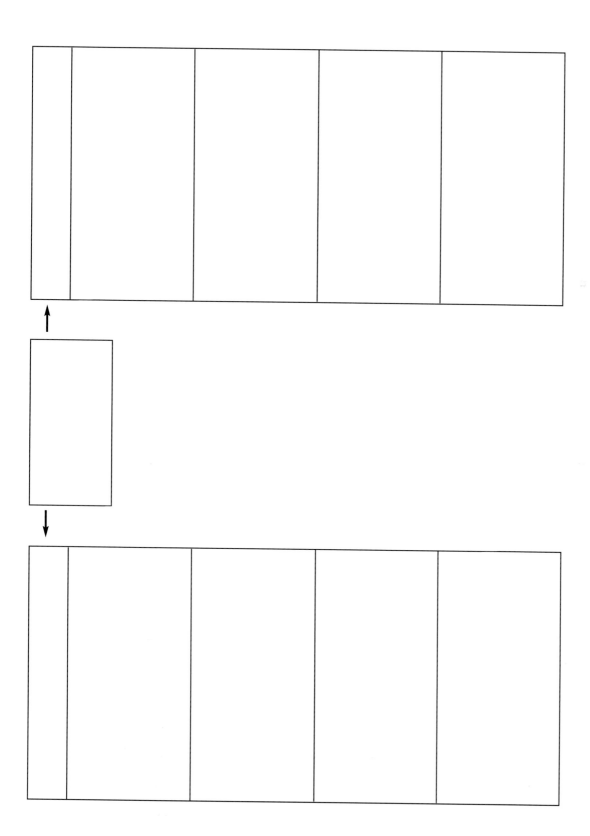

Instructions for Constructing a Concept Map

1. Work with your group to create a list of 15–20 words related to the main topic.

2. Discuss with your group how all of the words on your list are related, and sort your list of words into 3–5 categories based on these relationships. Listen to and consider the ideas of other members of your group. If you disagree with others in your group, explain to the rest of the group why you disagree.

3. Identify words that describe each category.

4. Work with your group to create a concept map on this topic. Follow these steps:

    a. Write the topic in the center of your paper, and circle it.

    b. Place the words describing each category around the topic. Circle each word.

    c. Draw a line between the topic and each category. On each line, explain the relationship between the topic and the category.

    d. Repeat steps 4b and 4c as you continue to add all of the words on your list to your concept map.

    e. Add lines to connect other related words. Explain the relationship between the words on the line.

5. View the concept maps of other groups. As you look at their concept maps, observe similarities and differences between their maps and yours. Discuss your observations with your group members.

KWL

What I know	What I want to know	What I learned

Venn Diagram Template

Compare two ideas by recording unique features of each term on the far side of each circle. Record features that are common to both of these terms in the space that overlaps.

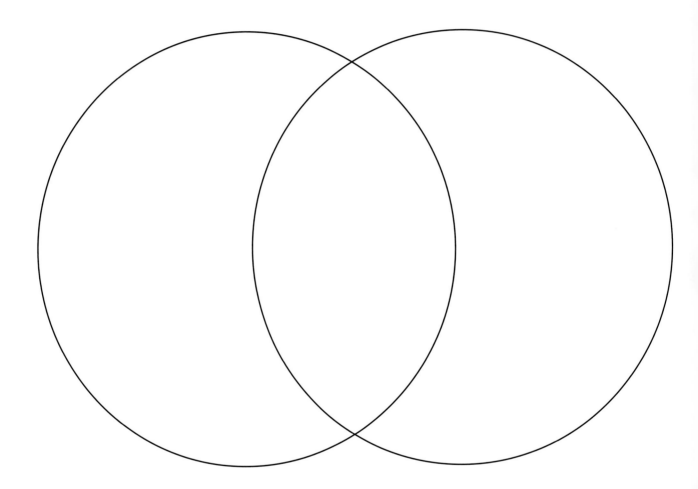

Read, Think, and Take Note Reading Strategy

As you read, from time to time, write one of the following on a sticky note:

- Explain a thought or reaction to something you read.

- Note something in the reading that is confusing or unfamiliar.

- List a word that you do not know.

- Describe a connection to something you learned or read previously.

- Make a statement about the reading.

- Pose a question about the reading.

- Draw a diagram or picture of an idea or connection.

After writing the sticky note, place it next to the word, phrase, sentence, or paragraph in the reading that prompted your note.

B Science Skills

ON THE FOLLOWING pages are instructions you can use to review the following important science skills:

Reading a Graduated Cylinder

Using a Dropper Bottle

Bar Graphing

Scatterplot and Line Graphing

Elements of Good Experimental Design

Reading a Graduated Cylinder

A graduated cylinder measures the volume of a liquid, usually in milliliters (mL). To measure correctly with a graduated cylinder:

1. Determine what measurement each unmarked line on the graduated cylinder represents.

2. Set the graduated cylinder on a flat surface and pour in the liquid to be measured.

3. Bring your eyes to the level of the fluid's surface. (You will need to bend down!)

4. Read the graduated cylinder at the lowest point of the liquid's curve (called the meniscus).

5. If the curve falls between marks, estimate the volume to the closest mL.

The example below shows a plastic graduated cylinder that contains 42 mL of liquid.

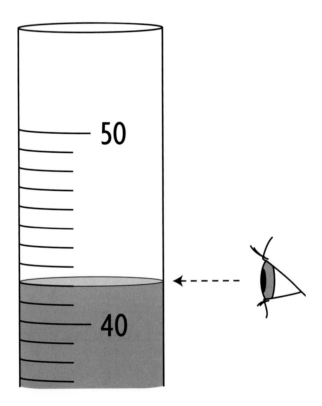

Using a Dropper Bottle

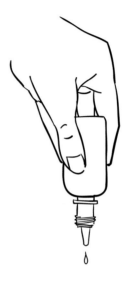

Incorrect

Holding the dropper bottle at an angle
gives drops that vary in size.

Correct

Holding the dropper bottle vertically gives
drops that are more consistent in size.

Bar Graphing Checklist

Sample Graph

Follow the instructions below to make a sample bar graph.

☐ Start with a table of data. This table represents the amount of Chemical A that the Acme Company used each year from 1999 to 2003.

Year	Chemical A used (kg)
1999	100
2000	80
2001	110
2002	90
2003	105

☐ Determine whether a bar graph is the best way to represent the data.

☐ If so, draw the axes. Label them with the names and units of the data.

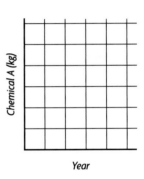

☐ Decide on a scale for each axis. Be sure there is enough space for all the data, but that it's not too crowded.

Year axis: 1 block = 1 year
Chemical A axis: 1 block = 20 kilograms

☐ Mark intervals on the graph, and label them clearly.

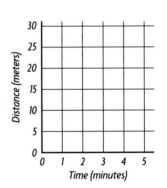

Bar Graphing Checklist (continued)

☐ Plot your data on the graph.

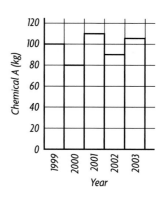

☐ Fill in the bars.

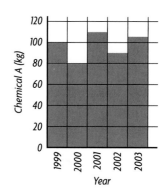

☐ Title your graph. The title should describe what the graph shows.

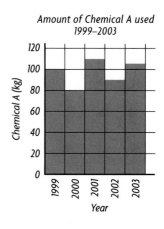

Scatterplot and Line Graphing Checklist

Sample Graph

Follow the instructions below to make a sample line graph.

☐ Start with a table of data.

MOTION OF A BALL

Time (minutes)	Distance (meters)
0	0
1	5
2	9
3	16
4	20
5	27

☐ Determine whether a line graph or a scatterplot is the best way to represent the data.

LINE GRAPH

☐ Draw the axes. Label them with the names and units of the data.

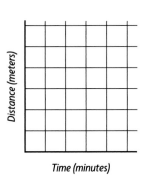

Distance (meters)

Time (minutes)

☐ Decide on a scale for each axis. Be sure there is enough space for all the data, but that it's not too crowded.

Time axis: 1 block = 1 minute

Distance axis: 1 block = 5 meters

☐ Draw intervals on the graph, and label them clearly.

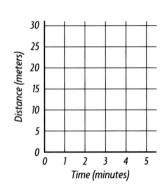

Scatterplot and Line Graphing Checklist (continued)

☐ Put a dot on the graph for each data point.

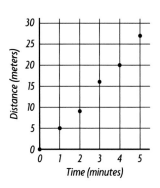

☐ For a scatterplot, leave the points unconnected.

For a line graph, draw a smooth line or curve that follows the pattern indicated by the position of the points.

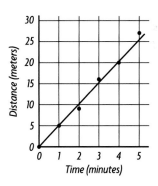

☐ Title your graph. The title should describe what the graph shows.

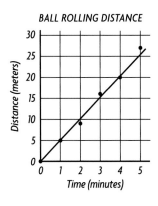

☐ If more than one data set has been plotted, consider whether to include a key

● = *large ball*
○ = *small ball*

Elements of Good Experimental Design

An experiment that is well designed:

- builds on previous research.

- is based on a question, observation, or hypothesis.

- describes all steps in a procedure clearly and completely.

- includes a control for comparison.

- keeps all variables—except the one being tested—the same.

- describes all data to be collected.

- includes precise measurements and all records of data collected during experiment.

- may require multiple trials.

- can be reproduced by other investigators.

- respects human and animal subjects.

Note: Elements may vary, depending on the problem being studied.

Using Microscopes

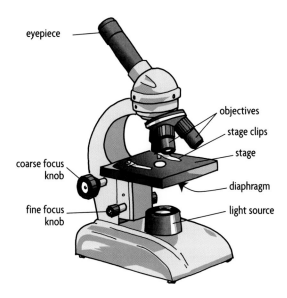

eyepiece

objectives

stage clips

stage

coarse focus knob

diaphragm

fine focus knob

light source

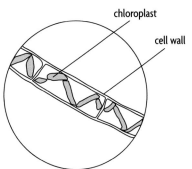

Spirogyra (algae) x 400

chloroplast

cell wall

Focusing a Microscope

Be sure that your microscope is set on the lowest power before placing your slide onto the microscope stage. Place the slide on the microscope stage. Center the slide so that the sample is directly over the light opening, and adjust the microscope settings as necessary. If the microscope has stage clips, secure the slide in position so that it does not move.

- Observe the sample. Focus first with the coarse-focus knob, and then adjust the fine-focus knob.
- After switching to a higher power magnification, be careful to adjust the focus with the fine-focus knob only.
- Return to low power before removing the slide from the microscope stage.

Safety

Always carry a microscope properly with both hands—one hand underneath and one holding the microscope arm. When you are working with live organisms, be sure to wash your hands thoroughly after you finish the laboratory.

Some Tips for Better Drawings:

- Use a sharp pencil and have a good eraser available.
- Try to relax your eyes when looking through the eyepiece. You can cover one eye or learn to look with both eyes open. Try not to squint.
- Look through your microscope at the same time as you do your drawing. Look through the microscope more than you look at your paper.
- Don't draw every small thing on your slide. Just concentrate on one or two of the most common or interesting things.
- You can draw things larger than you actually see them. This helps you show all of the details you see.
- Keep written words outside the circle.
- Use a ruler to draw the lines for your labels. Keep lines parallel—do not cross one line over another.
- Remember to record the level of magnification next to your drawing.

C Assessment in *Science and Global Issues*

WITHIN SCIENCE AND GLOBAL ISSUES there are many opportunities for you and your teacher to evaluate your progress in developing the skills and knowledge you will need to best understand the science being taught. Some of these opportunities involve an assessment system that has been specifically developed to work with a course like *Science and Global Issues*. You are likely familiar with traditional assessment systems of tests and quizzes. This assessment system works in a different way.

The assessment opportunities may appear as a Procedure Step or as one or more of the Analysis Questions you see at the end of each activity. Your teacher will discuss with you when you are being assessed on a Procedure Step or Analysis Question. He or she will assess you in seven areas, but generally only one, possibly two, areas within one activity. These seven areas are:

Analyzing Data

Communication Skills

Designing Investigations

Evidence and Trade-offs

Group Interaction

Organizing Data

Understanding Concepts

In this system your teacher scores your work or response to a question from zero to four, with four being the highest level. The score indicates the following:

SCORE	INDICATES STUDENT WORK IS:
4	Advanced, above and beyond
3	Complete and correct
2	Partially correct
1	Incorrect
0	Missing or off task

The pages that follow offer an outline, called a rubric, for each assessment area, showing what your teacher looks for in a complete and correct response. Note that a Level-3 response is considered complete and correct.

Your teacher will discuss his or her expectations for your work on specific assessments as you come to them in the course.

Scoring Guide: Analyzing Data (AD)

What to Look For

Student's response accurately summarizes data, detects patterns and trends, and draws valid conclusions based on the data used.

LEVEL 4 *Above and beyond*	*Student accomplishes Level 3 AND goes beyond in some significant way, such as* • *explaining unexpected results.* • *judging the value of the investigation.* • *suggesting additional relevant investigation.*
LEVEL 3 *Complete and correct*	*Student analyzes and interprets data correctly and completely, AND draws a conclusion compatible with the analysis of the data.*
LEVEL 2 *Almost there*	*Student notes patterns or trends, BUT does so incompletely.*
LEVEL 1 *On your way*	*Student attempts an interpretation, BUT ideas are illogical, OR ideas show a lack of understanding.*
LEVEL 0	*Student's analysis or interpretation of data is missing, illegible, or irrelevant.*
X	*Student had no opportunity to respond.*

Scoring Guide: Communication Skills (CS)

What to Look For

Student's response presents ideas clearly in the following formats:
- *written (such as a report): sentence structure, grammar, spelling*
- *oral (such as a presentation): enunciation, projection, and eye contact*
- *visual (such as a poster): balance of light, color, size of lettering, clarity of image*
- *multimedia (such as a computer slide show): effective use of available technology*

LEVEL 4 Above and beyond	Student accomplishes Level 3 and enhances communication in some significant way, such as: • including additional images or diagrams effectively. • using additional formats of communication effectively
LEVEL 3 Complete and correct	Student communicates ideas clearly with few or no technical errors.
LEVEL 2 Almost there	Student may make several technical errors, BUT those errors do not prevent the audience from understanding the message.
LEVEL 1 On your way	Student's communication is unclear, OR technical errors seriously distract the audience from understanding the message.
LEVEL 0	Student's response is missing, illegible, or irrelevant.
X	Student had no opportunity to respond.

Scoring Guide: Designing Investigations (DI)

What to Look For

Student's response states the purpose of the investigation, describes the investigation, and specifies data to be collected for the investigation.

Descriptions of procedures are complete and accurate.

LEVEL 4 Above and beyond	Student accomplishes Level 3 and goes beyond in some significant way, such as • identifying alternate procedures. • suggesting improved materials. • relating clearly to scientific principles and approaches.
LEVEL 3 Complete and correct	Student's design is appropriate and has a reproducible procedure, if required.
LEVEL 2 Almost there	Student's design or procedure is incomplete or has significant errors.
LEVEL 1 On your way	Student's design or procedure is incorrect or demonstrates a lack of understanding of the goals of the investigation.
LEVEL 0	Student's design or procedure is missing, illegible, or irrelevant.
X	Student had no opportunity to respond.

Scoring Guide: Evidence and Trade-offs (ET)

What to Look For

Student's response applies relevant evidence in comparing multiple options in order to make a choice.

Student's response states a position, supports it with evidence, and describes what advantages the chosen option gives up (trades off).

LEVEL 4 *Above and beyond*	*Student accomplishes Level 3 and goes beyond in some significant way, such as* • *including relevant evidence that was not studied in class.* • *evaluating the source, quality, or quantity of evidence.* • *proposing relevant experiments or research.* • *including a diagram or other visual aid to clarify his or her ideas.*
LEVEL 3 *Complete and correct*	*Student takes a position, supports the position with accurate and relevant evidence, and describes the trade-offs of his or her decision.*
LEVEL 2 *Almost there*	*Student discusses one or more options using accurate and relevant evidence, and takes a position supported by the evidence, BUT reasoning is incomplete or part of evidence is missing.*
LEVEL 1 *On your way*	*Student takes a position BUT provides reasons that are subjective, inaccurate, or unscientific.*
LEVEL 0	*Student's response is missing, illegible, or irrelevant.*
X	*Student had no opportunity to respond.*

Scoring Guide: Group Interaction (GI)

What to Look For

Group members work as a team and the ideas of all members are valued and weighed in working toward the common goal.

LEVEL 4 Above and beyond	Group members accomplish Level 3 and go beyond in some significant way, such as • asking helpful questions about each other's ideas. • helping each other accomplish the task. • building on each other's ideas.
LEVEL 3 Complete and correct	All group members participate and respectfully consider each other's ideas.
LEVEL 2 Almost there	Group participation is unbalanced, OR group considers some members', but not everyone's, ideas with respect.
LEVEL 1 On your way	Participation is significantly unbalanced OR group totally disregarded some members' comments and ideas.
LEVEL 0	Members do not work together, OR single individual does entire task.
X	Student had no opportunity to respond.

Scoring Guide: Organizing Data (OD)

What to Look For

Student's response accurately records and logically displays data.

LEVEL 4 *Above and beyond*	*Student accomplishes Level 3 and goes beyond in some significant way, such as* • *using innovation in the organization or display of data.*
LEVEL 3 *Complete and correct*	*Student logically presents complete and accurate data.*
LEVEL 2 *Almost there*	*Student reports data logically BUT records are incomplete.*
LEVEL 1 *On your way*	*Student reports data BUT records are illogical OR records contain major errors in the data.*
LEVEL 0	*Student's data is missing, illegible, or irrelevant.*
X	*Student had no opportunity to respond.*

Scoring Guide: Understanding Concepts (UC)

What to Look For

Student's response identifies and describes scientific concepts relevant to a particular problem or issue.

LEVEL 4 *Above and beyond*	*Student accomplishes Level 3 AND goes beyond in some significant way, such as* • *providing relevant information not provided in class that enhances the response.* • *using a diagram to clarify scientific concepts.* • *relating the response to other scientific concepts.*
LEVEL 3 *Complete and correct*	*Student accurately and completely explains or applies relevant scientific concept(s).*
LEVEL 2 *Almost there*	*Student explains or applies scientific concept(s) BUT omits some information OR includes some errors.*
LEVEL 1 *On your way*	*Student incorrectly explains or applies scientific concept(s) OR shows a lack of understanding of the concept(s).*
LEVEL 0	*Student's response is missing, illegible, or irrelevant.*
X	*Student had no opportunity to respond.*

D Science Classroom Safety

IT IS ESSENTIAL that you read and understand all safety procedures in the science classroom. Following these procedures will help you recognize and avoid potentially hazardous situations when you conduct science laboratories. In *Science and Global Issues: Biology,* you will work with chemicals and with organisms, such as duckweed and bacteria. By following these safety procedures, you will reduce risk to yourself, others, and the environment.

Before the Investigation

- Listen carefully to your teacher's instructions, and follow any steps recommended for preparing for the activity.
- Use only those materials or chemicals needed for the investigation.
- Know the location of emergency equipment, such as a fire extinguisher, fire blanket, and eyewash station.
- Tie back or remove dangling or bulky items, such as long hair, jewelry, sleeves, jackets, and bags. Do not wear open-toed shoes in the science lab.
- Tell your teacher if you wear contact lenses, or have allergies, injuries, or any medical conditions that may affect your ability to perform the lab safely.
- Make sure both the work surface and floor in your work area are clear of books, backpacks, purses, or any other unnecessary materials.

During the Investigation

- Follow all written instructions and those your teacher gives you.
- Read the activity procedure carefully.
- Don't eat, drink, chew gum, or apply cosmetics in the lab area.
- Wear safety goggles for any investigation that uses chemicals.
- Do not wear contact lenses when conducting activities that involve chemicals. If your doctor says you must wear them, notify your teacher before conducting any activity that involves chemicals.
- Read all labels on chemical bottles, and be sure you are using the correct chemical.
- Keep all chemical containers closed when not in use.

- Do not touch, taste, or smell any chemical unless you are instructed to do so by your teacher.
- Mix chemicals only as directed.
- Use caution when working with hot plates, hot liquids, and electrical equipment.
- Follow all directions when working with live organisms or microbial cultures.
- Be mature and cautious, and don't engage in horseplay.
- Report any accidents to your teacher immediately.
- Not sure what to do? Ask!

After the Investigation

- Dispose of all materials as instructed by your teacher.
- Clean up your work area, wash out trays, replace bottle caps securely, and follow any special instructions.
- Return equipment to its proper place.
- Wash your hands after every laboratory activity.

E The International System of Units

MEASUREMENTS THAT APPEAR in *Science and Global Issues* are expressed in metric units from the International System of Units, otherwise known as SI units (from Système Internationale d'Unités), which was established by international agreement. Virtually all countries in the world mandate use of the metric system exclusively. The United States does not use the metric system for many measurements, although it has been the standard for the scientific community in the United States for more than 200 years. A U.S. government effort to convert from the United States customary system to metric measurements in all realms of life has yet to extend far beyond governmental agencies, the military, and some industries.

The reason that many countries have replaced their traditional measurement systems with the metric system is its ease of use and to improve international trade. There are far fewer units to understand in comparison to the system commonly used in the United States. The metric system has only one base unit for each quantity and larger or smaller units are expressed by adding a prefix. The table below shows the base units in the International System of Units.

QUANTITY	BASE UNIT
Length	meter (m)
Mass	kilogram (kg)
Time	second (s)
Temperature	kelvin (K)
Electric current	ampere (A)
Luminous intensity	candela (cd)
Mole	mole (mol)

Other international units appearing in *Science and Global Issues* are shown in the table below.

QUANTITY	UNIT	COMMON EXAMPLE
Temperature	Celsius (°C)	Room temperature is about 20° Celsius.
Volume	liter (l)	A large soda bottle contains 2 liters.
Mass	gram (g)	A dollar bill has the mass of about 1 gram.
Electrical resistance	ohm (Ω)	Standard computer power cables have about .06 ohms resistance.
Electric potential	volt (V)	A typical battery provides 1.5 volts.
Power	watt (W)	One commonly used household incandescent light is about 60 watts.
Frequency	hertz (Hz)	Humans can typical hear sounds from 20 to 20,000 hertz.
Wavelength	nanometer (nm)	Visible light is in the range of 400 to 780 nanometers.

The International System's prefixes change the magnitude of the units by factors of 1,000. Prefixes indicate which multiple of a thousand is applied. For example, the prefix kilo- means 1,000. Therefore, a kilometer is 1,000 meters and a kilogram is 1,000 grams. To convert a quantity from one unit to another in the metric system, the quantity needs only to be multiplied or divided by multiples of 1,000. The chart below shows the prefixes for the metric system in relation to the base units. Note: Although it is not a multiple of 1,000 the prefix *centi-* is commonly used, for example, in the unit centimeter. Centi- represents a factor of one 100th.

METRIC PREFIX	FACTOR	FACTOR (NUMERICAL)
giga (G)	one billion	1,000,000,000
mega (M)	one million	1,000,000
kilo (k)	one thousand	1,000
<UNIT>	one	1
milli (m)	one one-thousandth	1/1,000
micro (μ)	one one-millionth	1/1,000,000
nano (n)	one one-billionth	1/1,000,000,000

F Elements and Organisms

OF THE **92** naturally occurring elements, 11 make up most of the human body. Additional elements, called trace elements, are present in humans in very small amounts.

The Big Four: C, H, O, and N

Approximately 96% of the mass of all living matter, including humans, is made of just four elements—carbon (C), hydrogen (H), oxygen (O), and nitrogen (N). They are indicated in the periodic table on the following page in green. These elements are the building blocks of all biological macromolecules, which are the proteins, carbohydrates, lipids, and nucleic acids.

Seven More

Seven more elements constitute about 4% of the human body. They are indicated in the periodic table on the following page in blue. Sulfur (S) is present in one of the amino acid building blocks of proteins, and phosphorus (P) is in both DNA and RNA, as well as in such molecules as ATP and NADPH, which provide energy for many reactions within cells. The elements calcium (Ca), chlorine (Cl), magnesium (Mg), potassium (K), and sodium (Na) are generally present in small molecules or charged particles called ions, and they play a number of roles in the human body. For example, calcium and phosphorus are important in bone strength, and calcium regulates many cellular activities, including muscle contraction and cell division. Sodium and potassium ions are essential for nerve cells' ability to transmit electrical signals.

Trace Elements

Less than 0.01% of humans' body mass is composed of trace elements, and scientists have not yet established their exact number or the roles that all of them play. You are most likely to be familiar with the biological role of iron (Fe), which is found in hemoglobin in red blood cells. You may also know that thyroid hormone contains iodine (I). Additional trace elements include cobalt (Co), copper (Cu), fluorine (F), manganese (Mn), molybdenum (Mo), selenium (Se), and zinc (Zn).

Periodic Table of the Elements

Color Key:
- Four elements make up 96% of the mass of all living matter.
- Seven elements constitute about 4% of the human body.

Shading Key:
- A Solid at room temperature
- A Liquid at room temperature
- A Gas at room temperature

1	2	3	4	5	6	7	8	9	10	11	12	13	14	15	16	17	18
1 H hydrogen 1.008																	2 He helium 4.003
3 Li lithium 6.941	4 Be beryllium 9.012											5 B boron 10.81	6 C carbon 12.01	7 N nitrogen 14.01	8 O oxygen 16.00	9 F fluorine 19.00	10 Ne neon 20.18
11 Na sodium 22.99	12 Mg magnesium 24.31											13 Al aluminum 26.98	14 Si silicon 28.09	15 P phosphorus 30.97	16 S sulfur 32.07	17 Cl chlorine 35.45	18 Ar argon 39.95
19 K potassium 39.10	20 Ca calcium 40.08	21 Sc scandium 44.96	22 Ti titanium 47.88	23 V vanadium 50.94	24 Cr chromium 52.00	25 Mn manganese 54.94	26 Fe iron 55.85	27 Co cobalt 58.93	28 Ni nickel 58.69	29 Cu copper 63.55	30 Zn zinc 65.39	31 Ga gallium 69.72	32 Ge germanium 72.58	33 As arsenic 74.92	34 Se selenium 78.96	35 Br bromine 79.90	36 Kr krypton 83.80
37 Rb rubidium 85.47	38 Sr strontium 87.62	39 Y yttrium 88.91	40 Zr zirconium 91.22	41 Nb niobium 92.91	42 Mo molybdenum 95.94	43 Tc technetium (98)	44 Ru ruthenium 101.1	45 Rh rhodium 102.9	46 Pd palladium 106.4	47 Ag silver 107.9	48 Cd cadmium 112.4	49 In indium 114.8	50 Sn tin 118.7	51 Sb antimony 121.8	52 Te tellurium 127.6	53 I iodine 126.9	54 Xe xenon 131.3
55 Cs cesium 132.9	56 Ba barium 137.3	57 La* lanthanum 138.9	72 Hf hafnium 178.5	73 Ta tantalum 180.9	74 W tungsten 183.9	75 Re rhenium 186.2	76 Os osmium 190.2	77 Ir iridium 190.2	78 Pt platinum 195.1	79 Au gold 197.0	80 Hg mercury 200.5	81 Tl thallium 204.4	82 Pb lead 207.2	83 Bi bismuth 208.9	84 Po polonium (209)	85 At astatine (210)	86 Rn radon (222)
87 Fr francium (223)	88 Ra radium (226)	89 Ac~ actinium (227)	104 Rf rutherfordium (257)	105 Db dubnium (260)	106 Sg seaborgium (263)	107 Bh bohrium (262)	108 Hs hassium (265)	109 Mt meitnerium (266)	110 Ds darmstadtium (271)	111 Uuu (272)	112 112 (277)		114 Uuq (296)		116 Uuh (298)		118 Uuo (?)

*Lanthanide Series

58 Ce cerium 140.1	59 Pr praseodymium 140.9	60 Nd neodymium 144.2	61 Pm promethium (147)	62 Sm samarium (150.4)	63 Eu europium 152.0	64 Gd gadolinium 157.3	65 Tb terbium 158.9	66 Dy dysprosium 162.5	67 Ho holmium 164.9	68 Er erbium 167.3	69 Tm thulium 168.9	70 Yb ytterbium 173.0	71 Lu lutetium 175.0

~Actinide Series

90 Th thorium 232.0	91 Pa protactinium (231)	92 U uranium (238)	93 Np neptunium (237)	94 Pu plutonium (242)	95 Am americium (243)	96 Cm curium (247)	97 Bk berkelium (247)	98 Cf californium (249)	99 Es einsteinium (254)	100 Fm fermium (253)	101 Md mendelevium (256)	102 No nobelium (254)	103 Lr lawrencium (257)

G Classifying Living Organisms

THE INFORMATION IN this appendix describes the common characteristics of the major groupings of living organisms. Over the centuries scientists have created and revised classification systems by which to categorize and group living organisms. One system uses seven basic levels of organization. From largest to smallest they are:

kingdom

   phylum

      class

         order

            family

               genus

                  species

Human beings, for example, are classified in the following way:

kingdom: Animalia

   phylum: Chordata

      class: Mammalia

         order: Primates

            family: Hominidae

               genus: *Homo*

                  species: *sapiens*

Note that to designate the species of an organism, both the genus and species names are used. The genus name is capitalized, but the species name is not. Both words should be italicized. The correct format for the scientific name of humans is *Homo sapiens*.

Scientific classification was originally based on the work of Carl Linnaeus, who, in the 1700s, worked on grouping organisms based on their physical characteristics. Modern scientific classification includes other information, such as organisms' genomes, as scientists continually update the classification of organisms when new information is discovered. As we have learned about the relationships among different groups of organisms, the system of classification has become more refined, with the addition of such groupings as superorders and subfamilies that reflect new findings.

In many instances currently, scientists are debating how to classify different groups and organisms based on new information. Exact designations within the classification system often change, with scientists proposing differing classifications for a group or a specific organism. Some of these proposed classifications are noted in the information that follows. Phylogenetics is another classification system, based on evolutionary relationships rather than overall similarity.

Domain Archaea

Kingdom Archaebacteria

The Archaebacteria are single-celled prokaryotes with genes and metabolic pathways that are more closely related to eukaryotes than they are to eubacteria. They are found in a wide range of habitats (some of them extreme), including oceans, soil, marshlands, salt lakes, and hot springs.

Examples: methanogens (*Methanobacterium*), which produce methane gas; thermonacidophilic bacteria (*Thermoplasma*), which grow in environments with high temperatures; and salt-loving bacteria (*Halococcus*)

Domain Bacteria

Kingdom Eubacteria

The Eubacteria, single-celled prokaryotes, may be shaped as spheres, rods, or spirals. They sometimes group themselves into chains or clumps. Some bacteria cause diseases, such as tuberculosis and strep throat, while others are beneficial to humans, such as those with which we make cheese and yogurt.

typical bacterium (plural: bacteria)

Examples: spore-forming bacteria (*Bacillus*); chemoautotrophs (*Nitrobacter*); blue-green bacteria (cyanobacteria); spirochetes (*Treponema*); obligate internal parasites, such as *Chlamydia*

Domain Eukarya

Kingdom Protista

Protists are mostly single-celled eukaryotes, but some are multicellular. Some are consumers, and others are producers.

protist

Phylum Ciliophora (ciliates)

Characterized by hair-like cilia at some point in their development, almost all of these organisms use cilia for motility. Ciliates have two types of nuclei: a micronucleus, and a macronucleus. In most, genetic information is exchanged between cells through direct contact or by a bridge-like connection during a process called conjugation.

Examples: *Paramecium, Stentor*

Phylum Apicomplexa, formerly known as Sporozoa (sporozoans)

In sporozoans, disease-causing parasites, a group of organelles are located at one end, called the apical end. The organelles are involved in the interaction of the host cell and the parasite and the invasion of the host cell. The complex life cycle includes both sexual and asexual stages.

Examples: *Plasmodium, Cryptosporidium*

Stentor

Phylum Dinoflagellata (dinoflagellates)

The dinoflagellates are heterotrophic or autotrophic, and most have two flagella. Most are marine, but there are some freshwater species. Some species are bioluminescent, some are parasitic, and some marine species are symbionts. They reproduce asexually. An algal bloom of dinoflagellates produces neurotoxins and forms what is called red tide.

Examples: *Noctiluca, Gonyaulax*

Phylum Foraminifera (forams)

Forams, single-celled marine protists, have shells (or tests) made of organic compounds, cemented sand, or other particles. They have pseudopods (projections of the cell) for feeding, locomotion, and anchoring.

Examples: *Discorbis vesicularis*, foraminiferan

Phylum Rhizopoda (amoebas)*

typical amoeba

The amoebas are consumers that move and feed with pseudopods. They are naked or shelled and found in freshwater, saltwater, and soil.

*Note that some classifications put cellular slime molds in Rhizopoda.

Phylum Bacillariophyta (diatoms)

Diatoms are photosynthetic and are characterized by shells made of silica that have ornate patterns. Most are single-celled and grow in colonies of filaments or ribbons in marine and freshwater.

Examples: *Striatella, Hydrosira, Fragilaria*

various diatoms

Phylum Chrysophyta (golden algae)

Golden algae are mostly photosynthetic, and most are single-celled. They live in freshwater sometimes in colonies or filaments.

Example: Dinobryon

Phylum Oomycota (water molds)

The water molds are filamentous, their cell walls are made of cellulose, and they produce large oogonia that contain the female gametes and smaller gametes (sperm). They absorb their food from water or soil, or some invade another organism.

Examples: *Phytophthora infestans* (causes potato blight), *Plasmopara* (downy mildew on grapes)

Phylum Phaeophyta (kelps and brown algae)*

Phaeophyta are all photosynthetic, and most are marine. Their complex life cycle alternates between diploid and haploid forms.

Examples: *Fucus distichous,* kelp

kelp

*Note: Some classifications use the phylum heterokontophyta to describe a group of eukaryotes made up mostly of diatoms. The name refers to the motile stage of the life cycle in which the cells have two flagella of different shapes. The classification system followed in this taxonomy appendix places Bacillariophyta, Chrysophyta, Phaeophyta, and Oomycota in phyla.

Some classifications have designated a separate kingdom called Chromista to group the colored algae with chloroplasts that contain chlorophyll a and c, and other closely related colorless algae.

Phylum Chlorophyta (green algae)

The green algae are producers, and their chloroplasts give them a bright green color. They may be single-celled or colonial flagellates that form colonies or long filaments. They are mostly aquatic.

Examples: *Chlamydomonas, Tetraselmis, Ulva*

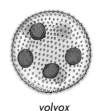

volvox

Phylum Rhodophyta (red algae)

The red algae are marine organisms, most are multicellular, and most reproduce sexually.

Examples: *Corallina, Porphyra, Chondrus*

Phylum Myxomycota (slime molds)*

The slime molds are characterized as plasmodial (large single cells with many nuclei) or cellular (separate, single-celled amoeboid protists). They reproduce sexually and form clusters of spores that are dispersed to start a new life cycle as amoeba-like cells.

Example: *Physarum, Acrasida*

*Some classifications put cellular slime molds in Rhizopoda.

Phylum Radiolaria (radiolarians)

The Radiolaria are consumers and are characterized by a silica skeleton that has several pseudopodia called axopods containing bundles of microtubules. Their reproduction is sexual or asexual.

Examples: radiolarian, *Actinophyrs*

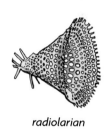

radiolarian

Kingdom Fungi

The fungi are eukaryotes—consumers and key decomposers. Most are multicellular, their structures are made of thin tubes called hyphae, and their cell walls are made of chitin. They reproduce both asexually and sexually.

Phylum Zygomycota (bread molds)

Most of the bread molds lack cross walls that divide the hyphae. Most reproduce asexually via spores, but some reproduce sexually by conjugation of adjacent hyphae.

Examples: *Rhizopus, Pilobolus*

Phylum Basidiomycota (club fungi: mushrooms, smuts, rusts, puffballs, stinkhorns)

These fungi have cross walls that divide the hyphae. Most reproduce sexually through spores on the surface of club-shaped structures, but some reproduce asexually.

Examples: shelf fungus, *Cryptococcus*

mushroom

Phylum Ascomycota (sac and cup fungi, yeasts, mildew)

These fungi have cross walls that divide the hyphae. They are also characterized as having a structure called an ascus where sexual spores are formed. Some reproduce asexually.

Examples: *Saccharomyces*, lichen

cup fungus

Kingdom Plantae

Plants are eukaryotic producers, multicellular, and nonmotile (not capable of movement). They have cell walls and chloroplasts containing chlorophyll. Vascular plants have tissues for transporting water and minerals through the plant; non-vascular plants lack these tissues. Most are terrestrial, but some are aquatic. They reproduce sexually with alternation between a haploid (gametophyte) and a diploid (sporophyte) phase or generation of the life cycle.

Phylum Bryophyta (mosses)

Mosses are nonvascular, live in moist habitats, and lack true leaves, stems, and roots. They reproduce with a dominant gametophyte generation.

Examples: *Sphagnum, Polytrichum*

moss

Phylum Hepaticophyta (liverworts)

The nonvascular liverworts have a flat-lobed structure, live in moist habitats, and lack true leaves, stems, and roots. Sexual reproduction is through gametes; asexual reproduction occurs through spores.

Examples: *Marchantia*

Phylum Anthcerophyta (hornworts)

Hornworts are nonvascular and characterized by tall stalked sporophytes that grow from the top of the plant throughout the plant's life.

Examples: *Anthoceros,* Dendroceros

Phylum Lycophyta (club mosses)

The club mosses are vascular, low growing, usually evergreen, and have roots, stems, and small leaves; dominant gametophyte generation. Some club mosses form carpets in the understory of wet tropical forests.

Examples: *Lycopodium, Selaginella*

hornwort

Phylum Pteridopsida (ferns)

Ferns are vascular and live in damp or seasonally wet habitats; dominant sporophyte generation.

Examples: tree fern, climbing fern, grape fern

Phylum Sphenopsida (horsetails)

The horsetails are vascular, weedy plants that store granules of silica in their cells; reproduction is by spores. Most horsetails live in wet sandy soil; some are semi-aquatic and some live in wet clay soil.

Examples: *Equisetum, Calamitaceae*

tree fern

Phylum Cycadophyta (cycads)

Cycads are vascular, tropical and subtropical, evergreen seed plants with large compound leaves. Their cones are either male pollen-producing or female seed-producing.

Phylum Ginkgophyta (ginkgoes)

Ginkgoes, vascular woody trees, have fan-shaped leaves. There are male pollen-producing trees, and female seed-producing trees, which have fleshy ovules. Only one species (*Ginkgo biloba*) exists.

horsetail

Phylum Gnetophyta (gnetophytes)

The gnetophytes are woody vascular plants that live mostly in desert environments with some elements of flowering plants.

Example: Welwitschia

ginkgo

Phylum Coniferophyta (conifers)

Most of the conifers, woody vascular trees with seed-bearing cones, are evergreen and have needle-like leaves.

Examples: juniper, blue spruce, hemlock, white pine

Phylum Anthophyta (flowering plants)

The flowering plants are vascular and seed-producing plants. They have fruits that enclose the seeds, and an endosperm within the seeds.

Examples: iris, lily, corn, dandelion, wild rose

dandelion

Kingdom Animalia

Animals are eukaryotic, multicellular, heterotrophs. Their body plans become fixed as they develop, their cells are organized into tissues and organs, and most reproduce sexually.

Phylum Porifera (sponges)

Most of the sponges are marine; adults are sessile (attached to the ground) asymmetrical, and specialized filter feeders. They reproduce both sexually and asexually. Sponges are found in oceans worldwide.

Examples: Venus' Flower Basket, barrel sponge, red volcano sponge

barrel sponge

Phylum Cnidaria (cnidarians)

Most cnidarians are marine, radially symmetrical, and have a digestive cavity and tentacles with stinging cells (nematocysts). Many reproduce both asexually and sexually at different stages in their life cycle.

CLASS ANTHOZOA (CORALS AND SEA ANEMONES)

Corals and sea anemones are polyps and have a subdivided digestive cavity. They may be solitary or colonial. Some reproduce asexually by budding. Some produce calcium-based skeletal structures, such as reefs.

Examples: sea pens, reef-building corals, sea fans.

CLASS HYDROZOA (HYDRAS)

Most hydras are marine. Most have medusa (bell-shaped body) and polyp (cylindrical-shaped body) stages during their life cycle. They are solitary or colonial and reproduce both sexually and asexually.

Examples: Portuguese man o'war, by-the-wind sailors, hydra

Portuguese man o' war

CLASS SCYPHOZOA (JELLIES)

True jellies spend most of their lives as free-swimming medusa forms. They all have a divided digestive sac and basic sense organs. They are found in marine and fresh water ecosystems.

Examples: Moon jellies, Lion's mane jelly, box jelly

Phylum Ctenophora (comb jellies)

Of these free-living (not attached to the ground), marine organisms, some have tentacles, but none have stinging cells. They reproduce sexually. Many have rows of cilia that beat synchronously to move the organism through the water.

Examples: sea gooseberries, sea walnuts

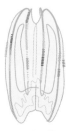

comb jelly

Phylum Platyhelminthes (flatworms)

Flatworms are bilaterally symmetrical and have three tissue layers. They may be free-living or parasitic, and reproduce sexually or sexually.

CLASS CESTODA (TAPEWORMS)

Cestoda are internal parasites which have a head with hooks or suckers, but no digestive tract. In different life stages they depend on multiple kinds of hosts.

Examples: beef tapeworm

CLASS TREMATODA (FLUKES)

Trematoda are parasites that in different life stages depend on multiple types of hosts (for example a snail and then a bird). They all have digestive systems, and most have suckers at their mouths and ventral surfaces. They have no external cilia. They are found on land and in marine and fresh water ecosystems.

Examples: human lung fluke, liver fluke, bird fluke

CLASS TURBELLARIA

These are mostly free living and usually have external cilia for movement. Some are carnivores and some are scavengers. They are found on land and in marine and fresh water ecosystems. Most reproduce sexually and are hermaphroditic (one individual has functional male and female reproductive systems).

Examples: planarians, Bedford flatworm, Hurt flatworm

flatworm

Phylum Nemertini [ribbon (or proboscis) worms]

Also known as Nermertina or Nemertea, these worms are free living and capture prey with a large tubular appendage called a proboscis. They have bilateral symmetry, are unsegmented, their digestive tubes have two openings, and they reproduce sexually and asexually (by fragmenting). They are found on land and in marine and fresh water ecosystems. Most ribbon worms are less than 8 cm long, but the largest species grows to nearly 30 m.

Examples: Giant ribbon worm, milky ribbon worm, yellow-bellied ribbon worm

Phylum Nematoda (roundworms)

Roundworms are found in nearly every ecosystem, and are either free living or parasitic. There are more than 15,000 described species, with estimates of up to 500,000 species existing. Their digestive systems have two openings. Roundworms are pseudocoelomate: they have a body cavity but no muscular or connective tissues.

Examples: hookworm, pinworm, Guinea worm, elegant worm (*C. elegans*)

roundworm

Phylum Annelida (segmented worms)

In these worms the body is segmented with internal partitions, and the circulatory system is closed. Their digestive system has two openings. They are coelomates: they have a fluid-filled body cavity with muscular and connective tissues. Segmented worms are found in fresh and marine waters and on land.

CLASS POLYCHAETA (POLYCHAETES OR BRISTLE WORMS)

These have on each segment a pair of parapodia (leg-like appendages) with bristles. They are primarily found in marine ecosystems, at all depths and in extreme marine environments such as hydrothermal vents.

Examples: feather-duster worm, fire worm, sea mice

SUBCLASS HIRUDINEA (LEECHES)

Most leeches live in freshwater, others in terrestrial or marine environments. Some (but not all) are parasitic. They are hermaphroditic, have a fixed number of segments (normally 34), and no appendages or bristles.

Examples: medicinal leech, Japanese mountain leech

SUBCLASS OLIGOCHAETA

The oligochaetes include terrestrial and aquatic worms. They have no appendages and few bristles. They are hermaphroditic.

Examples: earthworm, ice worms, blackworms

earthworm

Phylum Rotifera (rotifers)

Rotifers have cilia that form a wheel shape around their mouths. They are pseudo-coelomates with bilateral symmetry, most live in freshwater, some are motile and some sessile. Some species can reproduce sexually and asexually. Most rotifers are between 0.1 and 0.5 mm in length.

Examples: bdelloids, monogononts

Phylum Mollusca (mollusks)

The mollusks are the largest marine phylum (at least 50,000 species). They are: coelomates; free living; sessile or motile; marine, freshwater, or terrestrial; have bilateral symmetry or are asymmetrical; are not segmented; and have developed digestive, circulatory, and nervous systems. Many have a calcified shell and a muscular foot. Most reproduce sexually, through external fertilization.

CLASS BIVALVIA (BIVALVES)

In this class of 10,000 species are clams, oysters, mussels, and scallops. All have two-part hinged shells. They may be marine or freshwater, and most adults are sessile.

Examples: razor clam, blue mussels, bay scallop

scallop

CLASS CEPHALOPODA (CEPHALOPODS)

Cephalopods are squids, octopi and other marine animals in which the foot is divided into tentacles and which propel themselves by jetting water for locomotion. They have a closed circulatory system.

Examples: vampire squid, giant pacific octopus, chambered nautilus, Pfeffer's Flamboyant Cuttlefish

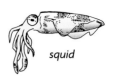
squid

CLASS GASTROPODA (SNAILS AND SLUGS)

Found in marine, freshwater, and terrestrial environments, these animals use a foot for movement. Most have a spiraled shell and a distinct head, and many are hermaphroditic.

Examples: Roman snail, abalone, sea hare

garden snail

Phylum Arthropoda* (arthropods)

Arthropods are the largest animal phylum, and all of them have an external skeleton made of chitin, which they molt. Their appendages are jointed, bodies are segmented, and circulatory systems are open. They reproduce sexually.

*Note that there is an ongoing debate within the scientific community about the classification of arthropods. Some systems no longer use Arthropoda as a phylum, and instead classify arthropods into the phyla Chelicerata, Mandibulata, Orthoptera, Coleoptera, and Crustacea.

beetle

Subphylum Chelicerata (chelicerates)

Chelicerates include spiders, scorpions, ticks, mites, and horseshoe crabs. They have segmented bodies, jointed limbs, and are covered with a cuticle made of chitin and proteins. Their first pair of appendages are feeding structures called chelicerae.

Examples: spiders, scorpions, ticks, mites, horseshoe crabs

typical spider

Subphylum Crustacea (crustaceans)

Most crustaceans are aquatic and free living, but some are parasitic. They have exoskeletons made of chitin, gills for gas exchange (intake of oxygen and respiration of carbon dioxide), and appendages with two branches.

Examples: crabs, lobsters, shrimp, barnacles, copepods, pill bugs

snow crab

Subphylum Hexapoda

The Hexapoda include insects, collembola, protura, and diplura. All have three pairs of appendages and a body divided into head, thorax and abdomen. Many have wings (one or two pairs), and many undergo metamorphosis (dramatic change in body form during different life-cycle stages).

Examples: silverfish, mayflies, dragonflies, termites, cockroaches, lice, beetles, fireflies, butterflies, mosquitoes, ants, bees

Subphylum Myriapoda

All of the myriapoda are terrestrial and have 10 to several hundred pairs of appendages. Their sizes range from almost microscopic to 30 cm long.

Examples: centipedes, millipedes

Hexapoda:
honey bee, beetle, grasshopper

Subphylum Trilobitomorpha (trilobites)

This entire group is extinct, and known only through the fossil record. They all had one pair of appendages on each body segment, and each appendage had a branch with a gill and a branch with a leg for walking.

Phylum Echinodermata (echinoderms)

These are free-living marine animals that have water vascular systems and tube feet for feeding, locomotion, and gas exchange. Their larvae have bilateral symmetry, and adults are radially symmetrical. Most species reproduce sexually, but some can reproduce asexually as well.

CLASS ASTEROIDEA (SEA STARS)

Usually having five arms that form a star shape, these carnivorous animals have a mouth on the lower surface of their bodies, and many can turn their stomachs to the outside of the body when digesting prey.

Examples: crown-of-thorns sea star, sun star, leather star

CLASS CRINOIDEA

These filter feeders found mostly in deep-water ecosystems have five arms that branch at the base. Some are sessile.

Examples: sea lilies and feather stars

CLASS ECHINOIDEA

These have spherical or disc-shaped bodies covered with spines or short hair-like projections. They have no arms, and their rigid skeletal structures are formed of interlocking plates.

Examples: sand dollars, sea urchins, sea biscuits

sea urchin

CLASS HOLOTHUROIDEA (SEA CUCUMBERS)

These have a cylindrical body shape, feeding tentacles around the mouth, and have no arms. They are detritus or filter feeders. Their skeletons are made of small particles joined by connective tissue.

Examples: conspicuous sea cucumber, sea apple, sea pig

CLASS OPHIUROIDEA

The Ophiuroidea have small disc-shaped bodies and long slender arms, rather than tube feet, with which they crawl. Most are filter or detritus feeders.

Examples: brittle stars and basket stars

brittle star

Phylum Chordata

The animals have a dorsal hollow nerve cord, notochord, and a brain within a skull. Pharyngeal gill slits (slits on the throat or neck) are present during at least one stage of development. Except for the urochordates, animals in the chordata phylum reproduce sexually.

Subphylum Urochordata

Sometimes classed as a separate phylum, these marine animals go through a free-swimming larval stage, during which they exhibit chordate characteristics, including notochord and dorsal nerve cord. The adults lose chordate characteristics, are usually sessile, and have no brains.

Examples: sea squirts, sea peaches, salps

Subphylum Cephalochordata

Sometimes classed as a separate phylum, these marine, free-swimming creatures have a hollow dorsal nerve cord, a notochord, and pharyngeal slits, but no internal skeleton, and no brain.

Examples: Florida lancelet, amphioxus

sea squirts

Subphylum Craniata*

Craniata have a single, hollow nerve cord that develops into a brain and spinal cord, and a well-developed head with skull. Some have a bony vertebral column (spine).

* Subphylum Craniata is a new grouping based on current research. Scientists have not clearly defined the classification of Craniata. They are part of the chordates, but have not been designated as a phylum or subphylum. Historically chordates included the Urochordata, Cephalochordata, and Vertebrata under the phylum Chordata.

CLASS CYCLOSTOMATA (JAWLESS FISHES)

These fishes have a cartilaginous skeleton and two-chambered heart, and exchange gas through gills. They lack true jaws.

Examples: lampreys, hagfish

CLASS CHONDRICHTYES (CARTILAGINOUS FISHES)

The Chondrichtyes have a cartilaginous skeleton, true jaws, calcified teeth and sometimes vertebrae, a two-chambered heart, and paired fins. They exchange gas through gills and have external gill slits. They are found in marine and freshwater ecosystems. Their bodies are covered in tooth-like scales called denticles.

tiger shark

Examples: tiger shark, manta ray, guitar skate

CLASS OSTEICHTHYES (BONY FISHES)

Bony fishes have a bony skeleton, true jaws, a two-chambered heart, paired fins, and scales. They exchange gas through gills, and their gill slits are covered. They are found in marine and freshwater environments.

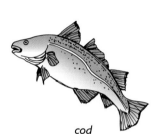

cod

Examples: tuna, lungfishes, coelacanth, perch, goldfish, salmon

CLASS AMPHIBIA (AMPHIBIANS)

Amphibians have a bony skeleton, moist skin, and a three-chambered heart. Adults exchange gas through their skin or lungs, but larvae have gills for gas exchange. Adults of most species live on land, but lay their eggs in water where the young develop.

frog

Examples: salamanders, frogs and toads, caecilians

CLASS REPTILIA (REPTILES)

Reptiles have a bony skeleton, lungs, and dry and scaly skin. Most have two pairs of limbs, three-chambered hearts, and are ectothermic (cold-blooded). Females' eggs are fertilized internally, and they lay eggs with leathery shells.

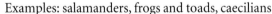

lizard

Examples: tuataras, lizards, snakes, turtles, alligators, crocodiles

CLASS AVES (BIRDS)

Birds have a bony skeleton with hollow and lightweight bones, lungs, feathers (modified scales) over much of the body, a beak with no teeth, and a four-chambered heart. They are endothermic (warm-blooded) and lay hard-shelled eggs.

owl

Examples: owls, chickens, penguins, flamingoes, honeycreepers

CLASS MAMMALIA (MAMMALS)

Mammals have a bony skeleton, lungs, hair, and are endothermic. They have a four-chambered heart, mammary glands for nursing their young, and most give live birth (as opposed to laying eggs).

ORDER ARTIODACTYLA (EVEN-TOED HOOFED MAMMALS)

Of these varied herbivores, most have complex stomachs adapted for plant material, most have two toes and some have four, and many have horns or antlers.

Examples: hippopotamus, sheep, cows, pigs, giraffes, deer.

pig

ORDER CARNIVORA (CARNIVORES)

These animals have small incisors and large canines, and often have sharp claws.

Examples: bears, dogs, cats, hyenas, sea otters

sea otter

ORDER CETACEA (CETACEANS)

The cetaceans may be marine or freshwater, the front limbs are modified into flippers, they breathe through a blowhole at the top of the head, and they have no external hind limbs. They live in water their entire lives, including giving birth and nursing their young. Some navigate by echo-location (biological sonar).

Examples: whales, dolphins, porpoises

sperm whale

ORDER CHIROPTERA (BATS)

The bats have webbed skin between the fingers and between front and hind limbs for flight. They are mostly nocturnal, and navigate by echolocation (biological sonar). Most feed on insects, nectar, or fruits.

Examples: fruit bat, flying fox

ORDER INSECTIVORA

The Insectivora have numerous and unspecialized teeth, long and narrow snouts, and sharp claws for digging.

Examples: shrews, moles, hedgehogs

bat

ORDER LAGOMORPHA

The Lagomorpha have four incisors in the upper jaw, and a total of 26 or 28 teeth. They have very short tails, and most are herbivores.

Examples: rabbits, hares, pikas

ORDER MARSUPIALIA (MARSUPIALS)

Marsupialia young are born in an undeveloped state and complete development in the mother's pouch.

Examples: opossum, koalas, kangaroos

ORDER MONOTREMATA

The Monotremata are egg-laying and produce milk for their young from mammary glands without nipples.

Examples: platypus, echidna (spiny anteaters)

platypus

ORDER PERISSODACTYLA (ODD-TOED HOOFED MAMMALS)

The Perissodactyla herbivores have teeth and a digestive system adapted for grazing on plant material. All species in this order have an odd number of toes, often in the form of one fused hoof.

Examples: rhinoceros, tapir, horse

ORDER PHOLIDOTA (SPINY ANTEATERS)

Spiny anteaters have no teeth, the body is covered in scales developed from modified hairs, and strong, clawed limbs are suited for digging. They eat social insects, such as termites and ants.

Example: Sunda pangolin, tree pangolin, Asian giant pangolin

Caspian seal

ORDER PINNIPEDIA (AQUATIC CARNIVORES)

The Pinnipedia may be marine or freshwater animals. They have limbs modified as flippers for swimming, and give birth and nurse their young on land.

Examples: seals, sea lions, and walruses

ORDER PRIMATES

Primates are distinguished as having large brains, eyes usually set directly forward, and five digits on their hands and feet. Most species live in trees in tropical regions.

Examples: gorilla, chimpanzee, lemurs, humans, monkeys

ORDER PROBOSCIDEA (ELEPHANTS)

Elephants, the largest living land animals, are herbivorous, with upper incisors modified as tusks, and nose and upper lips modified to become trunks.

Examples: African elephant, Asian elephant

human

ORDER RODENTIA (RODENTS)

In addition to some molars, rodents have two continuously-growing chisel-shaped incisors in the upper and lower jaws, but no canine teeth.

Examples: squirrels, rats, hamsters, beavers, porcupines

mouse

ORDER SIRENIA

These aquatic herbivorous mammals have forelimbs modified as flippers, little body hair, a flat tail modified as a fin, and no hind limbs.

Examples: manatees and dugongs

ORDER TUBULIDENTATA

These animals have small tubular mouths, they eat ants and termites, and the adults have few teeth. The aardvark is the only living species.

ORDER XENARTHRA

armadillo

In most of the Xenarthra, the teeth are either reduced in size and or number or absent entirely. They primarily eat social insects, such as termites and ants.

Examples: anteaters, sloths, armadillos

H The Geologic Time Scale

The Geologic Time Scale

GEOLOGIC ERA OR EVENT	GEOLOGIC PERIOD	GEOLOGIC EPOCH	TIME (MYA)	MAJOR EVOLUTIONARY EVENT
Earth is formed	—	—	4,500	There is no free oxygen.
Archean	—	—	4,300	Hydrosphere forms and supports life. At 3,500 mya, prokaryotes diversify.
Proterozoic	—	—	2,500	Eukaryotes evolve.
Paleozoic	Cambrian	—	542	Marine animals diversify.
Paleozoic	Ordovician	—	488	First vertebrates (jawless fish) evolve.
Paleozoic	Silurian	—	444	Earliest vascular plants and arthropods on land. Jawed fishes evolve.
Paleozoic	Devonian	—	416	Bony fishes diversify. Amphibians, insects, ferns, and seed plants evolve.
Paleozoic	Carboniferous	—	359	Insects and amphibians diversify. First "reptiles" evolve.
Paleozoic	Permian	—	299	Mostly mammal-like reptiles exist. Major mass extinction occurs at end of period.
Mesozoic	Triassic	—	251	"Reptiles," including first dinosaurs, diversify. Cone-bearing plants are dominant. First mammals evolve.
Mesozoic	Jurassic	—	200	Dinosaurs diversify. First birds evolve. Cone-bearing plants are still dominant. First flowering plants evolve.
Mesozoic	Cretaceous	—	145	Dinosaurs, birds, mammals, flowering plants continue to diversify. Mass extinction of many taxa including dinosaurs, occurs at end of period.
Cenozoic	Tertiary	Paleocene	65	Mammals, birds, snakes, flowering plants, pollinating insects, bony fishes diversify.
Cenozoic	Tertiary	Eocene	55.8	Mammals, birds, snakes, flowering plants, pollinating insects, bony fishes diversify.
Cenozoic	Tertiary	Oligocene	33.9	Mammals, birds, snakes, flowering plants, pollinating insects, bony fishes diversify.
Cenozoic	Tertiary	Miocene	23	Mammals, birds, snakes, flowering plants, pollinating insects, bony fishes diversify.
Cenozoic	Tertiary	Pliocene	5.3	Mammals, birds, snakes, flowering plants, pollinating insects, bony fishes diversify.
Cenozoic	Quaternary	Pleistocene	1.8	Extinctions of large mammals and birds occur. *Homo erectus* and *Homo sapiens* evolve.
Cenozoic	Quaternary	Recent (Holocene)	0.01	Extinctions of large mammals and birds occur.

Media Literacy

IMAGINE YOURSELF READING a magazine. A feature article summarizes recent studies on the effectiveness of vitamin supplements and concludes that taking vitamin pills and liquids is a waste of money. A few pages later, an advertisement from a vitamin company claims that one of its products will protect you from all sorts of diseases. Such wide differences in claims that you will see in the popular media are common, but how can you tell which one is correct? "Media literacy" is the term that encompasses the skills we need to develop to effectively analyze and evaluate the barrage of information we encounter every day. Media literacy also includes the ability to use various media to create and communicate our own messages.

A strong background in the process of science helps you build two important skills of media literacy: being able to identify valid and adequate evidence behind a claim and evaluating if the claim is a logical conclusion based on the evidence. The skills share much in common with the process of scientific inquiry, in which you learn to seek out information, assess the information, and come to a conclusion based on your findings.

Evaluating Media Messages

A "media message" is an electronic, digital, print, audible, or artistic visual message created to transmit information. Media messages can include newspaper articles, political advertisements, speeches, artwork, or even billboards. The following are some of the kinds of questions you might ask as you learn to critically analyze and evaluate messages from various kinds of media. On the next page are three examples of media messages, all related to a common theme. Use these three examples to analyze and evaluate the messages.

1. *Who created this message?*

   Is this person an expert in the content of the message? What credentials does this person have that would make them an expert in this topic? Does this person have any conflicts of interest that may make him or her biased in any way? Who sponsored (or paid for) the message? Does the source of funding have any conflicts of interest?

2. *What creative techniques in the message attract a person's attention?*

   Are there any sensational or emotional words, images, or sounds that grab the viewer's attention? Do any of these words, images, or sounds try to stir up emotions and influence the viewer's ideas?

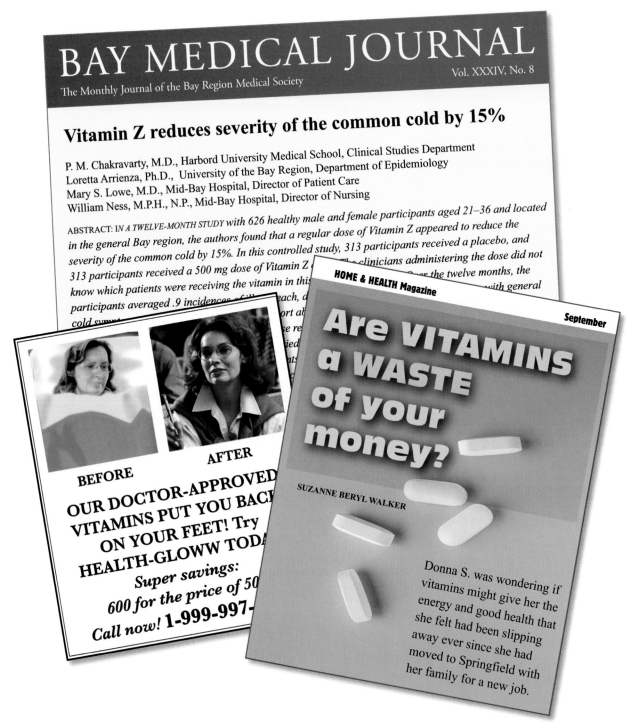

BAY MEDICAL JOURNAL

The Monthly Journal of the Bay Region Medical Society

Vol. XXXIV, No. 8

Vitamin Z reduces severity of the common cold by 15%

P. M. Chakravarty, M.D., Harbord University Medical School, Clinical Studies Department
Loretta Arrienza, Ph.D., University of the Bay Region, Department of Epidemiology
Mary S. Lowe, M.D., Mid-Bay Hospital, Director of Patient Care
William Ness, M.P.H., N.P., Mid-Bay Hospital, Director of Nursing

ABSTRACT: IN A TWELVE-MONTH STUDY with 626 healthy male and female participants aged 21–36 and located in the general Bay region, the authors found that a regular dose of Vitamin Z appeared to reduce the severity of the common cold by 15%. In this controlled study, 313 participants received a placebo, and 313 participants received a 500 mg dose of Vitamin Z ... the clinicians administering the dose did not know which patients were receiving the vitamin in this ... Over the twelve months, the participants averaged .9 incidences ... each, ... with general cold sympt...

BEFORE · **AFTER**

OUR DOCTOR-APPROVED
VITAMINS PUT YOU BACK
ON YOUR FEET! Try
HEALTH-GLOWW TODA

Super savings:
600 for the price of 50
Call now! **1-999-997-**

HOME & HEALTH Magazine

September

Are VITAMINS a WASTE of your money?

SUZANNE BERYL WALKER

Donna S. was wondering if vitamins might give her the energy and good health that she felt had been slipping away ever since she had moved to Springfield with her family for a new job.

3. *Does the message cite or mention appropriate sources of factual information?*
   Does the author cite first-person sources when reporting facts? Are the author's sources from credible organizations?

4. *Does the presented evidence completely support the claim?*
   Might there be other information that could support or discredit the message? Does the author make logical inferences and conclusions from the evidence presented in the article?

5. *Who is the target audience of this message?*

How is this message directed at this particular audience?

6. *Is the message promoting certain values, lifestyles, positions, or ideas either directly or indirectly?*

Are there any positions or ideas that are being promoted that are not explicit in the message?

Evaluating Internet Sources

Imagine that you want to search the Internet to find out about the effectiveness of vitamin supplements so that you can come to your own conclusion. When you are searching for information online, a search engine is searching from over one trillion websites[1]. Determining which websites and sources of information are reliable and which are biased is difficult. To make an informed decision about this topic, you will need to identify accurate and unbiased websites. Below is a suggested list of questions that will help you determine if a particular website is an accurate and unbiased source of information.

1. *Are the authors' names, contact information, and credentials clearly labeled on the website?*

Accurate websites will usually contain information from knowledgeable authors who have their names, credentials, and contact information clearly labeled on the website. Some websites are managed by a collection of people or an organization, and information on the exact author may not be clearly stated. However, these organizations should state the names, contact information, and credentials somewhere on their website of the people who represent the organization.

2. *Is the information and the website up to date?*

Some information that you may be seeking needs to be current. For example, if you were looking for the number of cars in the United States, you would want the most recent data. A study conducted in 1982 would not be helpful in this case. When seeking information that needs to be current, determine if the date the article or information was written is clearly indicated on the website so you can be sure you are accessing the most recent information. Credible websites will usually indicate the date the article or information was created or last updated. Also, the person or organization maintaining the website should be regularly updating the website, so that the majority of links to other websites work.

---

1. Alpert, Jesse & Hajaj, Nissan. (July 25, 2008). We knew the Web was big. . . . *The Official Google Blog. Retrieved August 2010 from* http://googleblog.blogspot.om/2008/07/we-knew-web-was-big.html.

3. *Are sources of information clearly cited?*

When factual information is stated in a website, is the source clearly cited so you can refer back to it?

4. *Are there links to more resources on this topic?*

Authoritative websites will often provide links to further information from other sources that support their claim. Authors of websites that contain information that is biased or inaccurate usually do not provide additional information that supports their claims.

5. *What are other people saying about the author or the organization that produced this information?*

If you come across information from an author or organization that you are unfamiliar with, perform a search for other information about the author or organization. What are experts writing about the author's or organization's other work?

6. *Why is this website on the Internet?*

Was this information put on the Internet to inform or to persuade people? Is the author selling something? What is the author's motivation for providing this information?

FURTHER RESOURCES

Marlene Thier & Bennett Daviss. (2002). *The New Science Literacy*. Heinemann: Portsmouth, NH.

Center for Media Literacy. http://www.medialit.org.

PBS Teachers. Media literacy. http://www.pbs.org/teachers/media_lit.

What is Science?

The Nature of Science

If someone asked you the question, "What is science?" how would you answer?

You might reply that it is knowledge of such subjects as Biology, Chemistry, and Physics. That would be only partly correct. Although science is certainly related to the accumulation and advancement of knowledge, it is much more than that. Science is a way of exploring and understanding the natural world.

According to the American Association for the Advancement of Science (AAAS), two of the most fundamental aspects of science are that the world is understandable and that scientific ideas are subject to change.

Scientists believe that the world is understandable because things happen in consistent patterns that we can eventually understand through careful study. Observations must be made and data collected for us to discover the patterns that exist in the universe. At times scientists have to invent the instruments that allow them to collect this data. Eventually, they develop theories to explain the observations and patterns. The principles on which a theory is based apply throughout the universe.

When new knowledge becomes available, it is sometimes necessary to change theories. This most often means making small adjustments, but on rare occasions it means completely revising a theory. Although scientists can never be 100% certain about a theory, as knowledge about the universe becomes more sophisticated most theories become more refined and more widely accepted. You will see examples of this process as you study the history of the sciences of evolution and genetics in this course.

Scientific Inquiry

Inquiry is at the heart of science, and an important component of inquiry is scientific investigation, including experimentation. Although scientists do not necessarily follow a series of fixed steps when conducting investigations, they share common understandings about the characteristics of a scientifically valid investigation. For example, scientists obtain evidence from observations and measurements. They repeat and confirm observations and ask other scientists to review their results. It is important for scientists to avoid bias in designing, conducting, and reporting their investigations and to have other unbiased scientists duplicate their results. Some types of investigations allow scientists to set up controls and vary just one condition at a time. They formulate and test hypotheses, sometimes collecting data that lead them to develop theories.

When scientists develop theories they are constructing explanations of the patterns and relationships associated with natural phenomena. These explanations must be logically consistent with the evidence they have gathered and with evidence other scientists have gathered. Hypotheses and theories allow scientists to make predictions. If testing turns out to not support a prediction, scientists may have to look at revising the hypothesis or theory on which the prediction was made.

REFERENCE

American Association for the Advancement of Science (AAAS). (1990). Project 2061: Science for all Americans. New York: Oxford University Press.

Glossary

abiotic. Describes factors in an environment that are not, and have never been, living, including temperature, light, and precipitation. See also **biotic.**

active transport. Movement of a substance from lower to higher concentration through a protein carrier, requiring energy input usually provided by conversion of ATP to ADP.

adaptation. The change through natural selection of a population's physical, biochemical, or behavioral traits that better suit the population's environment.

adaptive radiation. The relatively rapid evolution from a common ancestor of multiple species that occupy newly available environments. Same as **biological adaptation.**

adenosine triphosphate (ATP). A small molecule that is the primary carrier of usable energy within the cell.

aerobic respiration. Reactions of cellular respiration that use oxygen to further break down the products of glycolysis, releasing energy in the form of ATP. See also **anaerobic respiration.**

allele. One of several forms of the same gene. A sexually reproduced organism has two alleles for each gene, one from each parent, which may or may not be the same form. See also **gene.**

amensalism. A symbiotic relationship in which one species is harmed, while the other species neither benefits nor is it harmed. See also **symbiotic relationship.**

amino acid. The basic building block of proteins; varying arrangements of 20 amino acids make up all natural proteins found in living organisms. See also **protein.**

anaerobic respiration. A form of cellular respiration that does not require oxygen, resulting in incomplete breakdown of sugars and generation of less usable energy than produced by aerobic respiration. See also **anaerobic respiration.**

antibiotic. A chemical substance that kills microorganisms and is used to treat infections.

aquaculture. The growing of fish and other aquatic species for human consumption.

asexual reproduction. Reproduction of genetically identical offspring from a single parent through mitosis. See also **mitosis, sexual reproduction.**

bacteria. A domain of single-celled prokaryotic organisms. While some cause infections in humans, others are harmless or even essential to human life.

base pair. Two nucleotides in double-stranded DNA connected by hydrogen bonds. See also **DNA, hydrogen bonds, nucleotides.**

binding site. A region on a protein or nucleic acid where other molecules attach, or bind. For example, an enzyme's substrate fits into a three-dimensional binding site on the enzyme.

biodiversity. The assortment of species on earth; within and between ecosystems; and the variation in the genetic composition of a species. Same as **biological diversity.**

biofuel. Fuel compounds, such as bioethanol and biodiesel, that are produced from renewable biological sources, such as corn.

biological adaptation. Same as **adaptation.**

biological diversity. Same as **biodiversity.**

biological evolution. Changes in the genetic composition of a population that eventually give rise to other diverse life forms. See also **evolution.**

biological species. The individuals of a population that breed or can potentially breed to produce fertile offspring. See also **species, species diversity.**

biological species concept. One definition of species as: a population or populations that can breed or potentially breed to exchange genes and produce fertile offspring.

biome. A large region classified by the interaction of the living organisms, climate, and geographical features.

biotic. Describes factors in an environment that are associated with living organisms. See also **abiotic**.

Calvin cycle. The series of light-independent, enzyme-catalyzed reactions that take place in the stroma of the chloroplast. During these reactions carbon dioxide combines with the hydrogen ions and electrons produced from water during light-dependent reactions. These reactions result in the production of the high-energy sugar glucose. See also **light-independent reactions**.

cancer. Any of more than 100 diseases that result when cells lose the normal controls that regulate their growth and division in the cell cycle. They may invade nearby tissues or spread to other locations in the body.

carbon cycle. The cycle in which carbon moves between reservoirs. See also **carbon reservoir.**

carbon footprint. The estimated amount of land and sea area (acres or hectares) that would be needed to completely absorb one person's carbon emissions. It is a subset of ecological footprint. See also **ecological footprint.**

carbon reservoir. A natural feature, such as a rock, a pinch of soil, or an organism, that stores carbon-containing molecules and exchanges them with other carbon reservoirs. See also **carbon cycle.**

carrier. An individual who carries a genetic trait for a disease but is not afflicted, usually identified through genetic testing. See also **trait**.

carrying capacity. The largest population of a species that an ecosystem can support long-term based on the resources available.

catalyze. The action of a catalyst, a chemical that speeds up a chemical reaction without being used up in the reaction.

causal relationship. An occurrence between two correlated events when one event (called the cause) directly produces another event (called the effect). In a causal relationship, the cause(s) alone produce the effect.

cell. The basic unit of life and where many life processes occur.

cell biology. The study of the compositions and functions of cells, cell structures, and cell molecules.

cell cycle. The complete sequence of phases in which a cell prepares for and undergoes cell division; the period from the end of one cell division to the end of the next.

cell membrane. A semipermeable biological membrane that provides a barrier between the interior of the cell and its external environment. See also **membrane.**

cell principle. The principle that states that all living organisms are made of cells, cells are the basic units of structure and function in living organisms, and new cells are only produced by the division of existing cells.

cell wall. A structure made of fibers of carbohydrate and protein that provides support and protection to cells of plants, fungi, and many prokaryotes.

cellular respiration. The process by which cells break down complex molecules, such as sugars, to release energy.

centrioles. A pair of small organelles found near the nucleus of a cell and that help to organize the system of tubules and filaments that move chromosomes during mitosis. See also **mitosis**.

centromere. A constricted region of DNA, usually at the center of the duplicated chromosome, where two sister chromatids are joined during cell division. See also **chromatid, chromosome, DNA.**

character. A recognizable structure, function, or behavior of an organism, such as fangs with which a rattlesnake delivers venom. See also **homologous character, shared derived character.**

chemical indicator. A chemical that indicates the presence, absence, or concentration of a particular substance.

chloroplast. A pigment-containing organelle with an inner and outer membrane layer that is the site of photosynthesis within the cells of plants and some other producers.

chromatid. The DNA that forms one-half of a duplicated chromosome, joined at the center to a second chromatid by a centromere. Once pulled apart during cell division the structures are called sister chromosomes. See also **centromere, chromosomes.**

chromosome. A structure composed of DNA wrapped with proteins.

cilia *(plural),* **cilium.** Short hair-like fibers, or fiber, that projects from a cell; many cells use them for movement.

clade. A group of taxa (species level or higher) that includes a common ancestor and all of its descendants.

co-opted feature. A feature that evolved to serve a certain function that was then modified through natural selection to serve another function.

codominant. A trait produced by two alleles that are both fully expressed in an individual who is heterozygous for that trait. See also **heterozygous.**

commensalism. A symbiotic relationship in which one species benefits, while the other species does not benefit but is not harmed. See also **symbiotic relationship.**

community. In ecological terms, populations of multiple species living in the same area. In sustainability terms, any group of people with a common interest living in a particular area.

consumers. Organisms that must eat other organisms to obtain energy.

control. Subjects, chemicals, or objects used in experimental tests that provide a standard of comparison in judging experimental results.

correlation. A relationship between one event or action and another. A positive correlation means that as one event or action becomes large, the other also becomes large, and vice versa. A negative correlation means that when one event or action becomes larger, the other becomes smaller, and vice versa.

cristae. Finger-like projections of the inner membrane of a mitochondrion that provide a large surface area for the reactions of cellular respiration.

crossing over. A phenomenon during prophase in meiosis I where pairs of chromosomes exchange portions. See also **meiosis.**

cyclins. Proteins that control progress of cells through the cell cycle. See also **protein.**

cytokinesis. The process following mitosis in which two daughter cells form from a parent cell. See also **daughter cell, mitosis, parent cell.**

cytoplasm. A semifluid mixture of substances found within the cell membrane but outside the nucleus and organelles, when a nucleus and organelles are present.

cytoskeleton. A network of microscopic tubules and filaments that supports and maintains the shape of a cell and may also function in movement of cells or structures within cells.

daughter cell. Any cell produced by the division of a parent cell. See also **mitosis.**

dead zone. An area of water that is so depleted of oxygen that organisms must migrate away from it or die. See also **eutrophication.**

decomposers. Organisms that obtain energy by eating dead or decaying organisms or waste from living organisms.

deep time. A vast time scale of billions of years, related to the geological and evolutionary history of the earth. Same as **geologic time.**

density-dependent factor. A factor, such as amount of food per individual, that changes when the population density changes.

density-independent factor. A factor that is not directly affected by population density, such as the effect of a natural disaster.

deoxyribonucleic acid (DNA). The macromolecule that makes up genes, present in every living organism.

diabetes. A noninfectious disease that disrupts the body's ability to process sugars.

differentiation. The process by which stem cells produce differentiated, or specialized, cells.

diffuse *(verb)*, **diffusion** *(noun)*. To move, or the movement of, substances down a concentration gradient from higher to lower concentration.

dihybrid cross. A cross between two first-generation individuals where two traits of interest are studied.

diploid. Somatic (nonreproductive) cell, which has pairs of chromosomes. Also called **2n.**

disease. Any breakdown in the structure or function of an organism. See also **infectious disease, noninfectious disease.**

disease intervention. Any method used to prevent, treat, or eradicate a disease.

disturbance. An abrupt event in an ecosystem that suddenly and significantly changes the resources available, the number or type of organisms, or the kinds of species present. See also **ecological succession.**

diversification *(noun)*, **diversify** *(verb)*. An increase in the number of species in a clade due to evolution; to evolve into a number of diverse species.

DNA. Same as **deoxyribonucleic acid.**

DNA construct. A piece of DNA made of three specific parts: a start region, the desired gene, and a selectable marker.

dominant. A trait that masks another version of the trait. See also **trait.**

double helix. The shape formed by two intertwined spirals. Each helix has a regularly curved shape like that of a coiled spring or the handrail of a spiral staircase. Used to describe the physical shape of a DNA molecule.

ecological footprint. A quantitative measurement that estimates the amount of resource consumption and waste production of an individual, community, population, or manufactured product. It is expressed in terms of land and sea area (acres or hectares) needed to sustain the resource consumption and absorb the wastes produced. See also **carbon footprint.**

ecological succession. The natural process in which a disturbed area is gradually taken over by a species or groups of species that were not there before. See also **disturbance.**

ecology. The study of how living organisms interact with each other and with their physical environment.

ecosystem diversity. Variation in biodiversity within and between ecosystems on earth.

ecosystem services. The benefits that humans and non-human species receive from ecosystems, such as food and water, materials for shelter and energy, and employment related to natural resources.

ecosystem. A community of various organisms interacting with each other within a particular physical environment.

electron transport chain. The final series of reactions in aerobic cellular respiration, which take place on the cristae of mitochondria.

embryonic stem cell. Stem cells from an embryo capable of differentiating into all or most specialized cell types. See also **stem cell.**

endemic. In terms of species, restricted to only one region or area.

endocytosis. The process by which a cell membrane engulfs particles or molecules outside the cell and pinches around it to form a vesicle that carries the material into the cell.

endoplasmic reticulum (ER). A system of sac-like compartments surrounded by a single membrane that produces lipids and some proteins in eukaryotic cells.

energy pyramid. A diagram that shows how much energy is available for each level of organism, such as producers and consumers. See also **food web.**

enzyme. A protein that catalyzes (speeds up) a specific chemical reaction within an organism; important for many biological processes including photosynthesis, cellular respiration, DNA replication, and protein synthesis. See also **protein.**

eukaryote (*noun*), **eukaryotic** (*adj.*). Organisms, or pertaining to organisms, that have cells that contain a nucleus.

eukaryotic cell. A cell that contains a membrane-bound nucleus, which is the location of the genetic material.

eutrophication. A dramatic increase in nutrients in an aquatic environment, resulting in increased plant growth, especially of algae. See also **dead zone.**

evidence. Information that refutes or supports a claim or hypothesis; information that leads to the development of a claim or hypothesis.

evolution (*noun*), **evolve** (*verb*). A process in which something changes gradually or by intervals over time. In biology, changes in the genetic composition of a population that eventually give rise to other diverse life forms.

evolutionary tree. A branched diagram for classifying taxa that represents a hypothesis about the history of descent of groups of taxa.

exocytosis. The process by which a vesicle transports particles or molecules from within the cell to the cell membrane, where it fuses with the membrane and deposits its contents outside the cell.

expressed (gene). A gene that is active in producing its RNA or protein product.

extinct (*adj.*), **extinction** (*noun*). Pertaining to the death of the last existing member of a species; the process leading to the death of the last existing member of a species.

facilitated diffusion. Movement of a substance from higher to lower concentration through a protein channel, without the need for input of energy.

fishery. An industry that catches or raises a specific type of fish or shellfish to be processed or sold.

fishery management. The development and application of rules and procedures, ideally based on scientific evidence, to maintain the sustainability of a fishery. See also **fishery.**

fit (*adj.*), **fitness** (*noun*). Pertaining to an organism that is likely to reach reproductive age and to reproduce offspring; the probability of an organism surviving to reproductive age and producing offspring.

flagella (*plural*), **flagellum.** Long tail-like structures, or structure, with which many cells move.

fluid mosaic model. A model of biological membrane structure and function that describes the ability of embedded proteins (the mosaic) to move laterally within the membrane bilayer.

food web. A diagram of the relationships between interacting food chains within an ecosystem, showing how each organism derives energy required for survival. See also **consumer, decomposer, producer, energy pyramid.**

fossil. The physical evidence left behind from a living organism after it dies that is preserved in the rock layers of the earth.

fossil record. The collection of all of the fossils within the earth's strata that have existed in the 4.5 billion years of earth's history, including those that have been discovered and those that have not.

gamete. A sexual reproductive cell, such as a sperm or an egg, that contains half of the normal number of chromosomes in the genetic material of the organism.

gel electrophoresis. A laboratory technique by which electricity is applied to a gel to move and separate molecules based on size and/or charge, often used to identify DNA samples.

gene. A segment of an organism's genetic material (DNA) that produces a specific RNA or protein product.

gene expression. The activity of genes in a cell.

gene flow. The movement of genes from one population to another.

gene pool. All of the genes of a given population.

genetic diversity. The variation in the genes within a population of organisms.

genetic drift. Unpredictable changes in the proportion of genes in a population.

genetic engineering. Genetic manipulation in which a gene from one species is inserted into another species in order to give the target organism and its offspring a new trait that improves it in some way. Same as **genetic modification.**

genetic modification. Same as **genetic engineering.**

genetically modified organism (GMOs). An organism whose genes have been directly manipulated by scientists, often by inserting or deleting one or more genes. Inserted genes are typically from another species. See also **genetic engineering.**

genome. The complete sequence of an organism's genetic material (DNA).

genomics. The study of the genomes of organisms. See also **genome.**

genotype. The genetic makeup of an organism, composed of pairs of alleles with one from each parent for each gene. See also **allele.**

geographic isolation. The separation of two populations by physical changes on the earth, such as the formation of mountains, canyons, or rivers.

geologic time. Same as **deep time.**

geologic timeline. All of the periods of the earth's history.

glycolysis. The series of reactions in cellular respiration that break glucose into two molecules of pyruvic acid and release ATP.

GMOs. Same as **genetically modified organism.**

Golgi apparatus. In eukaryotic cells, a compartment that looks like a stack of flattened balloons surrounded by a single membrane that modifies and sorts the lipids and proteins produced in the endoplasmic reticulum.

habitat. The specific environment that an organism lives in based on what the organism requires to survive.

haploid. A gamete, which contains one set of chromosomes. Also called **n**. See also **diploid.**

heredity. The passing of genetic traits from one generation to the next.

heterozygous. A genotype with two different alleles, such as Ss. The prefix hetero- means different. See also **homozygous.**

HIV/AIDS. Human immunodeficiency virus causing an infectious, sexually transmitted disease that reduces the function of the immune system. Also called AIDS (acquired immune deficiency syndrome) virus. See also **virus.**

homeostasis. Stable internal conditions within a cell or organism.

hominid. The taxonomic family made up of humans and the African apes (gorillas, chimpanzees, bonobos).

hominin. A taxonomic group made up of humans, both living and extinct.

homologous character. A character that is shared between species and is present in their common ancestor, such as bird wings and bat forelimbs. See also **homology, shared derived character.**

homology. A similarity between characteristics of two or more species that is also present in their common ancestor. See also **homologous character, shared derived character.**

homozygous. A genotype with two identical alleles, such as SS or ss. The prefix homo- means same. See also **heterozygous.**

hotspot. An area that has a high number of endemic species and an extraordinary loss of habitat.

hydrogen bond. A force of attraction between a hydrogen atom and an oxygen, nitrogen, or other atom in another molecule or part of the same molecule; typically considered a weak chemical bond. Hydrogen bonds are important in the three-dimensional structure of proteins and nucleic acids.

hypothesis. A tentative theory explaining a set of facts. A hypothesis may lead to further investigation to test whether the hypothesis is valid.

incomplete dominance. When neither of two traits is dominant and a combination of the two traits produces a third trait that is blended or intermediate between the two.

indicator. An observation or calculation that shows the presence or state of a condition or trend.

infectious disease. A disease caused by a microbe, such as a bacteria or virus, and transmitted from one individual to another, either directly or by a disease vector. See also **disease, virus.**

intervention. An action taken to interfere with or prevent a problem. See also **disease intervention.**

invasive species. A nonnative species that enters a new area, causing harm to the native species and environment, the economy, or human health. See also **nonnative species.**

isolation. The separation of one chemical or group of chemicals from others in a mixture, such as the separation of DNA from a cellular extract.

karyotype. An image of the chromosomal makeup of an individual, produced by staining the chromosomes from one cell of an organism, photographing them, and arranging them in pairs. Geneticists use karyotypes to test for chromosome abnormalities in humans.

Krebs cycle. A series of reactions that are part of aerobic cellular respiration and take part within the matrix of the mitochondria.

lactase. An enzyme that catalyzes the breakdown of lactose.

lactose. A sugar found in milk that can be broken down to glucose and galactose.

land degradation. A decline of the overall quality of soil, water, or vegetation in an area, caused by human activities or natural events.

latent. In the case of an infectious disease, such as tuberculosis, not clinically active; without symptoms.

law of independent assortment. Proposed by Gregor Mendel, states that it is equally likely for a heterozygous dihybrid organism to produce any of four kinds of gametes. For example a parent cell with genotype P̲pS̲s could produce the gametes P̲S̲, P̲s, pS̲, and ps.

light-dependent reactions. The series of reactions in photosynthesis that rely on chlorophyll and other pigments in the thylakoid membranes to harness the energy of light. In this complex series of reactions, water breaks down into oxygen, hydrogen ions (protons), and electrons.

light-independent reactions. The series of reactions in photosynthesis that takes place in both the presence and absence of light. See also **Calvin cycle.**

limiting factor. A component in a system that prevents further change in a particular variable.

lineage. A series of populations of a single species or several species descended from a common ancestor.

lipid. A group of organic compounds in cells that do not dissolve in water; includes fats, waxes, and phospholipids.

lipid bilayer. The double layer of lipids (phospholipids) in cell or organelle membranes. See also **lipid.**

lysosome. A bubble-like compartment surrounded by a single membrane that breaks down and recycles materials in animal cells and protists.

macroevolution. Evolution shaped by speciation and extinction leading to large-scale patterns of biodiversity on earth.

macromolecule. A large biological molecule—such as a protein, nucleic acid, or carbohydrate—made of one or more chains of smaller subunits linked together.

macrophage. A large white blood cell that is able to engulf microbes and other foreign material or wastes.

malaria. An infectious disease spread by mosquito vectors and caused by *Plasmodium,* a protist.

marine reserve. A protected area of ocean in which activities that upset the natural ecological functions of the area are prohibited.

mass extinction. The deaths of many major taxa in a relatively short period of time.

matrix. The fluid-filled space within the inner membrane of a mitochondrion.

meiosis. The process of cell division that produces sex cells (gametes), resulting in halving the number of chromosomes. See also **gametes, mitosis.**

membrane. A flexible layer of material that serves as a barrier between two compartments. In biology, any single or double phospholipid bilayer that bounds a cell or cellular organelle. See also **cell membrane.**

messenger ribonucleic acid (mRNA). A messenger molecule that during protein synthesis transmits the information in an organism's DNA to the ribosomes, where the messenger serves as a template for the synthesis of proteins.

metabolism. All of the chemical processes that maintain life and that occur within living organisms. Metabolism includes reactions involved in the breakdown and synthesis of cellular molecules, such as those that provide cells with energy.

microbe. A virus or microscopic cellular organism, such as a bacterium, or protist.

microevolution. Small-scale evolutionary changes, such as changes in gene frequencies, that lead to speciation and larger changes of macroevolution.

mitochondria *(plural)*, **mitochondrion.** Double-membrane-bound organelle that is the site of aerobic cellular respiration.

mitosis. The series of events in which the duplicated chromosomes of a parent cell are separated into two identical sets, resulting in two genetically identical daughter cells after the completion of cell division. See also **daughter cells, meiosis.**

motor protein. A type of protein involved in movement of and within cells. See also **protein.**

mRNA. Same as **messenger ribonucleic acid.**

multicellular organism. Organism made of more than one cell. Multicellular organisms range from organisms with a small number of cells to mammals with trillions of cells.

multipotent. A stem cell capable of differentiating into several kinds of specialized cells.

mutation. A change in the sequence of nucleotides in a strand of DNA.

mutualism. A symbiotic relationship in which both species benefit. See also **symbiotic relationship.**

natural selection. The main mechanism for evolutionary change by which heritable traits that increase the probability for an organism to survive and reproduce become more common in a population over many generations.

nitrate (and nitrite). A nitrogen-containing nutrient critical to the continuation of life on earth, but harmful at abnormal levels. See also **eutrophication.**

node. A point on an evolutionary tree where a single lineage splits into two or more lineages that represent the characteristics of a common ancestor.

nondisjunction. The failure of chromosomes to separate during cell division.

noninfectious disease. Diseases that are not transmitted from one person to another, and are caused by such factors as the environment, genetics, and aging. See also **disease.**

nonnative species. A species considered to be not naturally found in an environment. See also **invasive species.**

nucleotide. A repeating subunit that makes up DNA, made of a sugar, a phosphate group, and a nitrogen-containing base.

nucleus. The membrane-bound structure in eukaryotic cells that contains the genetic material, packaged in chromosomes.

organelle. A membrane-bound structure within a cell. Examples include mitochondria, chloroplasts, endoplasmic reticulum, and Golgi apparatus.

organism. An individual biological entity that performs basic life functions, such as growing, metabolizing, and reproducing.

osmosis. The diffusion of a fluid, such as water, across a membrane to equalize the concentrations of solutions on either side of the membrane.

parasitism. A symbiotic relationship in which one species benefits, while the other species is harmed, but not killed. See also **symbiotic relationship.**

parent cell. A somatic cell that reproduces to form daughter cells. See also **daughter cells.**

parts per million (ppm). The number of parts of a specific substance per million parts of the total mixture or solution in which it is contained.

passive transport. Same as **facilitated diffusion.**

pedigree. A diagram similar to a family tree that shows generations and relationships among biological parents and offspring. It also tracks which of those individuals have a specific trait.

pH. A measurement of the acidity of a solution.

phenotype. An organism's physical characteristics, which result from the organism's genes and their interaction with the environment. See also **genotype.**

phosphate. A phosphorous-containing nutrient essential to the growth of organisms and for animal metabolism. Many phosphate compounds are not very soluble in water, but some are released into solution. Phosphate runoff from animal waste and wastewater can deposit high levels of phosphate into rivers, lakes, and marine coastline waters. See also **eutrophication.**

phospholipid. Lipid with a phosphate head attached to two long lipid tails.

phospholipid (lipid) bilayer. The double layer of phospholipid molecules that makes up the membranes of a cell. See also **phospholipid**.

photosynthesis. The process by which the cells of producers, such as plants and phytoplankton, capture the sun's energy and store it in sugars, releasing oxygen as a by-product.

phylogenetic diversity. A measure of biodiversity using the pattern of the relationships of lineages to one another over time.

phylogeny. The history of the descent of taxa from their common ancestors.

phytoplankton. Plankton capable of photosynthesis. See also **plankton.**

pigment. A molecule that absorbs specific wavelengths of light energy, and is responsible for the colors of biological materials, such as the leaves of plants.

plankton. Any drifting aquatic organism that lives, at least during the planktonic stage of its life, in open waters of the ocean or other body of water. See also **phytoplankton, zooplankton.**

pluripotent. A stem cell capable of differentiating into most types of specialized cells.

population. A group of individuals of the same species that live in the same general area and are able to reproduce.

population growth rate. The rate of change in a population over specified intervals of time. See also **population.**

primary succession. Ecological succession that starts in an area where there are essentially no living organisms. See also **ecological succession.**

producers. Organisms able to produce their own food, often through photosynthesis. See also **photosynthesis.**

product life cycle. The amounts of resources and energy it takes to make a product, the duration of the product's usefulness to the consumer, and how the product is disposed of, recycled, or reclaimed when it is no longer needed.

prokaryote *(noun)*, **prokaryotic** *(adj.)*. An organism, or pertaining to an organism, that does not have a nucleus. The DNA of prokaryotes is located in the cytoplasm of the cell.

protein. A macromolecule made of one or more chains of amino acids folded together into a complex three-dimensional structure.

protein synthesis. The process by which all cells use their genetic code to produce proteins. It involves two phases: transcription and translation.

protist. A single-celled microscopic organism that has a nucleus. Examples include amoebas and *Plasmodium.*

Punnett square. A diagram that shows and helps predict the possible genotypes of offspring from two individuals that reproduce sexually.

radiometric dating. A method by which scientists measure the percentage of radioactive atoms of certain elements in fossils and rock layers to estimate how many years ago the rock layers and fossils formed.

receptor. Same as **receptor protein.**

receptor protein. A protein that mediates a cell's response to a stimulus, which is often provided by a signaling protein. See also **protein.**

recessive. A trait that will be hidden by a dominant trait in an individual that is heterozygous for that trait. See also **dominant, heterozygous.**

replication. The process by which DNA is copied within each cell.

repressed (gene). Genes that are turned off, but still present, in a cell. See also **expressed (gene).**

reproductive isolation. Any barrier that prevents two populations from reproducing successfully, thus preventing them from sharing a common gene pool and possibly leading to the evolution of the populations into separate species.

resilience. The ability of an ecosystem to recover after a major disturbance. The level of resilience depends on the state of the area prior to the disturbance. See also **disturbance.**

resistance. The ability of an ecosystem to resist an external influence, such as a disturbance. See also **disturbance.**

ribonucleic acid (RNA). A macromolecule composed of nitrogenous bases, sugar, and phosphate subunits, similar to DNA except formed of a single strand with the base uracil instead of thymine and sugar ribose instead of deoxyribose.

ribosome. A structure made of proteins and RNA that assembles proteins in eukaryotic and prokaryotic cells.

RNA. Same as **ribonucleic acid.**

rotavirus. An infectious disease causing severe diarrhea, found in infants worldwide and caused by a virus. See also **disease, virus.**

secondary succession. Ecological succession that occurs in an area where there is some component of the ecosystem, including soil, remaining after a disturbance. See also **disturbance, ecological succession.**

selective breeding. The process by which people mate organisms with desirable traits with the goal of producing even more desirable offspring.

selectively permeable. Allowing only certain substances (molecules and ions) to pass through, while blocking passage of other substances.

semipermeable. Same as **selectively permeable.**

sex-linked. An allele for a trait that is carried on one of the sex chromosomes.

sex-linked recessive. A sex-linked trait that is recessive.

sexual reproduction. Reproduction in which two parents contribute genetic material to the offspring. See also **asexual reproduction.**

sexual selection. Differential reproduction resulting from variation in the ability to obtain mates.

shared derived characters. Homologies shared by all populations of a single species or a group of species descended from a common ancestor. See also **homologous character, homology.**

sickle cell. A disease resulting from an inherited mutation that changes the hemoglobin protein, causing the proteins to stack on one another within the red blood cells, and producing sickle- or banana-shaped cells.

signaling protein. A protein that carries a signal from one cell to another, where it usually interacts with a receptor protein on the target cell's membrane. See also **protein.**

single-celled organism. Organisms made of a single cell, including archaebacteria, eubacteria, and many protists.

somatic cell. Body cells, but not reproductive cells.

speciation. The splitting of one lineage into two or more lineages as a result of barriers to gene flow that split the gene pool, followed by an accumulation of differences between the gene pools.

species. The basic unit of taxonomic classification. See also **biological species.**

species diversity. The number of species that exist in an area.

stakeholder. Individuals or groups who are affected by or involved in a decision.

stem cells. Undifferentiated cells that have the ability to produce a variety of types of specialized cells

strata. Layers of lava and compressed sediment.

stratigraphic dating. Provides the relative ages of rock layers and the fossils within them by interpreting the order of rock layers in light of geological evidence, such as the movement of the earth's surface from an earthquake.

stratigraphy. The study of rock layers.

stroma. Fluid-filled space within the inner membrane of a chloroplast that is the site of some of the reactions of photosynthesis.

sugar–phosphate backbone. The structure that forms the longitudinal support of a strand of DNA, composed of repeating bonded sugar and phosphate molecules.

sustainability. The ability to meet a community's present needs without compromising the ability of future generations to meet their own needs.

sustainable. See **sustainability.**

symbiosis. The close ecological relationships between organisms. See also **amensalism, commensalism, mutualism, parasitism.**

taxa *(plural),* **taxon.** Level of classification, such as genus or species.

terrestrial tetrapods. Four-limbed mammals, reptiles, amphibians, and birds that live on land.

theory. A well established and highly reliable explanation of a natural or physical phenomenon.

thylakoids. The stacks of connected inner membrane sacs within a chloroplast that contain chlorophyll.

totipotent. A stem cell capable of differentiating into all types of specialized cells.

trade-off. An exchange of one thing for another; giving up something that is a benefit or advantage, in exchange for some other benefit or advantage. Trade-offs usually involve balancing benefits and risks.

Tragedy of the Commons. A theory stating that the more people there are who have unrestricted access to a common resource, the more they will exploit it, without considering the consequences.

trait. A characteristic or condition determined by an organism's genes and their interaction with the environment.

transcription. The first phase of protein synthesis during which the information contained in DNA is converted into a messenger molecule (messenger ribonucleic acid, or mRNA) via a template mechanism. See also **mRNA** and **protein synthesis.**

transcription factor. A molecule that controls the transcription of DNA into RNA by activating or repressing transcription. See also **protein synthesis.**

transfer RNA (tRNA). The molecules that read the code in mRNA and add amino acids in the appropriate sequence to form a protein.

transitional features. Features of organisms that are not necessarily direct ancestors but have branched from the same line of descent leading to a specific taxon.

transitional fossils. Fossils that show an intermediate state for certain characters between an ancestor and its descendants.

translation. The second phase of protein synthesis during which the code in the mRNA is translated into the amino acid sequence of a protein. This happens on ribosomes in the cytoplasm of a cell. See also **mRNA, protein synthesis.**

transport protein. A protein that carries molecules and ions into a cell or throughout the body. See also **protein.**

tRNA. Same as **transfer RNA.**

tuberculosis. An infectious disease, caused by a bacterium, that mainly affects the lungs, but can affect other parts of the body. See also **bacteria, disease.**

vaccine. A substance that stimulates an organism's immune system to provide immunity to a specific disease.

vacuole. A storage compartment in eukaryotic cells that is surrounded by a single membrane and that helps maintain homeostasis.

variable. An element of an experiment or investigation that can be changed independently of all other elements.

vector. An organism that does not cause a disease itself, but spreads disease-causing microbes from one host to another. For example, rodent fleas are vectors for bubonic plague, and female Anopheles mosquitoes are vectors for malaria.

vesicle. A bubble-like cell compartment surrounded by a single membrane that carries materials to different places in eukaryotic cells.

virus. A microbe that must invade another cell in order to reproduce, composed of genetic material and a few proteins surrounded by a protein coat, and sometimes a lipid membrane.

zooplankton. Plankton that derive energy from the food that they eat, often other plankton. See also **plankton.**

Index

NOTE: *Italic* locators indicate pictures or illustrations; **bold** locators indicate definitions or first significant mention of the topic.

2n chromosomes, 574. *See also* diploid.

A

abiotic (nonliving). *See also* biotic (living).
    definition, **571**
    environmental factors, **62**
Acanthaster planci (crown of thorns), 53
Acanthostega, 450–451
acetyl CoA (coenzyme A), 225
active transport, **209**, *209*, **571**
active tuberculosis, 178
adaptation
    adaptive character, **492**
    co-opted features, 492
    definition, **571**
    examples of, 493
    genetic basis of, **484**–488
    honeybees, 493, *493*
    insect-pollinated orchids, 493, *493*
    rock pocket mouse, **484**–488
    scientific meaning of, 492
    venomous snakes, 493, *493*
adaptive character, **492**
adaptive radiation
    in biodiversity, **482**–483
    definition, **571**
    Hawaiian honeycreeper, *482*
    in speciation, 494–495
adenine, **329**, 331
adenosine triphosphate (ATP). *See* ATP (adenosine triphosphate).
Aequorea victoria jelly, genetically modifying, *269*–270
aerobic respiration
    in cells, **224**–225, *225*
    definition, **571**
AIDS. *See* HIV/AIDS.
algae
    in coral reefs, 52
    microscopic view of, *173*
    symbiosis with crabs, *116*
algal blooms, 423, *423*
alleles. *See also* genes; genotypes.
    definition, **571**
    different alleles. *See* heterozygous alleles.
    heterozygous, **295**
    homozygous, **295**
    human blood types, 297–298
    identical alleles. *See* homozygous alleles.
    purpose of, 286
alternative energy, implications of genomics, 340
amensalism, **571**. *See also* commensalism; mutualism; parasitism; symbiosis; symbiotic organisms.
amino acids. *See also* proteins.
    definition, **571**
    in mutations, 368–371
anaerobic respiration
    in cells, **225**–226
    definition, **571**
anchovy kilka (*Clupeonella engrauliformis*), 132
animal cells *vs.* plant, *221*
Anopheles mosquito, 168
antibiotics
    classes of, 182
    definition, **571**
    Penicillium mold, *182*
aquaculture. *See also* overfishing.
    along salmon migration routes, *125*
    definition, **571**
    net pens, 124, *124*, *125*, 144
    open-ocean, Hawaii, 143–144
    ponds, 124

raceways, 124

response to overfishing, **123**–128

systems for, 124, *124*, *125*

yellowtail farms, Hawaii, 143–144

"Ardi" skeleton, 464

arrow cichlid fish, species separation, 478, *478*

asexual reproduction. *See also* sexual reproduction.

definition, **571**

mitosis, *278*, **278**–281

Atlantic cod (*Gadus morhua*), 131

Atlantic salmon (*Salmo salar*), 350–351

ATP (adenosine triphosphate)

anaerobic respiration, 225–226

in the Calvin cycle, 223

definition, **571**

electronic transport chain, 225

glycolysis, 224

Krebs cycle, 225

light-dependent reactions, 222

light-independent reactions, 223

role of, 220

Australia

cane toad invasion, 50–51

coral reef bleaching, 52–53, *53*

freshwater crocodile, 51, *51*

Great Barrier Reef, 53

northern quoll, 51

B

Bacillus thuringiensis (Bt), 264–265

bacteria. *See also E. coli* bacteria; tuberculosis.

cell structure, 181, *181*

definition, **571**

genetically modified, 269–270

prokaryotes, **188**

Balaenoptera musculus (blue whale), 85, *85*

base pairs. *See also* DNA; hydrogen bonds; nucleotides.

definition, **571**

in DNA structure, **330**, *330*

bats, effects of human activities, *429*, 429–430

beans, cellular respiration, 103–106

Beddington Zero Fossil Energy Development. *See* BedZED.

BedZED, 14–18

binding sites

definition, **571**

in enzymes, 216

biodiversity. *See also* ecosystems.

across biomes, 68

by breeding. *See* breeding, effects on biodiversity.

definition, **571**

endemic species, **416**

genetic diversity, **422**

hotspots. *See* hotspots.

levels of, 422

by natural selection. *See* evolution; natural selection.

species diversity, **422**

sustainability, 415–421

taxa, **422**

taxon, **422**

biodiversity, effects of human activities

bats, *429*, 429–430

breeding, 423, *423*, 428–429, *428–429*. *See also* GMOs.

cichlids in Lake Victoria, *425*, 425–426

cloning, 423, *423*. *See also* GMOs.

disruption of networks, 423, *423*

dodo bird, 426, *426*

dogs, 428–429, *428–429*

Florida panther, 427, *427*

flying fox bats, *429*, 429–430

gray wolves, *428*, 428–429, *428–429*

habitat destruction, 422, *422*, 424, *424*

introduced species, 422, *422*, 425, 425–426

Lake Victoria, *425*, 425–426

Nile perch, *425*, 425–426

northern elephant seals, 430–431

overexploitation, 422, *422*, 426–427, 429–430, 430–431

potato blight (Ireland), 424–425, *425*

rainforests of Borneo, 424, *424*

biofarming, 393–399

biofuel

BedZED, 17

definition, **571**

from GMOs, **274**–276

biogeographical areas of the world, 441

biological adaptation. *See* adaptation.

biological diversity. *See* biodiversity.

biological evolution, **436**, **571**. *See also* evolution.

biological species. *See also* species; species diversity.

    classifying. *See* biological species concept.

    definition, **571**

biological species concept. *See also* species separation.

    basis for, **472**

    biological species, classifying, **473**

    definition, **572**

    formation of new species, 480–481. *See also*
        speciation.

    gene flow, **473**, 480

    gene pool, **473**, 480

    overview, 473

biomes

    abiotic (nonliving) factors, **62**

    biodiversity, 68

    biotic (living) factors, **62**

    chaparral, 65, *65*

    definition, **572**

    desert, 64, *64*

    savanna, 65, *65*

    taiga, 66, *66*

    temperate deciduous forests, 67, *67*

    temperate grassland, 66, *66*

    tropical rain forest, 64, *64*

    tundra, 67, *67*

biosphere, levels of organization, *186*

biotic (living). *See also* abiotic (nonliving).

    definition, **572**

    environmental factors, **62**

blastocysts, 241, *241*

blindness

    diabetes, 196–197

    LCA (Leber's congenital amaurosis), 372

    Vitamin A deficiency, 304–305

blood

    human types, selective breeding, 296–299

    studying under a microscope, 162–165

blue cichlid fish, species separation, 478, *478*

blue crab (*Callinectes sapidus*), 48–49, *48–49*

blue whale (*Balaenoptera musculus*), 85, *85*

bone marrow cells, *240*

bone marrow transplants, 242

Borneo, destruction of rainforests, 424, *424*

branches of evolutionary trees, 459

breathing *vs.* cellular respiration, 223

breeding, effects on biodiversity. *See also* evolution;
    natural selection.

    dogs, 428–429, *428–429*

    gray wolves, 428–429, *428–429*

    overview, 423, *423*

    pigeons, 440, *440*

brown tree snake, *70*

Bt (*Bacillus thuringiensis*), 264–265

BTB (bromothymol blue), 107–110

Bufo marinus (cane toads), *50*, 50–51

Burgess Shale, *432*, *446*

C

California sheephead, managing, 94–95

California spotted owls, species separation, 476, *476*

Callinectes sapidus (blue crab), 48–49, *48–49*

Calvin cycle. *See also* light-independent reactions.

    ATP, 223

    definition, **572**

    in photosynthesis, **222**

cancer

    burden of disease, 233

    causes, 233–234

    cervical, 233–234

    chemotherapy, 234

    death rate, by income level, *233*

    definition, **572**

    dietary factors, 234

    disease mechanism, 233–234

    environmental factors, 234

    HPV, 233–234

    occupational hazards, 235

    prevention, 234–235

    radiation therapy, 234

    screening for, 234, 235

    skin lesion, *233*

    smoking risk, 234

    surgical treatment, 234

    survival rates, 235

    symptoms, 233–234

    tobacco risk, 234

    treatment, 234–235

cane toads (*Bufo marinus*), *50*, 50–51

Canis lupus (wolves), biodiversity
    breeding, effects of, 428–429
      human activities, effects of, *428*, 428–429, *428–429*
      species separation from dogs, 477, *477*

Canis lupus familiaris (dogs), biodiversity
    effects of human activities, 428–429, *428–429*
    species separation from wolves, 477, *477*

carbon-14 dating, 448–449

carbon cycle. *See also* carbon reservoir.
    cellular respiration, **100**–102
    definition, **572**
    diagram of, *98–99*
    effects of human activity, 96–99
    photosynthesis, **100**–102

carbon dioxide emissions, case study, 17

carbon footprints, **572**. *See also* ecological footprints.

carbon reservoir, **572**. *See also* carbon cycle.

carriers (of disease traits), **572**

carrying capacity
    definition, **572**
    populations, **119**–122
    zebra mussels, *119*

cat (domestic), phylogenetic profile, *454*

catalyze, **572**

catalyzing chemical reactions with enzymes, **216**–218

causal relationships
    definition, **572**
    Jaffrey Lake case study, **30**

cell biology, **186**, **572**. *See also* cell structure.

cell cycle. *See also* mitosis.
    cell division, 229–232
    definition, **572**
    phases, **229**, *229*

cell differentiation. *See* differentiation.

cell division, 229–232

cell membrane structure
    fluid mosaic model, *207*, **207**–208
    macromolecules, 206
    phospholipid (lipid) bilayer, **207**, *207*
    phospholipids, **207**, *207*

cell membranes. *See also* membranes.
    definition, **572**
    function of, **188**

microscopic view, *188*
    movement of molecules, 200–202
    structure of, *191*, 191–195, *194*

cell membranes, permeability. *See also* osmosis.
    active transport, **209**, *209*
    diffusion, *198*, **198**–202
    endocytosis, **210**, *210*
    exocytosis, **210**, *210*
    facilitated diffusion, **209**
    inward, 210
    outward, 210
    passive transport, **209**
    selectively permeable, **208**
    semipermeable, **208**
    transport by vesicles, **210**, *210*
    to viruses, **211**

cell principle
    definition, **572**
    discovery of, **187**

cell structure
    bacterial cells, 181, *181*
    building blocks for, 206
    cilia, 181, *181*
    cytoplasm, **188**, *188*
    cytoskeleton, **189**
    DNA, 188
    flagella, 181, *181*
    macromolecules, 206
    membranes, 180, **188**, *188*
    nucleus, 188, **188**. *See also* eukaryotes; protists.
    organelles, 180
    ribosomes, 181, *181*
    specialization, 184–185
    walls, **572**

cell structure, functions of
    cell shape, 189
    containing genetic information, 188
    homeostasis, 189
    internal balance. *See* homeostasis.
    in multicellular organisms, 189–190

cell walls, **572**

cells. *See also* stem cells.
    bacteria, **188**
    definition, **572**

eukaryotes, **188**

genetic information. *See* cytoplasm; DNA.

metabolism, **189**

multicellular organisms, **171**

non-reproductive, 355

paramecium, *171*

plant *vs.* animal, *221*

plants, microscopic view of, *174*

prokaryotes, **188**

protein functions, **213**–215

proteins. *See* proteins.

protists, **188**

shape. *See* cytoskeleton.

somatic, 355

in the study of diseases, **161**–166

cells, under a microscope

algae, *173*

cell membrane, *188*

cork cells, 187, *187*

cytoplasm, *188*

microscope drawings, 173, *173*, *187*

paramecium, *171*

plant cells, *174*

preparing a slide, 174

prokaryotic cells, *188*

cellular respiration. *See also* photosynthesis.

aerobic respiration, **224**–225

breaking of sugar. *See* glycolysis.

in the carbon cycle, **100**–102

cristae, role of, **224**

definition, **572**

glycolysis, **224**–227

matrix, role of, **224**

mitochondria, role of, **224**

in plants, 107–110

vs. breathing, 223

cellular respiration, ATP

anaerobic respiration, 225–226

in the Calvin cycle, 223

electronic transport chain, 225

glycolysis, 224

Krebs cycle, 225

light-dependent reactions, 222

light-independent reactions, 223

role of, 220

cellular respiration rate

factors affecting, 103–106

oxygen levels in aquatic ecosystems, 111–115

centrioles, **572**. *See also* mitosis.

centromeres, *328*, **572**. *See also* chromatids; chromosomes; DNA (deoxyribonucleic acid).

cervical cancer, 233–234

Chaetodipus intermedius (rock pocket mouse), **484**–488

chaparral, 65, *65*

characters

definition, **572**

homologous, **454**, **576**

phylogenetic, **454**–455

shared derived, **455**, **581**

Chargaff, Erwin, 331

chemical indicators, **573**. *See also* indicators.

chemotherapy, 234

Chesapeake Bay

blue crab population, 48–49

dead zones, **112**–113

eutrophication, **112**–113

phytoplankton, 112–113

water pollution, 48–49, 112–113

Chesapeake Bay shoreline, 48–49

chloroplasts

definition, **573**

in photosynthesis, **221**, *221*, *223*

chromatids, *328*, **573**. *See also* centromeres; chromosomes.

chromosomes. *See also* centromeres; chromatids; genes.

abnormal meiosis, 358–359

definition, **573**

disorders related to, 359

in eukaryotes, 354

human variation, 356–358

independent segregation, 356

karyotypes, 354, *354*

law of independent assortment, 356

linked genes, 356

modeling, *328*

normal meiosis, 354–358, *357*

number per cell, 354

sex-linked traits, **317**, *317*

chromosomes, human
    male *vs.* female, 317, *317*, 354, *354*
    X *vs.* Y, 317, *317*, 354, *354*
cichlids
    arrow, 478, *478*
    blue, 478, *478*
    effects of human activities, *425*, 425–426
    Midas, 478, *478*
    red, 478, *478*
    species separation, 478, *478*
cilia, 181, *181*, **573**
cilium, **573**
clades, **458**, **573**
classifying
    biological species, **473**. *See also* biological species
      concept.
    species. *See* biological species concept;
      phylogenetics.
    taxa. *See* phylogenetics.
cleaner shrimp, symbiosis with moray eels, *117*
climate change, effects on malaria, 170, *170*
cloning, effects on biodiversity, 423, *423*
cloud forest ecosystems, 417
Clupeonella engrauliformis (anchovy kilka), 132
co-opted features
    adaptation, 492
    definition, **573**
    in the origin of tetrapods, **450**
codominance, in selective breeding, **296**
codominant traits, **573**. *See also* heterozygous.
coenzyme A (acetyl CoA), 225
comb jelly (*Mnemiopsis leidyi*), 132
commensalism, **573**. *See also* symbiosis; symbiotic
  organisms.
commons. *See* Tragedy of the Commons.
communities
    definition, **573**
    of multiple populations, **58**
comparative genomics, 341
conservative DNA replication, 344, *344*
consumers. *See also* energy pyramid; food webs.
    definition, **573**
    plankton, 85
control, **573**
Cope, Edward, 449

copper-resistant yellow monkey flower, species
  separation, 479, *479*
copper-tolerant yellow monkey flower, species
  separation, 479, *479*
copying DNA, 337. *See also* replication of DNA.
coral polyps, 52
coral reefs
    bleaching, 52–53
    crown of thorns, *53*
    ecosystems, 418
    global distribution, *52*
    Great Barrier Reef, Australia, 53
    Palau, South Pacific, 53
    polyps, 52
cork cells, microscopic view, 187, *187*
corn
    mapping the corn genome, 314
    predicting offspring, 285
    Punnett squares, **285**
    sexual reproduction, **282**
    U.S. crop, usage distribution, *311*
corn, genetically modified
    DNA fingerprinting, 385–387
    history of, 264–265
    identifying, 385–387
    illustration, *262*
    tracking origins of, 385–387
corn, selective breeding
    dihybrid cross, *300*, **300**–303
    growth in yield over time, *313*
    history of, 311–314
    for single traits, **282**, *283–284*
    for two traits, *300*, 300–303
    vs. teosinte (native Mexican corn), *311*,
      311–312, *312*
correlation
    definition, **573**
    Jaffrey Lake case study, **30**
countries, comparative sustainability, 8–13. *See also*
  geographic regions of the world.
crab jubilee, 48–49
crabs
    blue, 48–49, *48–49*
    symbiosis with algae, *116*

Crick, Francis, 330, 343

cristae

    definition, **573**

    role in cellular respiration, **224**

crossing over. *See also* meiosis.

    causing chromosomal variation, 358

    definition, **573**

    modeling, **348**

crown of thorns (*Acanthaster planci*), 53

cyclins, **573**. *See also* proteins.

cytokinesis, **573**. *See also* daughter cells; mitosis; parent cells.

cytoplasm

    definition, **573**

    function of, **188**

    microscopic view, *188*

cytosine, **329**, 331

cytoskeleton, **189**, **573**

D

Darewadi watershed restoration, 19–20

Darwin, Charles. *See also* evolution, theory of.

    biodiversity through breeding, 440

    The Descent of Man, 442

    on the Galapagos islands, 438–439, *438–439*

    On The Origin of Species, 441

    photograph, *436*

    predecessors, 437

Dasyurus hallucatus (northern quoll), 51, *51*

daughter cells, *346*, **573**. *See also* cytokinesis; mitosis; parent cells.

DDT insecticide, 168–169

dead zones. *See also* eutrophication.

    Chesapeake Bay, **112**–113

    definition, **573**

    Gulf of Mexico, *113*

    rate of increase, *113*

decomposers, **90**, **573**. *See also* energy pyramid; food webs.

deep time. *See* geologic time.

density-dependent factors

    aquaculture, 128

    definition, **573**

density-independent factors

aquaculture, 128

    definition, **574**

deoxyribonucleic acid (DNA). *See* DNA (deoxyribonucleic acid).

The Descent of Man, 442

desert, 64, *64*

diabetes

    burden of disease, 196

    correlation with income level, *196, 197*

    correlation with weight, *197*

    definition, **574**

    disease mechanism, 196–197

    insulin injections, 197

    prevention, 197

    symptoms, 196–197

    treatment, 197

    Type I *vs.* Type II, 196–197

diagramming inherited traits. *See* pedigrees.

diarrhea. *See* rotavirus.

dietary factors, cancer, 234

differentiation

    definition, **574**

    description, 376

    gene expression, *377*, 377–381

    gene repression, **379**

    human cells, *376, 377*

    stem cells, **236**

    transcription factors, **380**

diffuse, **574**

diffusion

    definition, **574**

    through cell membranes, *198*, **198**–202. *See also* cell membranes, permeability; osmosis.

dihybrid cross

    breeding corn, *300*, **300**–303

    definition, **574**

diploid, 355, **574**. *See also* haploid.

disease intervention

    benefits of, 250–251

    definition, **574**

    drawbacks, 250–251

    trade-offs, 250–251

    world health proposals, 252–253

disease proteins, 214

diseases. *See also* infectious diseases; noninfectious diseases; rotavirus; viruses; *specific diseases.*
  cellular study of, **161**–166
  definition, **574**
  factors affecting, 157–160
  large-scale epidemics, 157
  world health and sustainability, 157–160
dispersive DNA replication, 344, *344*
disruption of networks, effects on biodiversity, 423, *423*
disturbances of ecosystems. *See also specific disturbances.*
  caused by humans, 135. *See also* oil spills.
  definition, **574**
  natural, 135. *See also* forest fires; volcanic eruptions.
  recovery from. *See* ecological succession; primary succession; resilience; secondary succession.
  resistance to, 137
diversification, **574**. *See also* biodiversity.
diversify, **574**
DNA (deoxyribonucleic acid).
  classifying living cells, 188
  conservative replication, **344**, *344*
  copying, 337
  definition, **574**
  dispersive replication, **344**, *344*
  double helix, *328*, *330*, **574**
  electrophoresis, identifying GMOs, 391
  human, global comparisons, 340
  isolating, **324**–327
  mutations, 368–371
  PCR, 337
  replicating, **343**–345, **580**
  semi-conservative replication, **344**, *344*
  sequencing, *335*, *372*. *See also* Human Genome Project.
DNA (deoxyribonucleic acid), structure
  adenine, **329**, 331
  base pairs, **330**, *330*
  centromeres, *328*
  chromatids, *328*
  chromosomes, *328*
  cytosine, **329**, 331

discovery of, 330
double-stranded, *332*
guanine, **329**, 331
hydrogen bonds, **330**, *330*
modeling, *328*, 328–333, *332*
nucleotides, *328*, **329**, *329*, 331
nucleus, *328*
sugar-phosphate backbone, *332*, **581**
thymine, **329**, 331
DNA constructs
  definition, **574**
  edible vaccines, **396**, *396*
DNA fingerprinting
  gel electrophoresis, **385**, *385*, *386*
  genetically modified corn, 385–387
dodo bird, effects of human activities, 426, *426*
dogs (*Canis lupus familiaris*), biodiversity
  effects of human activities, 428–429, *428–429*
  species separation from wolves, 477, *477*
domestic cat, phylogenetic profile, *454*
dominant traits. *See also* codominant traits; recessive traits; traits.
  definition, **574**
  identifying, 316–323
  scientific notation, 286
  selective breeding, 293–296
donkeys, species separation, 477, *477*
double helix
  definition, **574**
  discovery of, 330
  in DNA structure, *328*
double-stranded DNA, *332*
Down syndrome, 359
drawings, from microscope images, 173, *173*
Dreissena polymorpha (zebra mussels)
  carrying capacity, *119*
  in the Great Lakes, 74, *74*
  history of, 74
  population growth rates, *119*, 119–122
drug resistance
  malaria, 170
  tuberculosis, 179
duckweed (*Lemna minor*), 57–61, *59*, *60*

E

E. coli bacteria. *See also* bacteria.
    DNA replication, 343–345
    edible vaccine, 399
    ethanol from, 275–276
    genetic engineering, 271–273
    safe handling, 272

eastern narrowmouth frogs, species separation, 476, *476*

ecological footprints. *See also* carbon footprints.
    calculating, 22–25
    definition, **574**

ecological succession. *See also* primary succession; secondary succession.
    definition, **574**
    recovering from disturbances, **136**

ecology, **574**

ecosystem biodiversity, sustainability implications of genomics, 341

ecosystem diversity, **574**

ecosystem services
    definition, **574**
    Tragedy of the Commons, **80**

ecosystems. *See also* biodiversity; *specific ecosystems.*
    California sheephead, 94–95
    changes to. *See* disturbances of ecosystems.
    cloud forest, 417
    coral reef, 418
    decomposers, **90**
    definition, **574**
    effects of change, **45**–47
    energy flow, 90–95
    energy pyramid, constructing, 93
    food webs, **90**–95
    managing, **417–421**
    mangrove forests, 418, *501*, 501–502
    roles of organisms, 92
    tropical rainforest, 417

ecovillages. *See* BedZED.

edible vaccines, *393*, 393–399, *395–398*

electrical power generation, photovoltaic solar panels, 17, *18*

electron transport chain, **225**, **574**

ELISA protein plate, 391

ELISA protein strips, 391

embryonic stem cells, **574**. *See also* stem cells.

endemic species, **416**, **574**

endocytosis, **210**, *210*, **574**

energy flow, in ecosystems, 90–95

energy pyramid, 93, **575**. *See also* consumers; decomposers; food webs; producers.

enzymes. *See also* proteins.
    binding sites, 216
    catalyzing chemical reactions, **216**–218
    definition, **575**
    examples, 214
    function, 214
    lactase, 216–218

ER (endoplasmic reticulum), **574–575**

eras of geologic time, 433

ethanol from genetically modified *E. coli* bacteria, 275–276

eucalyptus trees, *70*

eukaryotes
    in cell structure, **188**
    chromosomes in, 354
    definition, **575**

eukaryotic, **575**

eukaryotic cell, **575**

Eusthenopteron, 449–450

eutrophication. *See also* dead zones; nitrates; nitrites; phosphates.
    Chesapeake Bay, **112**–113
    definition, **575**
    Jaffrey Lake case study, **29**

evidence
    of biome quality, 62
    definition, **575**
    of water quality, 26
    of world health trends, 160

evidence, for human evolution
    molecular, 461–462
    physical, 460–461

evolution. *See also* biological evolution.
    definition, **575**
    extinction, **489**, 495–496
    fit organisms, competitive advantage, **490**
    fitness, components of, **490**

geologic timeline, *434–435*

Hawaiian honeycreepers, *341*

macroevolution, **489**, 495–496

microevolution, **489**, 490–491

organism fitness, components of, 490

scientific support for, 498–499. *See also* fossils.

speciation, **489**

sustainability, implications of genomics, 341

evolution, human

hominid lineage, 459–462

molecular evidence, 461–462

natural selection, 463–464

physical evidence, 460–461

evolution, theory of

biodiversity through breeding, 440

biodiversity through natural selection, 441–442

The Descent of Man, 442

finches, Galapagos Islands, 439, *439*, *494*, 494–495

human population growth, 440

Lamarck, Jean-Baptiste, 437

Malthus, Thomas, 440

Malthus on Population, 440

On The Origin of Species, 441

Principles of Geology, 438

sexual selection, 442, *442*

tortoises, Galapagos Islands, 439, *439*

Wallace, Alfred Russell., 441, *441*

Wallace's Line, 441

world biogeographical areas, 441

Zoological Philosophy, 437

evolutionary trees

branches, 459

creating, 456–458

definition, **575**

hominid lineage, 459–462

lineages, **459**

uses for, **455**

evolve, 575

exocytosis, **210**, *210*, **575**

exotic species. *See* nonnative species.

expressed genes, **575**. *See also* gene expression; repressed genes.

extinct

definition, **575**

evolutionary outcome, **489**

extinction

definition, **575**

in the evolutionary process, **489**, 495–496

mass extinctions, **496**

F

facilitated diffusion, **209**, **575**

family trees. *See* pedigrees.

fast-growing salmon case study, 349–351, *350*

female *vs.* male chromosomes, 317

fermentation, 225–226, *226*

fertilized human eggs, stem cells, 241, *241*

Fiers, Walter, 338

finches, Galapagos Islands. *See* Galapagos finches.

fisheries

anchovy kilka, 132

Atlantic cod, 131

Atlantic salmon, 350–351

comb jelly, 132

definition, **575**

importance of plankton, **88**

Pacific chinook salmon, 350–351

Pacific halibut, *129*, 129–131, *130*

Pacific perch, 132

salmon hybrids, 350–351

sustainability, 145–147

tiger shark, 132

fisheries, case studies

assessing viability, 139–140

Goat Island marine reserve, New Zealand, 141–142

open-ocean aquaculture, Hawaii, 143–144

yellowtail farms, Hawaii, 143–144

fishery management, **575**

fit (organisms)

competitive advantage, **490**

definition, **575**

fitness

components of, **490**

definition, **575**

Fitzroy, Robert, 438

flagella, 181, *181*, **575**

Florida panther, effects of human activities, 427, *427*

flower fossil, Eocene epoch, *489*

fluid mosaic model of a cell membrane, *207*, **207**–208, **575** flying fox bats, effects of human activities, *429*, 429–430

food webs. *See also* consumers; decomposers; energy pyramid; producers.

  definition, **575**

  mapping, **90**–95

forest fires, succession, *55*, 56, *137*. *See also* Yellowstone forest fires (1988).

fossil fuel reduction, case study, 14–18

fossil record

  definition, **575**

  evolution of whales, *443*, **443**–445

  missing links, 452

  origin of tetrapods (four-limbed animals), 449–453

  scope of, **446**

  transitional features, **453**

  transitional fossils, 452

fossil record, rock layers

  carbon-14 dating, 448–449

  radiometric dating, **448**–449

  relative ages, 448–449

  strata, *447*, **447**–448

  stratigraphic dating, **448**

  stratigraphy, *447*, **447**–448

fossils

  age, determining, *447*, 447–449

  "Ardi" skeleton, 464

  Burgess Shale, *432*, *446*

  definition, **575**

  flower, Eocene epoch, *489*

  "Lucy" skeleton, *460*

  Middle Cambrian worm, *446*

  Neanderthal skeleton, *459*

  transitional, 452

  wasp, Eocene epoch, *489*

four-limbed animals. *See* terrestrial tetrapods.

Franklin, Rosalind, 330, 343

frogs

  eastern narrowmouth, 476, *476*

  Great Plains narrowmouth, 476, *476*

  moor, *472*

  narrowmouth, 476, *476*

  pickerel, *472*

G

Gadus morhua (Atlantic cod), 131

Galapagos finches, 439, *439*, 494, 494–495

Galapagos islands, 438–439, *438–439*

Galapagos tortoises, 439, *439*

Galeocerdo cuvier (tiger shark), 132

gametes

  definition, **575**

  diploid, 355

  haploid, 355

  selective breeding, **294**, *294*

gel electrophoresis

  definition, **575**

  DNA fingerprinting, **385**, *385*, *386*

gene expression

  definition, **576**

  genetically modified bacteria, 269–270

  in humans, *377*, **377**–381

gene flow

  biological species concept, **473**

  definition, **576**

  formation of new species, 480

  microevolution, 490–491

gene pool

  biological species concept, **473**

  definition, **576**

  forming new species, 480

gene repression, **379**

gene spread, GMOs, *382*, 382–383, *383*

gene therapy, 372–373

genes. *See also* alleles; DNA (deoxyribonucleic acid); heredity; traits.

  in chromosomes, 354

  definition, **576**

  exchanging between organisms. *See* genetic engineering.

  law of independent assortment, 356

  selective breeding, **294**

genetic diversity, **422**, **576**. *See also* biodiversity.

genetic drift, 490–491, **576**

genetic engineering, **261**–262, **576**. *See also* GMOs (genetically modified organisms); selective breeding.

genetic testing, 372

genetically modified organisms (GMOs). *See* GMOs (genetically modified organisms).

genomes
    definition, **336, 576**
    mapping, 337–339
    sequencing, *337*, 337–339
    size, by organism, 336
    study of. *See* genomics.
    viral, 338
genomics
    comparative, 341
    definition, **576**
    DNA sequencing, *335. See also* Human Genome
        Project.
    future of, 342
    goals of, **336**
    history of, *338*, 338–339
    Human Genome Project, 339–340
genomics, implications for sustainability
    alternative energy, 340
    ecosystem biodiversity, 341
    evolution, 341
    human health, 341
genotypes. *See also* alleles.
    definition, **576**
    selective breeding, **294**
geographic isolation, **576**
geographic regions of the world. *See also* countries.
    comparative analysis of indicators, 3–7
    map, 4
geologic time
    definition, **576**
    eras, 433
    evolutionary timeline, *434–435*
    scale, **432**–435
geologic timeline, **576**
giant kelp (*Macrocystis pyrifera*), *90*, 90–91
Gilbert, Walter, 338
glowing mice, *269–270*
glycolysis, *224*, **224**–227, **576**
GMOs (genetically modified organisms). *See also* corn,
    genetically modified; genetic engineering.
    Aequorea jelly, *269–270*
    Atlantic salmon, 350–351
    biofarming, 393–399
    biofuels from, **274**–276
    Bt (*Bacillus thuringiensis*), 264–265

creating, **261**–262
crops, by country, 265
definition, **576**
DNA constructs, **396**, *396*
E. coli bacteria, 269–270, 275–276
edible vaccines, *393*, 393–399, *395–398*
ethanol from, 275–276
exchanging genes, 269–270
gene expression, 269–270
genetic engineering, **261**–262
glowing mice, *269–270*
insecticides, 264–265
mosquito larvae, *277*
Pacific chinook salmon, 350–351
procedure, 271–273
soybeans, 400–407
virus-resistant papaya, *388*, 388–392, *389*
GMOs (genetically modified organisms), identifying
    corn, 385–387
    detection tests, 391
    DNA electrophoresis, 391
    ELISA protein plate, 391
    ELISA protein strips, 391
    Southern blotting, 398
    tracking, 385–387
GMOs (genetically modified organisms), risks
    evaluating, 361–365
    gene spread, *382*, 382–383, *383*
    GURT restriction technology, 382–383
    pros and cons, 266–267
    salmon hybrids, 350–351
    sustainability issues, 361–363, *361–363*
    technology restricting, 382–383
    trade-offs, 400–407
Goat Island marine reserve, New Zealand, 141–142
Golden Rice, 304–305, *305*
Golgi apparatus, **576**
gray wolves. *See* wolves (*Canis lupus*).
Great Barrier Reef, 53
Great Lakes
    round goby, 72, *72*
    zebra mussels, 74, *74*
Great Plains narrowmouth frogs, species separation,
    476, *476*
green lacewings, species separation, 479, *479*

Grousbeck, Wycliffe, 372

growth rate of populations, 58–61

guanine, **329**, 331

Gulf of Mexico, *113*

GURT restriction technology, 382–383

H

habitats

    definition, **576**

    destruction, effects on biodiversity, 422, *422*, *424*, *424*

    within ecosystems, 70

haploid, **576**. *See also* diploid.

HapMap project, 340

harbor seals (*Phoca vitulina*), *90*

Hawaiian Islands

    Indian mongoose, 73, *73*

    open-ocean aquaculture, 143–144

    yellowtail tuna farms, 143–144

hemoglobin, model of, *213*

heredity. *See also* genes; selective breeding; traits.

    definition, **576**

    diagramming. *See* pedigrees.

Herpestes javanicus (Indian mongoose), 73, *73*

heterozygous, **576**. *See also* codominant; homozygous; recessive.

heterozygous alleles, selective breeding, **295**

Hippoglossus stenolepis (Pacific halibut), *129*, 129–131, *130*

HIV/AIDS virus. *See also* viruses.

    burden of disease, 203

    crossing the cell membrane, 211

    definition, **576**

    disease mechanism, 203–204

    electron microscope image of, *244*

    global distribution, *203*

    model of, *204*

    organelles, 244–246

    prevention, 204–205

    reproducing in human cells, 244–246

    research, 204–205

    symptoms, 203–204

    transmission vectors, 204

    treatment, 204–205

    tuberculosis co-infection, 179

HMS Beagle, 438

homeostasis, 189, **576**

hominids. *See also* hominins; human beings.

    definition, **576**

    lineage, 459–462

    locomotion methods, 463

hominins, **576**. *See also* hominids; human beings.

Homo sapiens (human beings). *See also* hominids; hominins.

    blood types, 296–299

    cell differentiation, *376*, *377*

    health sustainability, implications of genomics, 341

    population growth, resulting in natural selection, 440

    variation, causes of, 356–358

homologous characters, **454**, **576**. *See also* characters; shared derived characters.

homology, **454**, **576**. *See also* shared derived characters.

homozygous, **576**. *See also* heterozygous.

homozygous alleles, selective breeding, **295**

honeybees

    adaptation, 493, *493*

    invasive species, *70*

honeycreepers, *482*

Hooke, Robert, 187

horses, species separation, 477, *477*

hotspots

    definition, **576**

    global map, *420–421*

    Madagascar, *465–467*, 465–471, *469–470*

    mangrove forests, 418, *501*, 501–502

    tropical montane cloud forests, 504, *504*

    tropical rainforests (north), 502, *502*

    tropical rainforests (south), 503, *503*

household power efficiency, case study, 17

HPV (human papillomavirus), 233–234

human beings (*Homo sapiens*). *See also* hominids; hominins.

    blood types, selective breeding, 296–299

    cell differentiation, *376*, *377*

    health sustainability, implications of genomics, 341

    population growth, resulting in natural selection, 440

    variation, causes of, 356–358

Human Genome Project, 339–340

hydrogen bonds. *See also* base pairs.

    definition, **577**

    in DNA structure, **330**, *330*

hypothesis, **577**

I

ice plants, *70*

Icthyostega, 449–450

immune system proteins, 214

incomplete dominance

    definition, **577**

    selective breeding, **296**

independent assortment of genes, 356

independent segregation of chromosomes, 356

Indian mongoose (*Herpestes javanicus*), 73, *73*

indicators. *See also* chemical indicators.

    across geographic regions, **3**–7

    BTB (bromothymol blue), 107–110

    definition, **577**

    health of the commons, 80

    Lugol's iodine, 199

    methylene blue, 111–115

    phenol red, 104

infectious diseases. *See also* diseases; noninfectious diseases; viruses.

    definition, **577**

    global distribution, **157**, *157*

inherited traits, diagramming. *See* pedigrees.

insect-pollinated orchids, adaptation, 493, *493*

insecticides

    controlling malaria, trade-offs, 169

    genetically engineered, 264–265

insulin, model of, *213*

insulin injections, for diabetes, 197

intervention, **577**. *See also* disease intervention.

introduced species, effects on biodiversity, 422, *422*, *425*, 425–426. *See also* invasive species; nonnative species.

invasive species. *See also* nonnative species.

    brown tree snake, *70*

    cane toads, 50–51

    characteristics of, **70–71**

    comb jelly, 132

    definition, **577**

    duckweed, 57–61, *59*, *60*

    eucalyptus trees, *70*

    honey bees, *70*

    ice plants, *70*

    Indian mongoose, 73, *73*

    Japanese beetles, 422, *422*

    round goby, 72, *72*

Ireland, potato blight, 424–425, *425*

isolating DNA, **324**–327

isolation

    chemical, **577**

    geographic, **576**

    reproductive, **580**

isoniazid, for tuberculosis, 179

J

Jacobson, Samuel G., 373

Jaffrey Lake case study

    eutrophication, **29**

    proposing corrective action, 31–33

    stakeholders, **31**, 34–38

    testing water quality, 26–30

    trade-offs, **31**

Japanese beetles, 422

K

karyotypes

    definition, **577**

    human male, 354, *354*, *377*

kelp forest, symbiotic relationships, 116–119

Klinefelter syndrome, 359

Krebs cycle, **225**, **577**

L

lacewings, species separation, 479, *479*

lactase enzyme, 216–218, **577**

lactose, **577**

lactose intolerance, 216

Lake Victoria, effects of human activities on biodiversity, *425*, 425–426

Lamarck, Jean-Baptiste, 437

land degradation

    Darewadi watershed restoration, **19**

    definition, **577**

landscape, types of. *See* biomes.

latent, **577**

latent tuberculosis, 178

law of independent assortment, 356, **577**

LCA (Leber's congenital amaurosis), 372

Lee, Derrek, 372

Lemna minor (duckweed), 57–61, *59*, *60*

lemurs, *465*, 470, *470*

leptospirosis, 73

leukemia, stem cell treatments, 242

life cycle of products. *See* product lifecycle.

light-dependent reactions, **222**, *222*, **577**

light-independent reactions, **223**, *223*, **577**. *See also*
  Calvin cycle.

limiting factors, **577**

lineage
  definition, **577**
  evolutionary trees, **459**
  hominids, 459–462

linked genes, 356

lipid bilayer, **577**

lipid (phospholipid) bilayer
  cell membrane structure, **207**, *207*
  definition, **579**

lipids, **577**

locomotion methods for hominids, 463

"Lucy" skeleton, *460*

Lugol's iodine, 199

Lyell, Charles, 438

lysosome, **577**

M

Macrocystis pyrifera (giant kelp), *90*, 90–91

macroevolution
  definition, **577**
  in the evolutionary process, **489**
  extinctions, 495–496

macromolecules
  cell membrane structure, 206
  definition, **578**

macrophages, 178, **578**

Madagascar, *465–467*, 465–471, *469–470*

malaria
  Anopheles mosquito, 168
  burden of disease, *167*

DDT insecticide, 168–169

definition, **578**

diagnosing, 164

disease mechanism, 167–168

drug resistance, 170

effects of climate change, 170, *170*

global distribution, *167*

infection cycle, 168

insecticides, trade-offs, 169

mosquito nets, 169–170

plasmodium parasites, *167*, 167–170

prevention, 168–169

symptoms, 167–168

treatment, 168–169

vectors, 168

male *vs.* female chromosomes, 317

Malthus, Thomas, 440

Malthus on Population, 440

mangrove forests, 418, *501*, 501–502

mapping genomes, 337–339

marine reserve, **578**

mass extinctions, **496**, **578**

matrix
  definition, **578**
  role in cellular respiration, **224**

Maxam, Allan, 338

meiosis. *See also* crossing over; gametes; mitosis.
  abnormal, effect on chromosomes, 358–359
  chromosome abnormalities, 358–359
  definition, **578**
  failure of cell division, 358–359
  fast-growing salmon case study, 349–351, *350*
  modeling, 348–349
  nondisjunction, **358**
  normal, effect on chromosomes, 354–358, *357*
  in sexual reproduction, **346**–352

membranes, **578**. *See also* cell membranes.

Mendel, Gregor, 291–296, *292*, 356

Meselson, Matthew, 343

messenger ribonucleic acid (mRNA), 366, **578**. *See also*
  translation; tRNA.

metabolism
  cells, **189**
  definition, **578**

methylene blue, 111–115

mice, glowing, *269–270*

microbes

definition, **578**

in infectious diseases, **161**–166

microevolution

definition, **578**

in the evolutionary process, **489**

factors affecting, 490–491

gene flow, 490–491

genetic drift, 490–491

mutation, 490–491

natural selection, 490–491

microscope drawings, 173, *173*, *187*

microscope slides, preparing, 174

microscopes

focusing, 87

observing prepared slides, 86

proper handling, 86

studying blood, 162–165

Midas cichlid fish, species separation, 478, *478*

Middle Cambrian worm fossil, *446*

missing links, 452

mitochondria

aerobic respiration, *225*

definition, **578**

fermentation, *226*

glycolysis, *224*

plant *vs.* animal, *221*

role in cellular respiration, **224**. *See also*
photosynthesis, mitochondria.

mitochondrion, **578**

mitosis. *See also* asexual reproduction; centrioles;
cytokinesis; daughter cells; meiosis.

asexual reproduction, *278*, **278**–281

in the cell cycle, **229**, *229*

definition, **578**

onion root tips, *346*

Mnemiopsis leidyi (comb jelly), 132

molecular farming. *See* biofarming.

molecules, movement through cell membranes, 200–
202. *See also* diffusion; osmosis.

moor frog, species separation, *472*

moray eels, symbiosis with cleaner shrimp, *117*

mosquito larvae, genetically modifying, *277*

mosquito nets, controlling malaria, 169–170

motor proteins. *See also* proteins.

definition, **578**

examples, 214

function of, 214

mRNA (messenger ribonucleic acid), 366, **578**.
See also translation; tRNA.

multicellular organisms, **171**, **578**

multipotent, **578**

mutations

amino acid sequences, 368–371

definition, **578**

DNA, 368–371

microevolution, 490–491

protein synthesis, *368*, **368**–371

mutualism, **578**. *See also* amensalism; symbiosis.

Mycobacterium tuberculosis, 177, *178*

N

n chromosomes, **576**. *See also* haploid.

narrowmouth frogs, species separation, 476, *476*

natural selection. *See also* evolution.

adaptive radiation, *482*, **482**–483

definition, **578**

honeycreepers, *482*

human evolution, 463–464

macroevolution, **489**

microevolution, 490–491

resulting from human population growth, 440

role in biodiversity, 441–442

Neanderthal skeleton, *459*

Neogobius melanostomus (round goby), 72, *72*

net pens

aquaculture, 124, *124*, *125*

drawbacks, 144

farming salmon, 350–351, *351*

New Zealand, Goat Island marine reserve, 141–142

Nile perch, effects on biodiversity, *425*, 425–426

nitrates, **578**. *See also* eutrophication.

nitrites, **578**. *See also* eutrophication.

nodes, **578**

non-reproductive cells, 355

noncommunicable diseases. *See* noninfectious
diseases.

nondisjunction, **358**, **578**

noninfectious diseases, **157**, **578**. *See also* diseases;
  infectious diseases.
nonnative species. *See also* invasive species.
  characteristics of, **70**
  definition, **579**
northern elephant seals, effects of human activities,
  430–431
northern quoll (*Dasyurus hallucatus*), 51, *51*
northern spotted owls, species separation, 476, *476*
Norwalk virus, edible vaccine, 399
nucleotides. *See also* base pairs.
  comparison of selected organisms, 331
  composition of, *329*
  definition, **579**
  illustration, *328*
  types of, **329**
nucleus
  cell structure, 188, **188**
  definition, **579**
  DNA, *328*

O

occupational hazards for cancer, 235
oil spills, *134*
On The Origin of Species, 441
Oncorhynchus tshawytscha (Pacific chinook salmon),
  350–351
onion root tips, mitosis, *346*
open-ocean aquaculture, Hawaii, 143–144
orchids
  adaptation, 493, *493*
  species separation, 479, *479*
organelles
  in cell structure, 180
  definition, **579**
  HIV/AIDS, 244–246
organism fitness, components of, 490
organisms
  definition, **579**
  environmental factors. *See* biomes.
  roles in ecosystems, 92
osmosis, **208–209**, *209*, **579**. *See also* diffusion.
overexploitation, definition, 422
overexploitation, effects on biodiversity

dodo bird, *426*, 426–427
Florida panther, 427, *427*
flying foxes, *429*, 429–430
narrow-headed softshell turtles, *422*
northern elephant seals, *430*, 430–431
overfishing
  effect on blue crab population, 48–49
  solutions to. *See* aquaculture.
oxygen levels in aquatic ecosystems
  cellular respiration rate, 111–115
  depletion by phytoplankton, 112–113
  testing, 111–115

P

Pacific chinook salmon (*Oncorhynchus tshawytscha*),
  350–351
Pacific halibut (*Hippoglossus stenolepis*), *129*, 129–131,
  130
Pacific perch (*Sebastes alutus*), 132
Palau coral reefs, South Pacific, 53
papaya, virus-resistant, *388*, 388–392, *389*
paramecium, *171*
parasitism, **579**. *See also* symbiosis; symbiotic
  organisms.
parent cells, **579**. *See also* cytokinesis; daughter cells.
Parkinson's disease, stem cell treatments, 242
parts per million (ppm), **579**
passive transport, **209**, **579**
Pauling, Linus, 330
PCR (polymerase chain reaction), 337
peacocks, sexual selection, 442, *442*
pedigrees
  definition, **579**
  diagramming, **316–323**
  example, *317*
Penicillium mold, *182*
permafrost, 67
permeability of cell membranes. *See* cell membranes,
  permeability.
pH
  definition, **579**
  effect on lactase enzyme, 216–218
phases of the cell cycle, **229**, *229*. *See also specific phases.*
phenol red, 104

phenotypes
  definition, **579**
  selective breeding, **292–293**
Phoca vitulina (harbor seals), *90*
phosphates, **579**. *See also* eutrophication.
phospholipid (*lipid*) bilayer
  cell membrane structure, **207**, *207*
  definition, **579**
phospholipids
  cell membrane structure, **207**, *207*
  definition, **579**
photosynthesis. *See also* cellular respiration; producers.
  acetyl CoA (coenzyme A), 225
  aerobic respiration, *225*
  anaerobic respiration, **225**–226. *See also* fermentation.
  Calvin cycle, **222**
  in the carbon cycle, **100**–102
  chloroplasts, **221**, *221*, *223*
  definition, **579**
  electron transport chain, **225**
  fermentation, 225–226, *226*
  glycolysis, *224*
  Krebs cycle, **225**
  light-dependent reactions, **222**, *222*
  light-independent reactions, **223**, *223*
  pigments, **220**, *220*
  plant cells *vs.* animal cells, *221*
  in plants, 107–110
  stroma, **221**, *221*, *223*
  thylakoids, **221**, *221*, *223*
photovoltaic solar panels, 17, *18*
phylogenetic diversity. *See also* biodiversity.
  definition, **579**
  factor in conservation decisions, **465**–471
phylogenetics
  characters, **454**–455
  clades, **458**
  definition, **454**
  diagramming, 455
  of a domestic cat, *454*
  evolutionary trees, **455**, 456–458
  homologous characters, **454**
  homology, **454**
  shared derived characters, **455**

phylogeny, **579**
Phytophthora infestans fungus, 424–425, *425*
phytoplankton. *See also* plankton.
  in Chesapeake Bay, 112–113
  definition, **579**
  description, **85**
  in the Gulf of Mexico, *113*
  oxygen depletion, 112–113
pigeons, breeding effects on biodiversity, 440, *440*
pigment, **220**, *220*, **579**
plankton. *See also* phytoplankton; zooplankton.
  biomass, calculating, 88–89
  definition, **579**
  description, **85**
  diagrams of, *88*
  examining under a microscope, 85–87
  producers *vs.* consumers, 85
plant cells
  microscopic view of, *174*
  vs. animal cells, *221*
plants
  cellular respiration, 107–110
  photosynthesis, 107–110
plasmodium parasites, *167*, 167–170
pluripotent, **579**
pluripotent embryonic stem cells, 241, *241*
pollution. *See* water pollution.
polycythemia vera, diagnosing, 164
polymerase chain reaction (PCR), 337
polyps, coral reefs, 52
ponds, aquaculture, 124
population growth, changes caused by, 123–128
population growth rates
  definition, **579**
  density-dependent factors, 128
  density-independent factors, 128
  measuring, 58–61
  zebra mussels, *119*, 119–122
populations
  carrying capacities, **119**–122
  in communities, **58**
  definition, **579**
  of duckweed, 57–61
potato blight (Ireland), 424–425, *425*
ppm (parts per million), **579**

Prader-Willi syndrome, 359

primary succession. *See also* ecological succession.

    after volcanic eruptions, *136*

    definition, **579**

    recovering from disturbances, **136**, *136*

Principles of Geology, 438

producers, 85, **580**. *See also* energy pyramid; food webs; photosynthesis.

product lifecycle

    BedZED case study, **15**–16

    definition, **580**

    wooden boards, 16

prokaryotes

    cell structure, **188**

    definition, **580**

    microscopic view, *188*

prokaryotic, **580**

protein synthesis. *See also* transcription factors; translation.

    definition, **580**

    gene therapy, 372–373

    model key, *369*

    mRNA, creating, 366

    mutations, *368*, **368**–371

    phases, *366*, 366–368

    transcription, *366*, **366**–368

    translation, *366*, **366**–368

    tRNA, 366, *366*

proteins. *See also* amino acids; cyclins.

    classes of, 214. *See also specific proteins.*

    definition, **580**

    disease, 214

    enzymes, 214

    function in cells and viruses, **213**, *213*, **213**–215

    hemoglobin, model of, *213*

    immune system, 214

    insulin, model of, *213*

    motor, 214

    receptor, 214

    rhodopsin, model of, *213*

    signaling, 214

    storage, 214

    structural, 214

    transport, 214

protists

    cell structure, **188**

    definition, **580**

Punnett squares, **285**, **580**

purple sea urchins, species separation, 475, *475*

R

raceways, aquaculture, 124

radiation therapy for cancer, 234

radiometric dating, **448**–449, **580**

rainforests. *See* tropical rainforests.

receptor proteins. *See also* proteins.

    definition, **580**

    examples, 214

    function of, 214

receptors, **580**

recessive traits. *See also* dominant traits; heterozygous.

    definition, **580**

    identifying, 316–323

    scientific notation, 286

    selective breeding, 293–296

    sex-linked. *See* sex-linked, recessive traits.

red cichlid fish, species separation, 478, *478*

red sea urchins, species separation, 475, *475*

regions of the world. *See* geographic regions of the world.

replication of DNA, **343**–345, **580**. *See also* copying DNA.

repressed genes, **379**, **580**. *See also* expressed genes.

reproductive isolation, **580**

residential energy consumption, case study, 14–18

resilience, **580**. *See also* disturbances of ecosystems.

resistance to disturbances of ecosystems, 137, **580**

rhodopsin, model of, *213*

ribosomes, 181, *181*, **580**

rice, selective breeding

    for flood-prone areas, *307*, 307–309

    Golden Rice, 304–305, *305*

    vitamin A supplement, 304–305, *305*

rifampin, for tuberculosis, 179

ring-tailed lemurs, *465*

RNA (ribonucleic acid), **580**. *See also* mRNA; tRNA.

rock layers, study of. *See* stratigraphy.

rock pocket mouse (*Chaetodipus intermedius*), **484**–488

rotavirus. *See also* diseases; viruses.

    burden of disease, 247

    definition, **580**

    disease mechanism, 247–248

    global death rate for children, *247*

    model of, *248*

    prevention, 248–249

    symptoms, 247–248

    treatment, 248–249

    vaccine for, 248–*249*

round goby (*Neogobius melanostomus*), 72, *72*

S

Salmo salar (Atlantic salmon), 350–351

salmon, aquaculture

    along migration routes, *125*

    Atlantic salmon, 350–351

    density-dependent factors, 128

    density-independent factors, 128

    fast-growing salmon case study, 349–351, *350*

    hybrids, 350–351

    net pens, 124, *124*, *125*, 350–351, *351*

    Pacific chinook salmon, 350–351

    salmon hybrids, 350–351

    salmon species, 350–351

    systems for, 124, *124*, *125*

salmon hybrids, 350–351

salmon migration routes, *125*

Sanger, Frederick, 338

savanna, 65, *65*

Schleiden, Matthias, 187

screening for cancer, 234, 235

sea urchins, species separation, 475, *475*

Sebastes alutus (Pacific perch), 132

secondary succession. *See also* disturbances of ecosystems; ecological succession.

    definition, **580**

    recovering from disturbances, **136**, *137*

    from Yellowstone forest fire, *137*

sediment concentration, Gulf of Mexico, *113*

selective breeding

    codominance, **296**

    definition, **580**

    dihybrid cross, *300*, **300**–303

    dominant traits, 293–296

early practices, 291–296

    gametes, **294**, *294*

    genes, **294**

    genotypes, **294**

    heredity, **290**

    heterozygous alleles, **295**

    homozygous alleles, **295**

    human blood types, 296–299

    incomplete dominance, **296**

    independent segregation of chromosomes, 356

    law of independent assortment, 356

    linked genes, 356

    phenotypes, **292–293**

    recessive traits, 293–296

    sexual reproductive cells, 294, *294*

    for single traits, **282**, *283–284*

    for two traits, *300*, 300–303

selective breeding, corn

    dihybrid cross, *300*, **300**–303

    growth in yield over time, *313*

    history of, 311–314

    for single traits, **282**, *283–284*

    for two traits, *300*, 300–303

    vs. teosinte (native Mexican corn), *311*, 311–312, *312*

selective breeding, rice

    for flood-prone areas, *307*, 307–309

    Golden Rice, 304–305, *305*

    vitamin A supplement, 304–305, *305*

selectively permeable cell membranes, **208**, **580**

semi-conservative DNA replication, 344, *344*

semipermeable cell membranes, **208**, **580**

sequencing

    DNA, *335*, *372*

    genomes, *337*, 337–339

Seriola rivoliana (yellowtail tuna), 143–144

sex-linked

    definition, **580**

    recessive traits, 316–323, **580**

    traits, **317**, *317*

sexual reproduction. *See also* asexual reproduction; meiosis.

    corn, **282**

    definition, **581**

    human variation, 356–358

sexual reproductive cells, selective breeding, 294, *294*

sexual selection, 442, *442*, **581**

shared derived characters, **455, 581**. *See also* characters; homologous characters; homology.

sickle cell disease, diagnosing, 164

sickle cells, **581**

signaling proteins
    definition, **581**
    examples, 214
    function of, 214

single-celled organisms
    definition, **581**
    under a microscope, 172–176
    microscope drawings, 173, *173*
    paramecium, *171*
    vs. multicellular, **171**

skin lesion, cancer, *233*

smoking, cancer risk, 234

snakes, adaptation, 493, *493*

solar panels, photovoltaic, 17, *18*

somatic cells, 355, **581**

Southern, Edward M., 398

soybeans, genetically modified, 400–407

speciation
    adaptive radiation, 494–495
    definition, **581**
    description, 494–495
    in the evolutionary process, **489**
    Galapagos finches, *494*, 494–495

species. *See also* biological species.
    classifying. *See* biological species concept; phylogenetics.
    definition, **581**
    new, forming, 480–481

species diversity
    biodiversity, **422**
    definition, **581**

species separation. *See also* biological species concept.
    analyzing, 474–475
    arrow cichlid fish, 478, *478*
    blue cichlid fish, 478, *478*
    California spotted owls, 476, *476*
    cichlid fish, 478, *478*
    copper-resistant yellow monkey flower, 479, *479*

copper-tolerant yellow monkey flower, 479, *479*

dogs, 477, *477*

donkeys, 477, *477*

eastern narrowmouth frogs, 476, *476*

Great Plains narrowmouth frogs, 476, *476*

green lacewings, 479, *479*

horses, 477, *477*

lacewings, 479, *479*

Midas cichlid fish, 478, *478*

moor frog, *472*

narrowmouth frogs, 476, *476*

northern spotted owls, 476, *476*

orchids, 479, *479*

pickerel frog, *472*

purple sea urchins, 475, *475*

red cichlid fish, 478, *478*

red sea urchins, 475, *475*

sea urchins, 475, *475*

spotted owls, 476, *476*

wolves, 477, *477*

yellow monkey flower, 479, *479*

spherocytosis, diagnosing, 164

spotted owls, species separation, 476, *476*

Stahl, Franklin, 343

stakeholders
    definition, **581**
    Jaffrey Lake case study, **31**, 34–38

stem cell research
    bone marrow cells, *240*
    current scientific knowledge, 240–243
    social issues, 243

stem cell treatments
    bone marrow transplants, 242
    leukemia, 242
    Parkinson's disease, 242
    Type-I diabetes, 242

stem cells. *See also* embryonic stem cells.
    blastocysts, 241, *241*
    definition, **581**
    developing specialized cells, *236*, **236**–239
    differentiation, **236**
    fertilized human eggs, 241, *241*
    pluripotent embryonic, 241, *241*
    sources of, 242

totipotent, 241, *241*

types of, *241*, 241–242

umbilical cord, 242

zygotes, 241, *241*

storage proteins

examples, 214

function of, 214

strata

definition, **581**

in the fossil record, *447*, **447**–448

stratigraphic dating, **448**, **581**

stratigraphy, *447*, **447**–448, **581**

stroma, **221**, *221*, *223*, **581**

structural proteins, 214

sugar, breaking down. *See* diabetes; glycolysis.

sugar-phosphate backbone, *332*, **581**

surgical treatment for cancer, 234

sustainability

across countries, 8–13

across geographic regions, **3**–7

biodiversity, 415–421

definition, **581**

effects of change, 45–47

fisheries, 145–147

Madagascar, 465–471

United States compared to other countries, 8–13

world health and, 157–160

sustainability, implications of genomics

alternative energy, 340

ecosystem biodiversity, 341

evolution, 341

human health, 341

sustainability case studies

BedZED, 14–18

Darewadi watershed restoration, 19–20

symbiosis. *See also* amensalism; commensalism; mutualism; parasitism.

definition, **581**

in a kelp forest, 116–119

symbiotic organisms

advantages and disadvantages, 116–119

coral polyps and algae, 52

crabs and algae, *116*

moray eels and cleaner shrimp, *117*

T

taiga, 66, *66*

taxa

biodiversity, **422**

classifying. *See* phylogenetics.

definition, **581**

taxon

biodiversity, **422**

definition, **581**

TB. *See* tuberculosis.

temperate deciduous forests, 67, *67*

temperate grasslands, 66, *66*

temperature, effect on lactase enzyme, 216–218

terrestrial tetrapods (four-limbed animals)

Acanthostega, 450–451

co-opted features, **450**

definition, **581**

Eusthenopteron, 449–450

Icthyostega, 449–450

missing links, 452

origins of, **449**–453, *450*–*452*

Tiktaalik, 451–452

transitional features, **453**

transitional fossils, 452

testing

for GMOs, 391

water quality, 26–30

tetrapods. *See* terrestrial tetrapods (four-limbed animals).

theory, **581**. *See also specific theories.*

thylakoids, **221**, *221*, *223*, **581**

thymine, **329**, 331

tiger shark (*Galeocerdo cuvier*), 132

Tiktaalik, 451–452

tobacco, cancer risk, 234

tortoises, Galapagos Islands, 439, *439*

totipotent, **581**

totipotent stem cells, 241, *241*

tracking GMOs. *See* GMOs (genetically modified organisms), identifying.

trade-offs

controlling malaria with insecticides, 166, 169

controlling mosquitoes with insecticides, 166, 169

definition, **581**

    disease intervention, 250–251

    GMOs, 268, 400–407

    Jaffrey Lake case study, **31**

Tragedy of the Commons

    definition, **581**

    ecosystem services, **80**

    indicators, 80

    measuring the health of the commons, 80–84

traits. *See also* carriers (of disease traits); dominant traits; genes; heredity.

    definition, **581**

    diagramming individual histories. *See* pedigrees.

    sex-linked. *See* sex-linked, traits.

traits, selectively breeding

    codominance, **296**

    different alleles. *See* heterozygous alleles.

    dominant traits, 293–296

    early practices, 291–296

    gametes, **294**, *294*

    genes, **294**

    genetic makeup. *See* genotypes.

    genotypes, **294**

    heredity, **290**

    heterozygous alleles, **295**

    homozygous alleles, **295**

    human blood types, 296–299

    identical alleles. *See* homozygous alleles.

    incomplete dominance, **296**

    phenotypes, **292–293**

    physical appearance. *See* phenotypes.

    recessive traits, 293–296

    sexual reproductive cells, 294, *294*

transcription

    definition, **582**

    in protein synthesis, *366*, **366**–368

transcription factors, **380**, **582**. *See also* protein synthesis.

transitional features, **453**, **582**

transitional fossils, 452, **582**

translation, *366*, **366**–368, **582**. *See also* mRNA; protein synthesis.

transport by vesicles, **210**, *210*

transport proteins

    definition, **582**

    examples, 214

    function of, 214

tRNA (transfer RNA), 366, *366*, **582**

tropical montane cloud forests, 504, *504*

tropical rainforests

    description, 64, *64*, 417

    destruction of (Borneo), 424, *424*

    north, 502, *502*

    south, 503, *503*

tuberculosis. *See also* bacteria; disease.

    active, 178

    burden of disease, 177

    cause, 177

    definition, **582**

    disease mechanism, 177–178

    drug resistance, 179

    global distribution, *177*

    HIV/AIDS co-infection, 179

    infection cycle, 178

    isoniazid, 179

    latent, 178

    macrophages, 178

    Mycobacterium tuberculosis, 177, *178*

    prevention, 178–179

    rifampin, 179

    symptoms, 177–178

    treatment, 178–179

tundra, 67, *67*

Turner syndrome, 359

turtles, overharvesting, 422, *422*

2n chromosomes, **574**. *See also* diploid.

Type-I diabetes, stem cell treatments, 242

Type I diabetes *vs.* Type II, 196–197

U

umbilical cord stem cells, 242

United States sustainability, compared to other countries, 8–13

V

vaccines
  definition, **582**
  edible, *393*, 393–399, *395–398*, **396**, *396*
  for Norwalk virus, 399
  for rotavirus, 248–*249*
vacuoles, **582**
variable, **582**
vectors
  definition, **582**
  malaria, 168
venomous snakes, adaptation, 493, *493*
vesicles
  definition, **582**
  transport mechanisms, **210**, *210*
Virchow, Rudolf, **187**
virus-resistant papaya, case study, *388*, 388–392, *389*
viruses. *See also* HIV/AIDS; rotavirus.
  cell membrane permeability, **211**
  definition, **582**
  genomics of, 338
  protein functions, **213**–215
vitamin A deficiency, *304*, 304–305, *305*
volcanic eruptions
  immediate aftermath, *135*
  primary succession, *136*
  in progress, *134*

W

Wallace, Alfred Russell., 441, *441*
Wallace's Line, 441
wasp fossil, Eocene epoch, *489*
water conservation, Darewadi watershed restoration, 19–20
water pollution. *See also* Jaffrey Lake case study.
  Chesapeake Bay, 48–49, 112–113
  effect on blue crab population, 48–49
  oil spills, *134*
  oxygen levels, testing, 111–115
Watson, James, 330, 343

whales, fossil evidence of evolution, *443*, 443–445
Wilkins, Maurice, 330, 343
wolves (*Canis lupus*), biodiversity
  breeding, effects of, 428–429
  human activities, effects of, *428*, 428–429, *428–429*
  species separation from dogs, 477, *477*
wooden boards, product life cycle, 16
world biogeographical areas, 441
world health. *See* diseases.
world health proposals for disease intervention, 252–253
world regions. *See* geographic regions of the world.
worm fossil, *446*

X

X, human chromosomes, 317, *317*, 354, *354*

Y

Y, human chromosomes, 317, *317*, 354, *354*
yellow monkey flower, species separation, 479, *479*
Yellowstone forest fires (1988)
  description, 54–56
  scope of, 54
  secondary succession, *137*
  succession, 55
yellowtail tuna (*Seriola rivoliana*), 143–144

Z

zebra mussels (*Dreissena polymorpha*)
  carrying capacity, *119*
  in the Great Lakes, 74, *74*
  history of, 74
  population growth rates, *119*, 119–122
Zoological Philosophy, 437
zooplankton. *See also* plankton.
  definition, **582**
  description, **85**
zygotes, 241, *241*

Credits

All illustrations by Seventeenth Street Studios/Valerie Winemiller, except where noted below.

Front cover and title page photo: Georgette Douwma/Photo Researchers, Inc.Small fish hiding in a sea pen. Sea pens are colonial organisms related to sea feathers. Photographed off the coast of Rinca Island, Indonesia.

Abbreviations: T (top), M (middle), B (bottom), L (left) R (right), C (center)

Sustainability

Unit opener: Page 1 BioRegional/Marcus Lyon

Page 3 BL Jeffery Rotman/Photo Researchers, Inc.; BR Erin Spencer-Mullen

Page 9 TL Bryan & Cherry Alexander/Photo Researchers, Inc.; TR VOISIN/PHANIE/Photo Researchers, Inc.

Page 15 BioRegional/Marcus Lyon

Page 16 Houston-Galveston Area Council (H-GAC)

Page17 Moodboard/Corbis

Page18 BL Ashley Cooper/Corbis

Page 19 The Watershed Organisation Trust (WOTR) India

Page 22 Stephen Ausmus/USDA Agricultural Research Service

Page 23 Tammy Hanratty/Corbis

Page 26 Robert Warren/Getty Images

Page 31 Andrew Howe/Getty Images

Page 32 Martin Shields/Photo Researchers, Inc.

Ecology

Unit opener: Page 43 Andrew G. Wood/Photo Researchers, Inc.

Page 45 Terry Whittaker/Photo Researchers, Inc.

Page 46 TR ©Deddeda/Design Pics/Corbis; TL © Herwarth Voigtmann/Corbis

Page 48 ML istockphoto

Page 49 Millard H. Sharp/Photo Researchers, Inc.

Page 50 MT Wayne Lawler/Photo Researchers, Inc.

Page 51 TR ©Eric and David Hosking/CORBIS; BR ©M. Letnic

Page 52 ML ©Norbert Wu/Science Faction/Corbis

Page 53 TR ©Norbert Wu/Science Faction/Corbis; BR NOAA

Page 54 TL David R. Frazier Photolibrary, Inc./Photo Researchers, Inc.

Page 55 ©DLILLC/Corbis

Page 57 BR Ross & Diane Armstrong/Photo Researchers, Inc.; BL Andrew G. Wood/Photo Researchers, Inc.

Page 59 Raul Gonzalez Perez/Photo Researchers, Inc.

Page 60 Adam Jones/Getty Images

Page 62 BL Bob Gibbons/Photo Researchers, Inc.; BR James Steinberg/Photo Researchers, Inc.

Page 64 TR Jacques Jangoux/Photo Researchers, Inc.; BM Jerry Schad/Photo Researchers, Inc.

Page 65 TL Art Wolfe/Photo Researchers, Inc.; BR Earl Scott/Photo Researchers, Inc.

Page 66 TR Richard T. Nowitz/Photo Researchers, Inc.; BL Stephen J. Krasemann/Photo Researchers, Inc.

Page 67 TL James Steinberg/Photo Researchers, Inc.; BR Jim Zipp/Photo Researchers, Inc.

Page 70 ML John Mitchell/Photo Researchers, Inc.; M altrendo nature/Getty Images; MR John Wang/Getty Images; BL James Forte/Getty Images

Page 72 TR Ted Kinsman/Photo Researchers, Inc.

Page 73 TL E. Hanumantha Rao/Photo Researchers, Inc.; BR Simon Fraser/Photo Researchers, Inc.

Page 74 Peter Yates/Photo Researchers, Inc.

Page 75 TL Scott Robinson, Georgia Department of Natural Resources, Bugwood.org; BR Robert Vidèka, Doronicum Kft., Bugwood.org

Page 76 April Bahen, CBNERRVA, NOAA

Page 79 Hyunsoo Leo Kim/The Virginian-Pilot

Page 80 NOAA

Page 82 Joseph Smith, NOAA/NMFS/SEFSC/Beaufort Laboratory

Page 85 Francis Gohier/Photo Researchers, Inc.

Page 90 Gregory Ochocki/Photo Researchers, Inc.

Page 97 ML Inga Spence/Photo Researchers, Inc.; BL © Burke/Triolo Productions/Brand X/Corbis; BR Jeffrey Hamilton/Getty Images; MR Thinkstock Images/Getty Images

Page 100 Andrew G. Wood/Photo Researchers, Inc.

Page 113 BL, BR, MR NASA Goddard Space Flight Center Scientific Visualization Studio

Page 116 Tom Reamy

Page 117 Tim Laman/Getty Images

Page 119 NOAA

Page 125 BR fotosearch; TL fotosearch

Page 129 © Tim Thompson/Corbis

Page 130 ©Brandon D. Cole/Corbis

Page 134 TR © Dorian Weisel/Corbis; BL D C Lowe/Getty Images

Page 135 National Park Services

Page 136 B Thomas & Pat Leeson/Photo Researchers, Inc.

Page 137 BR Douglas Faulkner/Photo Researchers, Inc. ; BL ©DLILLC/Corbis

Page 139 Vanessa Vivk/Photo Researchers, Inc.

Cell Biology

Unit opener © Louise Gubb/Corbis

Page 163 Sotirus Zafeiris/Photo Researchers, Inc.

Page 167 London School of Hygiene & Tropical Medicine/Photo Researchers, Inc.

Page 168 Richard T. Nowitz/PhototakeUSA.com

Page 169 © Louise Gubb/Corbis

Page 171 BL Novastock/Photo Researchers, Inc.; MR David M. Phillips/Photo Researchers, Inc.

Page 173 Perennou Nuridsany/Photo Researchers, Inc.

Page 174 M. I. Walker/Photo Researchers, Inc.

Page 178 Kwangshin Kim/Photo Researchers, Inc.

Page 182 © James Webb/Phototake

Page 184 BR CNRI/Photo Researchers, Inc.; ML NIBSC/Photo Researchers, Inc.; BL Stem Jems/Photo Researchers, Inc.

Page 187 © Bettmann/Corbis

Page 188 TL Kwangshin Kim/Photo Researchers, Inc.; TR Medimage/Photo Researchers, Inc.; BR Michael Abbey/Photo Researchers, Inc.

Page 189 Dr. Torsten Wittmann/Photo Researchers, Inc.

Page 191 Biophoto Associates/Photo Researchers, Inc.

Page 204 Kalros, Latin Stock/Photo Researchers, Inc.

Page 213 BR Kenneth Eward/BioGrafx/Photo Researchers, Inc.; BM ©Corbis; BL Kallista Images/Getty Images

Page 216 Charles D. Winters/Photo Researchers, Inc.

Page 220 M. I. Walker/Photo Researchers, Inc.

Page 221 BR Marshall Sklar/Photo Researchers, Inc.; BL Biophoto Associates/Photo Researchers, Inc.

Page 223 BL Image Source/Getty Images; BR PHANIE/Photo Researchers, Inc.

Page 234 © iStockphoto.com/Diane Diederich (vegetable); © iStockphoto.com/Jacek Chabraszwski (meat); © iStockphoto.com/Tova Teitelbaum (rice)

Page 240 Astric & Hanns-Frieder Michler/Photo Researchers, Inc.

Page 244 CMSP/J.L. Carson/Getty Images

Page 248 © MedicalRF.com/Corbis

Page 250 Vèronique Burger/Photo Researchers, Inc.

Page 252 Mauro Fermariello/Photo Researchers, Inc.

Genetics

Unit Opener: Page 259 Ulrike Welsch/Photo Researchers, Inc.

Page 261 Mark Burnett/Photo Researchers, Inc.

Page 262 ML Scott Olson/Staff/Getty Images; BL SciMAT/Photo Researchers, Inc.

Page 264 TR Bugwood.com; BR Scott Camazine/Photo Researchers, Inc.

Page 269 T&B © Dr. Charles Mazel/Visuals Unlimited/Corbis

Page 274 Bob Nichols/USDA

Page 277 Sinclair Stammers/Photo Researchers, Inc.

Page 278 Dr. Gopal Murti/Photo Researchers, Inc.

Page 283 T © Maximilian Stock Ltd/photocuisine/Corbis; M Jon Edwards Photography/ Foodstock.com; B © Rick Miller/AgStock Images/Corbis

Page 284 Martin Shields/Photo Researchers, Inc.

Page 290 Michael P. Gadomski/Photo Researchers, Inc.

Page 292 BL © Bettmann/Corbis

Page 294 BL Biophoto Associates/Photo Researchers, Inc.; BR David M. Phillips/Photo Researchers, Inc.

Page 300 National Science Foundation

Page 305 Courtesy Golden Rice Humanitarian Board, www.goldenrice.org

Page 310 Ulrike Welsch/Photo Researchers, Inc.

Page 312 TL Hila Science Videos; BR Inga Spence/Photo Researchers, Inc.; BR Inga Spence/ Photo Researchers, Inc.

Page 313 Courtesy of John Doebley

Page 317 BL & BR Biophoto Associates/Photo Researchers, Inc.

Page 324 Simon Fraser/Photo Researchers, Inc.

Page 325 Inga Spence/Photo Researchers, Inc.

Page 332 Kenneth Eward/Photo Researchers, Inc.

Page 335 TL Patrick Landmann/Photo Researchers, Inc.; BL Spencer Grant/Photo Researchers, Inc.; BR Gregory G. Dimijian, M.D./Photo Researchers, Inc.

Page 337 TL Mark Bowler/Photo Researchers, Inc.; TR Nigel Cattlin/Photo Researchers, Inc.; ML David M. Phillips/Photo Researchers, Inc.

Page 341 T Michael Ord/Photo Researchers, Inc.; B Peter LaTourrette

Page 346 Eye of Science/Photo Researchers, Inc.

Page 347 © Visuals Unlimited/Corbis

Page 350 TL Tom McHugh/Photo Researchers, Inc.; BR Herve Berthoule/Jacana/Photo Researchers, Inc.

Page 353 Lawrence Migdale/Photo Researchers, Inc.

Page 354 Biophoto Associates/Photo Researchers, Inc.

Page 361 ©Benjamin Lowy/Corbis

Page 362 Nigel Cattlin/Photo Researchers, Inc.

Page 363 Jack Dykinga

Page 368 University of California Agriculture and Environment

Page 372 TL National Human Genome Research; BR Maggie Bartlett, NIHGRI

Page 373 Patrick Landman/Photo Researchers, Inc.

Page 376 T Biology Pics/Photo Researchers, Inc. B Steve Gschmeissner/Photo Researchers, Inc.

Page 377 Biophoto Associates/Photo Researchers, Inc.

Page 382 L Inga Spence/Photo Researchers, Inc.; R Adam Jones/Photo Researchers, Inc.

Page 383 © Vasily Fedosenko/Reuters/Corbis

Page 386 Gustoimages/Photo Researchers, Inc.

Page 388 TR Veronique Leplat/Photo Researchers, Inc.; MR Wayne Nishijima, University of Hawaii at Manoa

Page 389 StockTrek/Getty Images

Page 393 Adrian Bicker/Photo Researchers, Inc

Page 400 T Martin Bond/Photo Reseachers, Inc.; B © Queen's Printer for Ontario, 2009. Reproduced with permission.

Evolution

Unit Opener Page 413 Nigel J. Dennis/Photo Researchers, Inc.

Page 415 TL Bjamla Ladic/Photo Researchers, Inc.; TR Art Wolfe/Photo Researchers, Inc.; MR E.R. Degginger/Photo Researchers, Inc.; BR Gregory G. Dimijian, M.D./Photo Researchers, Inc.; BL John Maraventano/Photo Researchers, Inc.

Page 422 BL Paal Hermansen/Photo Researchers, Inc.; BM Larry Landolfi/Photo Researchers, Inc.; BR Shekar Dattatri © Chelonian Research Foundation

Page 423 BL Alexis Rosenfeld/Photo Researchers, Inc.; BR Jack Dykinga/USDA Agricultrural Research Service

Page 424 Cede Prudente/Photo Researchers, Inc.

Page 425 TL, TR Nigel Cattlin/Photo Researchers, Inc.; MR Tom McHugh/Photo Researchers, Inc.; BR Mark Smith/Photo Researchers, Inc.

Page 426 Fox Photos/Getty Images

Page 427 U.S. Fish and Wildlife Service

Page 428 ML U.S. Fish and Wildlife Service; MR Jose Reynaldo da Fonseca/Wikimedia commons; BL Adam.J.W.C./Wikimedia commons; BR Paddy Patterson/Wikimedia commons

Page 429 TR Mark Taylor/Photo Researchers, Inc.; BL © How Hwee Young/Corbis

Page 430 Gerald C. Kelley/Photo Researchers, Inc.

Page 432 L. Newman & A. Flowers/Photo Researchers, Inc.

Page 436 Mary Evans/Photo Researchers, Inc.

Page 439 ML Ralph Lee Hopkins/Photo Researchers, Inc.; MR Francois Gohier/Photo Researchers, Inc.; B Jeanne White/Photo Researchers, Inc.

Page 440 William Munoz/Photo Researchers, Inc.

Page 441 Science Source/Photo Researchers, Inc.

Page 442 Steve Maslowski/Photo Researchers, Inc.

Page 443 BR RIA Novosti/Photo Researchers, Inc.; ML Francois Gohier/Photo Researchers, Inc.; BL Saul Gonor/Photo Researchers, Inc.

Page 446 Alan Sirulnkoff/Photo Researchers, Inc.

Page 447 National Park Service

Page 454 iStockphoto

Page 459 Philippe Plailly/Photo Researchers, Inc.

Page 460 Tom McHugh/Photo Researchers, Inc.

Page 465 Nigel J. Dennis/Photo Researchers, Inc.

Page 466 Courtesy of David R. Parks

Page 469 National Park Service

Page 470 From top in order: Alan & Sandy Carey/Photo Researchers, Inc.; Jacana/Photo Researchers, Inc.; Sidney Bahrt/Photo Researchers, Inc.; Nigel J. Dennis/Photo Researchers, Inc.; Millard H. Sharp/Photo Researchers, Inc.

Page 472 BL DEA/A. Calegari/De Agostini/Getty Images; BR Rod Planck/Photo Researchers, Inc.

Page 475 BL Peter Skinner/Photo Researchers, Inc.; BR Neil McDaniel/Photo Researchers, Inc.

Page 476 TR Suzanne L. Collins/Photo Researchers, Inc.; MR Phil A. Dotson/Photo Researchers, Inc.

Page 477 Fotosearch

Page 478 Courtesy of Ad Konings

Page 479 TR Jack Kelly Clark, courtesy University of California Statewide IPM Program; MR ©Steve Schoenig

Page 482 T Michael Ord/Photo Researchers, Inc.; B Peter LaTourrette

Page 489 BL Barbara Strnadova/Photo Researchers, Inc. BR Francois Gohier/Photo Researchers, Inc.

Page 492 National Fish and Wildlife Service

Page 493 BM Tom McHugh/Photo Researchers, Inc.; M Scott Camazine/Photo Researchers, Inc.; BR Vaughan Fleming/Photo Researchers, Inc.

Page 501 Jacques Jangoux/Photo Researchers, Inc.

Page 502 Nigel Cattlin/Photo Researchers, Inc.

Page 503 Nigel Cattlin/Photo Researchers, Inc.

Page 504 Fletcher & Baylis/Photo Researchers, Inc.